Tailoring
Genes for
Crop Improvement

An Agricultural Perspective

BASIC LIFE SCIENCES

Alexander Hollaender, General Editor

Council for Research Planning in Biological Sciences, Inc., Washington, D.C.

Recent volumes in the series:

A Continuation Order Plan is available for this series. A continuation order will bring delivery of each new volume immediately upon publication. Volumes are billed only upon actual shipment. For further information please contact the publisher.

Tailoring Genes for Crop Improvement

An Agricultural Perspective

Edited by

George Bruening
John Harada and
Tsune Kosuge

University of California, Davis
Davis, California

and

Alexander Hollaender

Council for Research Planning in Biological Sciences, Inc.
Washington, D.C.

Technical Editors
Gregory Kuny and
Claire M. Wilson
Council for Research Planning in Biological Sciences, Inc.
Washington, D.C.

PLENUM PRESS • NEW YORK AND LONDON

Library of Congress Cataloging in Publication Data

Conference on Tailoring Genes for Crop Improvement (1985: University of California, Davis)
    Tailoring genes for crop improvement.

    (Basic life sciences; v. 41)
    "Proceedings of the Conference on Tailoring Genes for Crop Improvement: an
agricultural perspective, held September 9–12, 1985, at the University of California, Davis,
California."—T.p. verso.
    Includes bibliographical references and index.
    1. Crops—Genetic engineering—Congresses. I. Bruening, George. II. Title. III. Series.
SB123.57.C66   1985   631.5′2   87-2419
ISBN 0-306-42579-3

This book was copyedited and entirely retyped by the staff of the Council for Research Planning in Biological Sciences, located on the premises of Associated Universities, Inc., of which the Council is a guest.

The opinions expressed herein reflect the views of the authors, and mention of any trade names or commercial products does not necessarily constitute endorsement by the funding sources.

Proceedings of the Conference on Tailoring Genes for Crop Improvement: An Agricultural Perspective, held August 24–28, 1986, at the University of California, Davis, California.

© 1987 Plenum Press, New York
A Division of Plenum Publishing Corporation
233 Spring Street, New York, N.Y. 10013

DEDICATION

This volume is dedicated to Professor Paul K. Stumpf, emeritus professor, Department of Biochemistry and Biophysics, University of California, Davis. Professor Stumpf's pioneering work in plant metabolism provides a foundation for the current research efforts in the molecular biology and molecular genetics of plant lipids. He was the first to elucidate the pathway of fatty acid synthesis in plants and determined that it occurs in the chloroplast coupled to the energy-generating machinery of photosynthesis. The important concept of coupling essential biosynthetic processes to the primary energy-generating systems in the plant is revealed by these observations. His studies on oleic acid synthesis in the chloroplast, the transport of oleic acid to the cytoplasm, and its conversion in the endoplasmic reticulum to the wax components, monounsaturated long chain fatty acids and alcohols, are other examples of exciting new avenues of inquiry his research has helped develop.

The impact of Professor Stumpf's research extends well beyond lipid biochemistry in plants, however. Plant lipids are essential components of the human and animal diet and also are important in industrial uses of vegetable products. Thus future attempts to improve lipid composition in plants for food and industrial uses will build upon the knowledge developed by Professor Stumpf's research programs.

The Editors

PREFACE

In August, 1982, a conference was held at the University of California, Davis, to discuss both molecular and traditional approaches to plant genetic analysis and plant breeding. Papers presented at the meeting were published in Genetic Engineering of Plants: An Agricultural Perspective. A second conference, entitled "Tailoring Genes for Crop Improvement," sponsored by the UC-Davis College of Agricultural and Environmental Sciences and the College's Biotechnology Program, was held at Davis in August, 1986, to discuss the notable advances that had been made during the intervening years in the technology for gene modification, transfer, and expression in plants. This volume contains papers that were presented at this meeting and provides readers with examples of how the new experimental strategies are being used to gain a clearer understanding of the biology of the plants we grow for food and fiber; it also discusses how molecular biology approaches are being used to introduce new genes into plants for plant breeding programs. We are grateful to the speakers for their excellent presentations for the conference and extend our sincere thanks to those who contributed manuscripts for this volume.

We are indebted to the University of California System-Wide Biotechnology Research and Education Program, Calgene Incorporated, the Ciba-Geigy Corporation, and the Monsanto Company for providing funds to support this conference. We also extend our sincere thanks to the following persons who contributed their time, efforts, and ideas for the planning and successful completion of this conference: program committee members Raymond Huffaker, Clarence I. Kado, Carole P. Meredith, Richard Michelmore, Raymond Valentine, and John Yoder; special events coordinator, Carroll Miller; assistant coordinator, Donna Hiatt; conference services coordinator, Carolyn Norlyn; and Debonny Barsky-Shoaf, assistant to the faculty coordinator, the Biotechnology Program of the College of Agricultural and Environmental Sciences, UC-Davis. The dedicated and superb editing efforts of Claire Wilson and Gregory Kuny are gratefully acknowledged.

The Editors

Addendum: During the final stages of the preparation of this volume, we were stunned by the death of Dr. Alexander Hollaender. Dr. Hollaender compiled a distinguished record of research in radiation biology at the Oak Ridge National Laboratory. Following his retirement from ORNL, he organized the Council for Research Planning in Biological Sciences in Washington, D.C. As President of this office, he was the driving force behind the organization of numerous conferences in new areas in biology. He was instrumental in calling the attention of policy makers at the national level to generate new funding initiatives in Congress. We owe him a great deal and we will miss him.

CONTENTS

POST-TRANSLATIONAL REGULATION

MODIFICATION OF GENES AND GENE EXPRESSION

SCIENTIFIC STRATEGIES FOR THE FUTURE

OPENING REMARKS

Charles E. Hess

College of Agricultural and Environmental Sciences
University of California
Davis, California 95616

It is a pleasure to welcome you to the Davis Campus and our summer of conferences. Some of you have already participated in the International Horticultural Congress last week, attended by 3,300 registrants from seventy countries.

The progress made since our last conference on genetic engineering in plants, held in 1972, is impressive. In some cases, commercial application of the new technology may be realized in a relatively short time, at least from a technological viewpoint as opposed to legal or regulatory viewpoints. One example is Calgene's glyphosate resistance in plants, such as in tobacco plants. Another example is the genetic modification of <u>Pseudomonas</u> <u>fluorescens</u> to contain the insect toxic gene from <u>Bacillus</u> <u>thuringiensis</u>, producing a natural pesticide in an attempt to control black cutworms in the root zone of corn plants. Lindow and Panopoulos at the University of California, Berkeley, have been ready to field test the ice-minus <u>Pseudomonas</u> <u>syringae</u> for several years to determine whether the frost protection achieved in greenhouse experiments can be obtained under natural conditions. As you probably know, the field tests have been postponed once again, this time by the Sacramento courts.

Plant tissue culture continues to be an interesting and useful source of genetic variation to effect tolerance to disease such as rootrot in celery (L. Rappaport), or resistance to stress such as high salt conditions or aluminum (C. Meredith).

The combination of conventional plant breeding and cytogenetics with molecular biology holds a lot of promise. ·One example here is Jan Dvorak's hybrid of wheat and a salt-tolerant grass in which the genes for the salt tolerance have been located on the chromosomes.

The bacterium <u>Agrobacterium</u> <u>rhizogenes</u> causes root formation in plants that are difficult to root, such as the transformed golden delicious apple (A.M. Dandekar).

1

The tools of molecular biology are also helping us understand physiological processes such as fruit ripening in the tomato. Alan Bennett has developed a library of genes involved in tomato fruit ripening, and can correlate the activation of the gene coded for polygalacturonase with an increase in endogenous ethylene. This makes one speculate on the possibility of regulating fruit softening by manipulating this gene.

Along with the scientific progress made in the past four years has been a persistent challenge to the application of this new technology by the public, or at least certain factions of the public. One cause of opposition is fear concerning unknown and unwanted side effects from the use of genetic engineering. This fear has been highlighted by Jeremy Rifkin and his lawsuits, one of which I mentioned above relative to the ice-minus bacteria.

Although many feel that the allegations made by Rifkin are without scientific merit, the wary response of the public reminds us that they are skeptical about the safety of the new technology and that we must provide them with answers and assurances. We must be sure that the proper risk assessments have been made and then discuss the issues in public forums, answering the concerns of the nonscientist and hopefully resolving the problems. Educational programs for the media and the legislature could be helpful here as well.

The problem has been complicated further because of the difficulty in developing regulatory guidelines among agencies such as the U.S. Department of Agriculture (USDA), the Environmental Protection Agency, and the Food and Drug Administration, and within the USDA between the Animal and Plant Health Inspection Service and Science and Education. Now that guidelines have been published, it is imperative that they be reviewed to be sure they are workable.

A second challenge we've had to face is the idea that research has caused surpluses and therefore the simple solution to the surplus problem is to stop research. You can understand the frustration of legislators who, after launching a multimillion dollar program to reduce milk surpluses, read about the development of a bovine growth hormone which increases milk production by fifteen percent. Again, it is our responsibility to explain to the legislators, the public, and even to the farmer that research can increase the efficiency of production, thereby providing a greater competitive advantage and the potential for greater profit. Further, it is the farmer's decision to take a variety or technique that is more efficient and use it to gain even greater profits. When overdone, however, this leads to overproduction and the resulting decrease in price. Research alone does not cause surpluses—it is how the benefits of that research are managed that can lead to difficulty. To stop research will only lead to a further erosion of the competitive advantage the United States has enjoyed in food and fiber production.

So as we launch this Conference on Tailoring Genes for Crop Improvement, we must not only share the excitement of the science and examine it from the technological aspects, we must also acknowledge and deal with the concerns of the public, the regulators, and the lawmakers to make sure that mistaken notions about genetic engineering are dispelled.

To conclude, I would like to recognize those who helped organize and sponsor this Conference.   The Scientific Organizing Committee has been chaired by George Bruening and Tsune Kosuge of the Department of Plant Pathology.   I'd like to thank the rest of our committee members as well: Debonny Barsky-Shoaf and Clarence Kado of the Department of Plant Pathology; Richard Michelmore and John Yoder of the Department of Vegetable Crops; Carole Meredith of the Department of Viticulture and Enology; Raymond Valentine of the Department of Agronomy and Range Science; and John Harada of the Department of Botany.

I'd like also to thank our sponsors for making this all possible: Calgene, Inc., the Monsanto Company, and the Biotechnology Research and Education Program at the University of California, Los Angeles.

IDENTIFICATION AND ANALYSIS OF PLANT GENES

GENES FOR THE EXTENSINS, AN ABUNDANT CLASS OF PROTEINS

J.E. Varner

Plant Biology Program
Washington University
St. Louis, Missouri 63130

INTRODUCTION

Hydroxyproline occurs in only a few classes of proteins; however, it is one of the most abundant amino acids. Most of these proteins are located in extracellular matrices, for example, the collagens of animals and the arabinogalactan proteins and extensins (hydroxyproline-rich glycoproteins or HRGPs) of plants. It is because of this that hydroxyproline is a major constituent of extracellular matrix proteins in both plants and animals.

In plants, the extensins accumulate in the cell walls (a) during normal development, (b) in response to injury, (c) in response to infection, (d) in response to ethylene, and perhaps (e) in response to signals not yet elucidated. In general, it appears that extensins in the cell wall are not degraded. The accumulation of extensins can be rapid; in carrot root slices, extensin synthesis can be as much as 6% to 8% of total protein synthesis. Hydroxyproline is 30 to 45 mole % of the amino acid content of the extensins. Thus, the extensins constitute 3% to 20% of the dry weight of dicot cell walls, and the wall is about 40% of the dry weight of the cell.

Recent work from Lamport's laboratory (4) and from my laboratory (3) makes it clear that the extensins are coded for by a multigene family; for example, at least four different extensin genes are expressed in tomato. Southern blots show the presence of four to eight extensin genes in tomato, carrot, soybean, lotus, and arabidopsis (J.E. Varner, unpubl. data). There is evidence that the expression of these different genes is tissue-specific. Details of the isolation and sequencing of a carrot extensin genomic clone (1), a tomato extensin clone (3), and several complementary DNA (cDNA) clones from tomato, petunia, and bean have been presented (3).

The goal of this chapter is to explore the likely architectural reasons for the abundance of the extensins in dicot cell walls.

THE FORM OF EXTENSIN

We know from physical data, CD spectra (6), the diffusion constant and sedimentation coefficient (2,5), and electron micrographs (5,6) that extensin is in the polyproline II conformation and has the appearance of a rod. It is about 80 nm long. The following are sequences of hydroxyproline-rich peptides that were obtained from tomato cell walls by partial hydrolysis (Ref. 4; hydroxyproline = 0):

-SOOOOK-
-SOOOOSOK-
-SOOOOTOV-
-SOOOOVYKYK-
-SOOOOSOSOOOOYYYK-

These data made it clear that the sequence

-SOOOO-

is abundant in extensin. Since then,

-SOOOOK-

has been found in partial hydrolysates from melon cell walls (3). Similar results were obtained for the deglycosylated extensins, P1 and P2, which were extracted from tomato cells grown in suspension culture (4). The sequences

-SOOOOTOV-   (from P1)
and   -SOOOOVYKYK- (from P2).

were obtained as abundant (and therefore repetitive) peptides from tryptic digests.

It is of great interest that P1 contains not only several repeats of

-SOOOOTOV-

but also several repeats of

-SOOOOVKPYHPTOV-

which is different from the first peptide by virtue of an inserted hexapeptide containing proline--the only extensin sequence known so far that contains proline.

In the amino acid sequence derived from the base sequence of a carrot genomic clone (1),

-SPPPP-   occurs 25 times,
-SPPPPK-   occurs seven times,
and   -SPPPPTPVYK- occurs eight times.

The sequence -SPPPPTPVYK- also is encoded by a cDNA clone from petunia callus (3).

In a tomato genomic clone (1),

	-SPPPP-	occurs a total of 37 times,
	-SPPPPVH-	occurs 21 times,
and	-SPPPPVA-	occurs 11 times.

The sequence encoding

-SPPPPSPSPPPPYYYK-

occurs in cDNA clones from tomato stem (3) and from petunia callus (3). The sequences

	-SPPPPVH-	
and	-SPPPPVA-	

also occur in cDNA clones prepared from potato tuber mRNA. The sequence encoding

-SPPPPYYYHSPPPPKH-

occurs repetitively in a cDNA derived from bean cell cultures (3).

These few examples seem to establish the widespread occurrence of genes encoding repetitive -SPPPP- sequences. Because most dicot cell walls contain much more hydroxyproline than proline, it seems safe to assume that -SOOOO- is an abundant sequence in most dicot cell wall proteins, even though it has been observed by direct sequencing of hydroxyproline-rich proteins only in tomato, sycamore, and melon (3).

In dicot extensins, most of the hydroxyproline residues are glycosylated with arabinose or linear oligosaccharides of two, three, four, or five arabinose residues. The precise arrangement of the sidechains along any -SOOOO- sequence is unknown. Because of the stabilizing effect of these oligosaccharides on the polyproline II structure (5,6), they must interact strongly with the peptide chain (either directly or through water molecules).

When we focus our attention beyond these hydroxyproline-rich segments, we see other repetitive sequences of a quite different character. In the carrot extensin gene-derived sequence, the sequence

	-EH-	occurs three times as
	-SPPPPEH-.	

The sequence

	-YKYK-	occurs eight times as
	-SPPPPTPVYKYK-.	

The sequence

	-MH-	occurs twice as
	-SPPPPMH-;	

the sequences

	-YHYE-	
and	-YHFE-	each occur once as
	-SPPPPYHYE-	
and	-SPPPPYHFE-,	respectively.

The sequence

	-HHYKYK-	occurs four times;
twice as	-SPAPVHHYKYK-,	
once as	-SPAPEHHYKYK-,	
and once as	-FPAPEHHYKYK-.	

The sequence

-HH-	occurs once as
-SPPPPKHHY-,	and once as
-SPPPPHHY.	

The sequence

-KH-	occurs seven times as
-SPPPPKH.	

In one tomato extensin that is elutable from the walls of living cells grown in suspension culture, one repetitive sequence is

-SOOOOTOV-,

and a second repetitive sequence in the same protein is

-SOOOOVKPYHPTOV-.

Another extensin from the same cell suspension culture has

-SOOOOVYKYK-

as the most abundant repetitive peptide.

It is obvious that the amino acid side chains in the regions between the -SPPPP- (-SOOOO-) sequences provide abundant opportunities for electrovalent and covalent bonding (i.e., connector sites) with other extensin molecules and/or other components of the cell wall.

THE FUNCTION OF EXTENSINS: SPECULATIONS

In my view, the following portion of the extensins constitutes rigid segments:

$$-S\ \underset{O}{\overset{-Ara_n}{|}}\ \underset{O}{\overset{-Ara_n}{|}}\ \underset{O}{\overset{-Ara_n}{|}}\ \underset{O-}{\overset{-Ara_n}{|}}$$

Many amino acid residues that fall between these segments have functional groups in their side chains which may act as connector sites. For example, the epsilon amino group of lysine could interact electrovalently with uronic acid residues in cell walls at pH values from 3 to 10. The protonated imidazole nitrogen of the histidine residue could interact electrovalently with uronic acid residues at pH values from 3 to 6. The epsilon amino group of lysine could interact reversibly with a polysaccharide aldehyde to form a covalent bond--a Schiff's base. If the sugar moiety underwent a rearrangement, such as an Amadori rearrangement, the reaction would no longer be reversible.

This exercise in speculation can be carried on until the possible reactions of the connector sites with cell wall components--and components brought into the cell wall by stress, wounding, and infection--are exhausted. The connector site hypothesis deserves experimental testing.

In addition, one should note from the values for extensin as percent of cell wall dry weight given in the "Introduction" above that, in some cell walls, the amount of polycations (extensins) may equal or exceed the amount of polyanions (polyuronic acids). We need to think more about the effects of immobilized polyelectrolytes in plant cell walls.

REFERENCES

1. Chen, J., and J.E. Varner (1985) An extracellular matrix protein in plants: Characterization of a genomic clone for carrot extensin. EMBO J. 4:2145-2151.
2. Leach, J.E., M.A. Cantrell, and L. Sequeira (1982) Hydroxyproline-rich bacterial agglutinin from potato: Extraction, purification and characterization. Plant Physiol. 70:1353-1358.
3. Showalter, A.M., and J.E. Varner (1986) Plant hydroxyproline-rich glycoproteins. In The Biochemistry of Plants: A Comprehensive Treatise. Vol. 11. Molecular Biology, A. Marcus, ed. Academic Press, Inc., New York (in press).
4. Smith, J.J., E.P. Muldoon, J.J. Willard, and D.T.A. Lamport (1986) Tomato extensin precursors P1 and P2 are highly periodic structures. Phytochemistry 25:1021-1030.
5. Stafstrom, J.P., and L.A. Staehelin (1986) Cross-linking patterns in salt-extractable extensin from carrot cell walls. Plant Physiol. 81: 234-241.
6. Van Holst, G.J., and J.E. Varner (1984) Reinforced polyproline II conformation in a hydroxyproline-rich wall glycoprotein from carrot root. Plant Physiol. 74:247-251.

MOLECULAR ANALYSIS OF PLANT PLASMA MEMBRANES

Christopher J. Lamb, Paul M. Norman, Mindy S. Fitter,
Michael G. Hahn, David R. Lerner, and Vincent P.M. Wingate

Plant Biology Laboratory
The Salk Institute for Biological Studies
San Diego, California 92138

INTRODUCTION

It has become clear that while rapid strides are now being made in the study of the structure and function of plant genomes, little is known in comparison to animal cells about the structure and function of the plant cell at the molecular level. For example, physiological and ultrastructural studies have shown that the plasma membrane is the site of a number of important cellular functions, including cellulose synthesis and wall deposition (16,19), hormone transport and action (8,21), transport of ions and metabolites (23), as well as recognition of, and response to, symbiotic and pathogenic microorganisms (3,14). However, despite its key role in plant cell division, differentiation, and development, investigation of the molecular properties of plant plasma membranes has been severely hampered by the lack of biochemical markers and attendant difficulties in membrane fractionation (10,11,20).

The central thrust of our research has been to develop the use of monoclonal antibody technology (15) to overcome these problems, thereby allowing study of the molecular architecture of the plant plasma membrane in relation to its function and biogenesis. Monoclonal antibodies have proved to be a valuable and powerful tool in the study of the plasma membrane of animal cells (12,24). The major advantage of this technology, with respect to plant plasma membranes, is that it is possible to obtain a series of pure and specific antibodies starting from impure, heterogenous immunogen preparations (15). Therefore, without being able initially to identify or purify antigens specifically located on the plasma membrane, it should nonetheless be possible to generate monoclonal antibodies that are specific to the (glyco)protein constituents of this membrane.

PRODUCTION OF MONOCLONAL ANTIBODIES

In our initial studies, Balb/c mice were immunized with a total cellular membrane preparation from suspension-cultured cells of _Nicotiana_ glutinosa, following a schedule similar to that previously used in the generation of monoclonal antibodies to lymphocyte plasma membrane antigens (18). In the absence of suitable biochemical markers for the plasma membrane of plant cells, a crude total cellular membrane preparation was used as immunogen so as to ensure that the antigens of interest were not lost during a prior fractionation process. Furthermore, by the use of undifferentiated suspension-cultured cells as a source of immunogen it was hoped that at least some of the antibodies generated would be directed against antigens that were widely distributed with respect to both cell type and plant species.

Antibody secretion by hybridoma cell lines was assayed by liquid-phase radioimmunoassay (RIA) using ^{125}I-labeled rabbit antimouse antibody to detect binding of murine antibodies to immunogens on total cellular membrane preparations equivalent to those used for immunization (18). Binding of test antibodies was measured relative to a control in which test antibody was replaced with either hybridoma culture medium or monoclonal antibodies directed against antigens present on bacterial surfaces. Only hybridoma cultures giving supernatants that exhibited test-to-control ratios greater than 3 in this assay were chosen for cloning. Following cloning by limiting dilution, 13 cell lines that stably secreted antibody were obtained from these initial experiments (18). These clonal cell lines were cryopreserved and the corresponding supernatants containing secreted monoclonal antibodies were retained for further characterization. Subsequently, further hybridoma cell lines were produced following immunization with (a) total cellular membrane preparations from suspension-cultured cells of N. plumbaginafolia, and (b) intact isolated mesophyll protoplasts from leaves of N. tabacum, leading to the generation, respectively, of 70 and 33 cell lines secreting antibody against the immunogen preparations (C.J. Lamb et al., unpubl. data).

ENZYME-LINKED IMMUNOSORBENT ASSAY

Subsequently, the radioimmunoassay for antibody-binding to membrane preparations was superceded by development of a sensitive and rapid enzyme-linked immunosorbent assay (ELISA) procedure which can analyze 200 to 1,000 samples within four to five hours, followed by computer-assisted data collection and analysis using a semiautomated ELISA plate reader (C.J. Lamb et al., unpubl. data). The ELISA was optimized and characterized with respect to length of exposure to first antibody (test) and second antibody (β-galactosidase-conjugated goat antimouse antibody), washing procedures, and method of immobilization of membranes or protoplasts. A key to successful development of this ELISA procedure, which is safer, more convenient, and more rapid than the RIA, was determination of the optimal conditions for immobilizing the antigen (particularly intact protoplasts) to the bottom of the microtiter plate wells. When intact protoplasts are used as the immobilized antigen, the ELISA becomes selective for antibodies that bind to plasma membrane antigens present on the external surface of protoplasts.

IDENTIFICATION OF MONOCLONAL ANTIBODIES TO PLASMA MEMBRANE EPITOPES

In order to determine which of these antibodies were directed against antigens present on the plasma membrane, a second screen was employed based on antibody binding to the surface of protoplasts isolated from N.

<u>glutinosa</u> suspension-cultured cells (18). Binding was monitored by immuno-fluorescence microscopy using fluorescein-labeled goat antimouse immuno-globulin as tracer second antibody. This procedure required elimination of background fluorescence associated with either autofluorescence of the pro-toplast preparation or nonspecific binding of antibody. Conditions were established in which zero background fluorescence was observed when first antibody was either omitted or was a monoclonal antibody directed against antigens present on bacterial cell surfaces. Initially, this screen was performed in bulk liquid phase such that the protoplasts were sedimented by centrifugation in conventional centrifuge tubes during the serial washings following the various antibody treatments and prior to microscopic exami-nation. This procedure allowed testing of about ten to 20 hybridoma super-natants per day. Subsequently, we developed a more rapid immunofluores-cence screen using protoplasts immobilized in 96-well culture plates for antibody treatment, washing, and direct in situ immunofluorescence micro-scopic observation. This procedure now routinely allows assay of 200 to 400 antibody preparations per day. Six of the 13 monoclonal antibodies directed against antigens present in the total cellular membrane prepara-tion from <u>N</u>. <u>glutinosa</u> cells also gave either zero or insignificant levels of fluorescence in this assay. In contrast, the remaining seven monoclonal antibodies exhibited strong binding to the protoplast surface, with partic-ularly intense fluorescence in a continuous ring at the periphery of the protoplast (Tab. 1).

None of the seven monoclonal antibodies that bind to antigens present on the protoplast surface membrane (plasma membrane) gave a positive signal in a parallel test using intact cells which retain the surrounding cell wall (18). However, of the six antibodies that did not bind to the proto-plast surface, two were found to bind to the surfaces of intact cells (Tab. 1). We concluded that these antibodies are directed against cell wall material present as contaminants in the total cellular membrane prep-aration used both for immunization and for the initial RIA screening. The

Tab. 1. Immunofluorescence assay of monoclonal antibody binding.

Clone	Plasma membrane	Cell wall	Neither
PN16.1B3	+		
PN16.2C6	+		
PN16.3C1	+		
PN16.4A6	+		
PN16.4B4	+		
PN17.2B4			+
PN17.3A3			+
PN17.3A6			+
PN17.3B4		+	
PN17.3D4	+		
PN17.4B5	+		
PN17.4C5			+
PN23.1D5			+
PN23.2D3		+	

other four monoclonal antibodies bound neither to the surfaces of protoplasts nor to the surfaces of intact cells. Presumably, these antibodies
are directed against cell-internal antigens. Radioimmunoassay of antibody
binding to membrane preparations confirmed that two of the antibodies were
directed against cell wall material, since these antibodies did not give a
signal with membrane preparations isolated from protoplasts derived from
suspension-cultured N. glutinosa cells. In contrast and as expected, significant binding to protoplast membrane preparations was obtained with
monoclonal antibodies directed against antigens present on the plasma membrane and with monoclonal antibodies directed against intracellular membrane antigens.

     More recently, by similar means we have determined that seven out of
the 70 monoclonal antibodies generated in the second series, by immunization with total cellular membranes from suspension-cultured cells of N.
plumbaginafolia, were directed to epitopes present on the plasma membrane.
Likewise, seven out of the 33 monoclonal antibodies generated in the third
series, by immunization with intact, isolated mesophyll protoplasts of N.
tabacum leaves, were directed against plasma membrane epitopes. Overall,
therefore, a panel of 21 monoclonal antibodies directed to plasma membrane
antigens has been generated.

     Of the remaining antibodies, while a small number appear to be direct-
ed to epitopes present on cell wall antigens (see above), the majority exhibit no activity with either plasma membrane or the cell wall and presumably are directed against cell-internal antigens. In some instances, this
has been directly confirmed by immunofluorescence microscopy of permeabilized protoplasts, leading to identification of antibodies that bind specifically with nuclear membrane, vacuolar membrane, starch granules, and various elements of the cytoskeletal system, respectively.

     Immunofluorescence assay of binding to the surface of intact proto-
plasts detects only plasma membrane antigens present on the external face
of the membrane. Interestingly, during immunofluorescence assay certain
antibodies (e.g., MH3.5E7) which did not bind to the surface of intact
protoplasts apparently bound to the plasma membrane of slightly damaged,
partially collapsed protoplasts, suggesting that these antibodies might be
directed against epitopes present on the internal surface of the plasma
membrane.

SPECIES AND ORGAN DISTRIBUTION OF ANTIBODY REACTIVITY

     The species distribution of these antigens was checked by RIA of anti-
body binding to total cellular membrane preparations isolated from cultured
cells. Some of the antigens present on the plasma membrane of suspension-
cultured N. glutinosa cells appear to be of relatively wide phylogenetic
distribution, being found not only in other solanaceous species and the
legumes soybean and bean but also in the monocots wheat and rice, whereas
other plasma membrane antigens were not found in the cell membrane preparations from the legumes or monocots (18). The species distribution was confirmed by immunofluorescence assay of binding to intact, isolated protoplasts. Within a mature plant, reactivity of the monoclonal antibodies to
plasma membrane antigens was observed with cell membranes isolated from all
organs tested: root, shoot, and juvenile and mature leaves. In the case
of leaf tissue, the cellular localization of these antigens was confirmed
by immunofluorescence visualization of antibody binding to the surface of

isolated mesophyll protoplasts. As expected, the panel of antibodies generated by immunization with total cellular membrane preparations from suspension-cultured cells of N. plumbaginafolia also showed wide reactivity
with membranes from different organs of the intact plant.

SELECTION TOOLS

     Antibody binding to the surfaces of animal cells has proved to be a
powerful approach for identifying and hence isolating specific subpopula-
tions of cells. We have used monoclonal antibodies to plant plasma membrane epitopes, in combination with fluorescein- or rhodamine-labeled goat
antimouse immunoglobulins, to identify heterokaryons in protoplast fusion
procedures (5). Antibody labeling did not inhibit callus formation or
plantlet regeneration. The antibodies are noninvasive, and surface labeling provides clear optical discrimination of true heterokaryons from un-
fused aggregates as well as parental protoplasts and homokaryons. Labeling
is stable throughout fusion, and hence by prelabeling parental protoplast
populations the strategy is both versatile and of general applicability
compared to use of other dominant selectable markers such as antibiotic resistance (22).

     Certain extant monoclonal antibodies are directed against plasma mem-
brane epitopes of limited species distribution (see above), and it was demonstrated that interspecies hybrids could be detected by postfusion labeling, in which the intrinsic specificity of the antibodies was exploited
(5). A major advantage arising from the generation of monoclonal antibodies of appropriate inherent specificity is that the efficacy of selection,
based on either pre- or postfusion labeling, can be directly checked by
immunoassay of membrane preparations from regenerating calli and plantlets.

     By analogy with animal cells (12,24), it is probable that monoclonal
antibodies reactive with plasma membrane epitopes characteristic of specific genotypes or cell types can be identified. The inherent specificity of
such monoclonal antibodies could then be exploited in a variety of applications in addition to somatic hybridization, e.g., to identify protoplasts
derived from juvenile, meristematic cells or to monitor the proportion of
embryogenic cells at early stages in the development of embryogenic cultures.

PLASMA MEMBRANE FRACTIONATION

     Following sucrose density gradient centrifugation of a crude cellular
membrane preparation from N. glutinosa cells, the distribution of reactivity with four independent monoclonal antibodies (PN16.2C6, PN16.4A6,
PN16.4B4, and PN17.4B5) directed against epitopes present on the plasma
membrane exhibited the same characteristic pattern with two peaks at 1.10
kg/1 and 1.14 to 1.17 kg/1 (18). This pattern of reactivity was different
from that observed with two monoclonal antibodies (PN17.3A6 and PN17.4C5)
directed against antigens present only on internal cellular membranes. The
bimodal distribution of reactivity with epitopes known to be present on the
plasma membrane suggests that these epitopes may also be present on an internal cellular membrane. Recently, it has been shown by immunoelectron-
microscopy that monoclonal antibodies to epitopes present on the peribacteroid membrane from Rhizobium-induced root nodules of pea also labeled

both the plasma membrane and Golgi body of uninfected plant cells, suggesting that the epitopes present on internal cellular membranes reside on biosynthetic precursors of the mature plasma membrane polypeptides (2).

In our studies, plasma membrane and reactive internal cellular membranes were distinguished by analysis of the distribution of radioactivity following surface labeling of intact protoplasts with monoclonal antibody and ^{125}I-labeled rabbit antimouse antibody prior to membrane extraction and fractionation (18). Topological specificity of this prelabeling procedure was demonstrated by the almost complete loss of reactivity using monoclonal antibody PN17.4C5, which is directed against epitopes present exclusively on internal cellular membranes. In contrast, while labeling of intact protoplasts with monoclonal antibody PN16.4B4 resulted in loss of reactivity with membranes banding at buoyant densities less than 1.14 kg/l, reactivity with membranes banding at buoyant densities of 1.14 kg/l and greater was fully retained.

Other monoclonal antibodies to plasma membrane epitopes bind exclusively to the membrane fraction ρ = 1.14 to 1.17 kg/l, further confirming this fraction as that which is specifically enriched for the plasma membrane. Treatment of protoplasts derived from suspension-cultured soybean cells with diazotized [^{35}S]sulfanilic acid (6) and protoplasts derived from suspension-cultured carrot cells with acetyl-concanavalin A (1) selectively labels membranes of this buoyant density, although in these studies there was no independent evidence to verify either reactivity with surface molecules or topological specificity.

Monoclonal antibodies to plasma membrane epitopes characterized here now provide markers for the plasma membrane in vitro, thereby allowing its purification and analysis of its properties at the biochemical and molecular levels. To this end, using reactivity with monoclonal antibody PN16.4B4 as a marker, we have investigated the partitioning of plasma membrane antigens between two-phase polyethylene glycol and dextran systems (17). At low concentrations of these solutes, most of the protein in total cellular membrane preparations partitions in the upper phase, whereas reactivity with monoclonal antibody PN16.4B4 is found in both the upper and lower phases. However, as the concentrations of polyethylene glycol and dextran are increased, virtually all the membrane protein accumulates in the lower phase, whereas reactivity with monoclonal antibody PN16.4B4 is now found principally in the upper phase, indicating an extensive enrichment for the plasma membrane. This was confirmed by sucrose density gradient centrifugation of the membranes partitioning into the upper phase at high polymer concentrations (Fig. 1). The distribution of reactivity with monoclonal antibody PN16.4B4 followed a similar pattern to that observed when plasma membrane was specifically tagged by topologically specific antibody labeling of intact protoplasts. Thus maximum reactivity was observed in a clearly defined peak at high buoyant density, with relatively little reactivity at intermediate and low buoyant densities compared to the pattern of monoclonal antibody PN16.4B4 reactivity following density gradient centrifugation of crude total cellular membrane preparations.

However, it should be noted that even at high polymer concentrations, reactivity with monoclonal antibody PN16.1B3, which is also directed against a plasma membrane epitope, did not efficiently partition into the upper phase compared to reactivity with monoclonal antibody PN16.4B4. This suggests the occurrence of more than one class of microsomal vesicle derived from the plasma membrane. While phase partitioning provides an

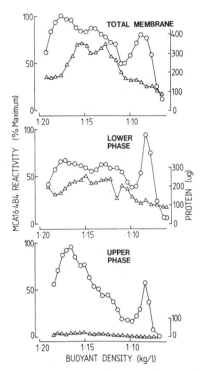

Fig. 1.   Fractionation of cellular membranes from suspension-cultured
           cells of Nicotiana glutinosa 14 days after subculture. Cells
           were homogenized in 50 mM Tris-malate buffer, pH 7.5, containing
           25 mM sucrose, 10 mM EGTA, and 20 mM sodium metabisulfite. Total
           cellular membranes were collected by centrifugation and then par-
           titioned between a two-phase system comprising 6.2% (w/w) poly-
           ethylene glycol (upper phase) and 6.2% (w/w) dextran T-500 (lower
           phase) in 10 mM Tris-malate, 25 mM sucrose, pH 7.8. Membranes
           were collected from upper and lower phases by centrifugation.
           The membrane pellets were resuspended in phosphate-buffered sa-
           line and centrifuged to equilibrium in a sucrose density gradient
           (15% to 45% w/w). Gradient fractions were analyzed for protein
           content (Δ) and reactivity with monoclonal antibody PN16.4B4 (o),
           and these data are presented as a function of buoyant density.

efficient procedure for purification of plasma membrane vesicles defined by
preferential reactivity with monoclonal antibody PN16.4B4, additional steps
may be required to obtain extensive enrichment of other classes of plasma
membrane-derived microsomal vesicles.

BIOCHEMICAL CHARACTERIZATION OF PLASMA MEMBRANE ANTIGENS

     Antibody reactivities with plasma membrane epitopes were insensi-
tive to prior treatment of membranes with proteinase, but reactivities
were destroyed by periodate treatment of membranes, suggesting that these

monoclonal antibodies are directed against glycan epitopes on the plasma membrane. In contrast, antibody reactivities with exclusively cell-internal epitopes were in general sensitive to proteinase rather than periodate treatment.

The molecular weights of (glyco)proteins containing epitopes reactive with specific monoclonal antibodies were determined by protein blots of total cellular membrane preparations fractionated by SDS-polyacrylamide gel electrophoresis. While satisfactory results were obtained using ^{125}I-labeled second antibody, significantly improved resolution and definition were subsequently obtained using immunoperoxidase or immunogold/silver as the second antibody. By this approach, plasma membrane epitopes corresponding to specific monoclonal antibodies were shown to reside on specific glycopolypeptides (e.g., MF3.1A1: a polypeptide of molecular weight 195 kDa) or on specific sets of glycopolypeptides as detailed in Tab. 2. Some antibodies reacted with unresolved sets of glycopolypeptides which exhibited smears of reactivity in protein blots (e.g., MH3.2B4).

In a few instances there were identical patterns of reactivity between different monoclonal antibodies (e.g., MH3.2B4, MH4.2A4, MH4.3E5, and MH4.4E1), suggesting that they are directed against a common plasma membrane epitope. However, in general, there was very little overlap in the pattern of reactivity of different monoclonal antibodies, such that from the set of 12 antibodies directed against plasma membrane epitopes reactive in protein blots, at least six distinct patterns of polypeptide reactivity were delineated. Overall, some epitopes appear quite widely distributed between different plasma membrane polypeptides, whereas other epitopes are characteristic of a limited number of, or even a single, polypeptide species. Specific plasma membrane polypeptides may carry both common and specific epitopes. Polypeptides containing specific epitopes restricted to internal cellular membranes were also identified by protein blotting and ranged in size between 22 kDa and 170 kDa.

Tab. 2. Western blot analysis of monoclonal antibody binding.

Clone	Apparent molecular weight of antigens
MF2.1B5	175
MF2.3D1	130-270
MF3.1A1	195
MH3.2B4	<15, 48-62, 82-200
MH4.2A4	<15, 48-62, 82-200
MH4.3E5	<15, 48-62, 82-200
MH4.4E4	<15, 48-62, 82-200
PN16.1B3	<15, 130-230
PN16.2C6	130-230
PN16.3C1	<15, 130-230
PN16.4A6	130-230
PN16.4B4	130-185

CHARACTERIZATION OF THE PLASMA MEMBRANE GLYCOPROTEIN FAMILY
CONTAINING THE EPITOPE REACTIVE WITH MONOCLONAL ANTIBODY PN16.4B4

To initiate the biochemical analysis required to study the molecular
structure, function, and biosynthesis of plant plasma membrane (glyco)pro-
teins, we have focused on the species containing the epitope reactive with
monoclonal antibody PN16.4B4. This antibody was generated by immunization
with crude total cellular membrane preparations from suspension-cultured
cells of N. glutinosa (18). The corresponding epitope is widely distributed in various organs of the plant, but has a relatively limited species
distribution, such that while monoclonal antibody PN16.4B4 exhibits strong
reactivity with cell membranes from Nicotiana and other solanaceous species (e.g., petunia), only weak activity is observed with soybean and bean
(Leguminoseae) or with monocots such as wheat and rice.

The epitope reactive with monoclonal antibody PN16.4B4 was shown to be
located on the external face of the plasma membrane by immunofluorescence
visualization of antibody binding to the surface of isolated protoplasts.
This was further confirmed by (a) specific agglutination of protoplasts,
(b) ELISA of antibody binding to the surface of intact protoplasts, and (c)
topologically specific labeling of intact protoplasts followed by analysis
of membrane partitioning on sucrose density gradients.

In protein (western) blots of solubilized membrane glycoproteins fractionated by SDS-polyacrylamide gel electrophoresis, monoclonal antibody
PN16.4B4 reacts with a set of glycoproteins (apparent molecular weights 130
to 185) which, depending on protein loading and the design of the electrophoretic separation, can be resolved into a discrete set of glycoproteins
(Tab. 2). Antibody reactivity was insensitive to prior proteinase treatment of the solubilized membrane preparation, but was destroyed by periodate treatment, indicating that the corresponding epitope is in the glycan
moieties of this set of plasma membrane glycoproteins. Immunoreactiv-
ity revealed that the glycoprotein family defined by monoclonal antibody
PN16.4B4 reactivity most markedly accumulates during the later stages of
the exponential phase of the cell culture cycle.

Hybridoma cell line PN16.4B4 was grown in the intraperitoneal cavity
to generate ascites fluid containing large amounts of monoclonal antibody
PN16.4B4, which was then purified by ion exchange chromatography and linked
to CNBr-activated Sepharose. Preparations of total cellular membranes were
solubilized with the zwitterionic detergent 3-[(3-cholamidopropyl)-dimeth-
ylamino]-1-propane-sulfonate (CHAPS). A set of plasma membrane glycoproteins was purified in one step from the solubilized total cellular membrane
preparation by immunoaffinity chromatography on the monoclonal antibody
PN16.4B4-Sepharose column, and the identity of the purified material was
confirmed by reactivity with this antibody on protein blots.

Immunoaffinity-purified material was used as immunogen to generate
monospecific polyclonal antisera and additional monoclonal antibodies (including PN27.1E8) which gave similar patterns of reactivity to monoclonal
antibody PN16.4B4 in western blots. Deglycosylation by treatment with tri-
fluoromethane sulfonic acid caused loss of reactivity with monoclonal antibody PN16.4B4 and a number of second-generation monoclonal antibodies, but
reactivity was retained with the polyclonal antisera and monoclonal antibody PN27.1E8. Following deglycosylation and subsequent SDS-polyacrylamide
gel electrophoresis, reactivity with monoclonal antibody PN27.1E8 and polyclonal antisera in western blots revealed a single parent polypeptide of

molecular weight 50. Thus it can be concluded that this family of glycoproteins arises from a single polypeptide, designated p50, which is glycosylated to different degrees in the various mature glycoproteins of the
family. Moreover, direct electrophoretic analysis of deglycosylated preparations of total cellular membranes reveals that p50 is one of the most
predominant species, and hence the family of glycoproteins based on p50
represents a major feature of the plasma membrane.

The amino acid composition of p50 has been determined and shows features characteristic of a heavily glycosylated membrane polypeptide, viz.,
high levels of serine and threonine, significant levels of proline, and
high levels of alanine and glycine. The amino acid composition of p50 is
similar to that of cell surface proteoglycans of animals. The glycan components of the p50 glycoprotein family contain large amounts of arabinose
and galactose, with smaller amounts of glucose, rhamnose, mannose, and
fucose. These features are reminiscent of arabinogalactan proteins (4),
although unlike the p50 plasma membrane glycoprotein family, cell wall
arabinogalactan proteins are highly soluble (4). However, reactivity with
the Yariv artificial antigen is a characteristic of arabinogalactan proteins, and agglutination of protoplasts by treatment with the Yariv antigen
has been observed, suggesting the occurrence in the plasma membrane of species that resemble arabinogalactan proteins (4) and which may be related to
the PN16.4B4 plasma membrane glycoprotein family based on p50.

FUTURE PROSPECTS

The generation and characterization of monoclonal antibodies to specific epitopes on the plant plasma membrane, together with concomitant
development of appropriate technical procedures such as rapid ELISA screening, provide the basis for molecular analysis of the structure, function,
and biogenesis of this membrane and its constituent glycoproteins, as well
as functional specialization during cell development and differentiation.

The recent generation of polyclonal antisera to the p50-derived,
PN16.4B4-reactive plasma membrane glycoproteins now allows, by pulse and
pulse-chase labeling experiments, analysis of processing events involved in
the biosynthesis of these glycoproteins and transport to the cell surface.
Furthermore, these polyclonal antisera can be used to identify cloned cDNA
sequences encoding p50 by antibody screening of cDNA libraries in the expression vector λgt11 (25). Identification and characterization of p50
cDNA clones will allow the use of recombinant DNA technology to generate
specific modifications in the encoded p50 polypeptide sequence and monitor
the effects of such mutations on p50 synthesis, processing, and trafficking
through the endomembrane system following reinsertion of the modified gene
or RNA into recipient plant cells. These studies will provide the basis
for development of chimeric constructs that target the accumulation of the
products of transferred genes specifically to the plasma membrane. This
will have considerable biotechnological utility, since certain classes of
transferred genes may have their greatest functional impact when the encoded proteins are specifically targeted to the plasma membrane, e.g., proteins involved in plant defense, wall biosynthesis, or modification of the
accumulation of insoluble solids in fruit ripening.

Molecular cloning of sequences encoding specific plasma membrane proteins such as p50 will allow functional analysis using gene transfer strategies, including the expression of antisense RNAs. Moreover, as discussed

above, reactivity of extant monoclonal antibodies as markers for the plasma membrane together with fractionation techniques such as phase partitioning and density gradient centrifugation can now be used to obtain extensive purification of plasma membrane-derived vesicles from crude microsomal preparations. A variety of strategies, including photoactivatable labels (9) and binding of appropriate anti-idiotype antibodies (7), should allow identification of proteins present in purified plasma membrane preparations that are involved in specific functions at the cell surface, such as metabolite partitioning, hormone transport, and action. Protein microsequencing/oligonucleotide probe synthesis (13) and microimmunization/antibody screening of expression libraries (25) permit direct molecular cloning of proteins tagged in this manner.

ACKNOWLEDGEMENTS

Research of the Plant Biology Laboratory of the Salk Institute was supported by grants from the McKnight Foundation, the Seaver Institute, and the U.S. Department of Agriculture, Competitive Grants Program (CRCR-1-1251). We thank Evelyn Wilson and Valerie Zatorski for help in preparation of the manuscript.

REFERENCES

1. Boss, W.F., and A.W. Ruesink (1979) Isolation and characterization of concanavalin A-labeled plasma membranes of carrot protoplasts. Plant Physiol. 64:1005-1011.
2. Brewin, N.J., J.G. Robertson, E.A. Wood, B. Wells, A.P. Larkins, G. Galfre, and G.W. Butcher (1985) Monoclonal antibodies to antigens in the peribacteroid membrane from Rhizobium-induced root nodules of pea cross-react with plasma membrane and Golgi bodies. EMBO J. 4:605-611.
3. Clarke, A.E., and P.A. Gleeson (1981) Molecular aspects of recognition and response in the pollen:stigma interaction. Rec. Adv. Phytochem. 15:161-211.
4. Fincher, G.B., B.A. Stone, and A.E. Clarke (1983) Arabinogalactan-proteins: Structure, function, and biosynthesis. Ann. Rev. Plant Physiol. 34:47-70.
5. Fitter, M.S., P.M. Norman, M.G. Hahn, V.P.M. Wingate, and C.J. Lamb (1986) Identification of somatic hybrids in plant-protoplast fusions with monoclonal antibodies to plasma membrane antigens. Planta (in press).
6. Galbraith, D.W., and D.H. Northcote (1977) The isolation of plasma membrane from protoplasts of soybean suspension cultures. J. Cell Sci. 24:295-310.
7. Gaulton, G.N., and M.I. Greene (1986) Idiotypic mimicry of biological receptors. Ann. Rev. Immunol. 4:253-280.
8. Goldsmith, M.H.M. (1977) The polar transport of auxin. Ann. Rev. Plant Physiol. 28:439-478.
9. Gronemeyer, H. (1985) Photoaffinity labelling of steroid hormone binding sites. Trends Biochem. Sci. 10:264-266.
10. Hall, J.L. (1983) Plasma membranes. In Isolation of Membranes and Organelles from Plant Cells, J.L. Hall and A.L. Moore, eds. Academic Press, Inc., New York, pp. 55-82.
11. Hall, J.L., and A.R.D. Taylor (1981) Isolation of the plasma membrane from higher plant cell. In Plant Organelles, E. Reid, ed. John Wiley, New York, pp. 103-111.

12. Hosking, C.S., and G.M. Georgiou (1982) Application of monoclonal antibodies to the study of human lymphocyte surface antigens. In Monoclonal Hybridoma Antibodies: Techniques and Applications, J.G.R. Hurrell, ed. CRC Press, Inc., Boca Raton, Florida, pp. 177-192.

13. Hunkapiller, M., S. Kent, M. Caruthers, W. Dreyer, J. Firca, C. Giffin, S. Horvath, T. Hunkapiller, P. Tempest, and L. Hood (1984) A microchemical facility for the analysis and synthesis of genes and proteins. Nature 310:105-111.

14. Keen, N.T. (1982) Specific recognition in gene-for-gene host-parasite interactions. Adv. Plant Pathol. 1:35-82.

15. Köhler, G., and C. Milstein (1975) Continuous cultures of fused cells secreting antibody of predefined specificity. Nature 256:495-497.

16. Lamb, C.J. (1981) Molecular approaches to the study of cell differentiation and development in higher plants: The biochemistry of xylem and phloem production. In Development and Differentiation, M.E. Buckingham, ed. CRC Press, Inc., Boca Raton, Florida, pp. 145-178.

17. Larsson, C. (1985) Plasma membranes. In Modern Methods of Plant Analysis. New Series Vol. 1. Cell Components, H.F. Linskens and J.F. Jackson, eds. Springer-Verlag, Berlin, pp. 85-104.

18. Norman, P.M., V.P.M. Wingate, M.S. Fitter, and C.J. Lamb (1986) Monoclonal antibodies to plant plasma membrane antigens. Planta 167:452-459.

19. Northcote, D.H. (1977) The synthesis and assembly of plant cell walls: Possible control mechanisms. In Synthesis, Assembly and Turnover of Cell Surface Components, Vol. 4, G. Poole and G.L. Nicholson, eds. Elsevier, Amsterdam, pp. 717-751.

20. Quail, P.H. (1979) Plant cell fractionation. Ann. Rev. Plant Physiol. 30:425-484.

21. Rubery, P.H. (1981) Hormone receptors. Ann. Rev. Plant Physiol. 32: 569-596.

22. Schieder, O. (1982) Somatic hybridization: A new method for plant improvement. In Plant Improvement and Somatic Cell Genetics, I.K. Vasil, W.R. Scowcroft, and K.J. Frey, eds. Academic Press, Inc., New York, pp. 239-253.

23. Spanswick, R.M. (1981) Electrogenic ion pumps. Ann. Rev. Plant Physiol. 32:267-289.

24. Williams, A.F. (1980) Cell-surface antigens of lymphocytes: Markers and molecules. Biochem. Soc. Symp. 45:27-50.

25. Young, R.A., and R.W. Davis (1983) Efficient isolation of genes by using antibody probes. Proc. Natl. Acad. Sci., USA 80:1194-1198.

METHODS AND APPLICATIONS OF RESTRICTION FRAGMENT

LENGTH POLYMORPHISM ANALYSIS TO PLANTS

Benoit S. Landry* and Richard W. Michelmore

Department of Vegetable Crops
University of California
Davis, California 95616

INTRODUCTION

The lack of markers has hindered genetic analyses in many important plant species. Molecular biology now provides an opportunity to develop large numbers of genetic markers. Cloned DNA sequences can be used to probe specific regions of eukaryotic genomes for the presence of polymorphism at the DNA sequence level. This polymorphism is detected as variation in the length of DNA fragments homologous to a labeled probe after digestion of the genomic DNA with restriction endonucleases. Such variation has been termed restriction fragment length polymorphism (RFLP).

Restriction fragment length polymorphisms were first used as a tool for genetic analysis in 1974 when a temperature-sensitive mutation of adenovirus was associated with a specific RFLP (45). Other studies demonstrated DNA differences which could be detected directly (e.g., in mitochondrial genomes) or following hybridization with specific sequences (83,88). The use of RFLPs as genetic markers of disease was first made by Kan and Dozy in 1978 for the analysis of sickle-cell anemia (56). Botstein et al. (19) described the theoretical basis of this method for mapping genes associated with disease in humans as well as defining the terminology and describing potential applications of RFLPs. Since then, RFLP analysis has been performed on many organisms and is the most efficient method for constructing detailed genetic linkage maps. Burr et al. (22) described the possible uses of this technique in improvement of crop plants. The methods for mapping, costs, and applications in breeding have been reviewed by Beckmann and Soller (13,14,100).

The majority of the methods and applications of RFLP analysis have been developed for human genetics. This review collates the different methods and surveys applications of RFLP analysis for plant improvement.

---

*Present address: Agriculture-Canada, P.O. Box 457, St.-Jean-sur-Richelieu, Quebec, Canada J3B 6Z8.

METHODS FOR THE DETECTION OF RESTRICTION FRAGMENT LENGTH POLYMORPHISMS

Southern Blots

Southern transfer and hybridization are the most commonly used techniques to detect variation in sizes of DNA fragments produced by restriction endonuclease digestions of eukaryotic genomes (102). The digested DNA
is separated by electrophoresis, transferred from the agarose gel to a solid support, and then hybridized to a labeled DNA sequence. Originally,
nitrocellulose membrane was used as a support for DNA. The disadvantage of
this membrane is its fragility, low DNA binding capacity, and the difficulty in using it for more than one hybridization. Diazobenzyloxymethyl (DBM)
and diazophenylthioether (DPT) membranes do not have these disadvantages,
but have complex and potentially dangerous preparation protocols. Charge-
modified nylon membranes are now available which do not have any of these
drawbacks and are particularly useful when repeated hybridizations are required. The DNA can be transferred from the gel to the membrane by capil-
larity or by the use of a parallel electrical field (31,102). A faster
capillary transfer method has been recently developed for nylon membranes
using NaOH as the transfer solution (89). Alternatively, for rapid, one-
time diagnostic uses, an in situ gel hybridization technique can be used
instead of membranes (108).

Techniques for labeling and hybridizing probes have improved in recent
years (68). Probes are most commonly labeled with ^{32}P; however, biotin-
labeled probes are being used increasingly for one-time hybridizations.
Current sensitivity with ^{32}P allows the detection of single copy sequences
in most organisms. Modifications of solutions for hybridization have
shortened the procedures and increased sensitivity. Calcium heparin has
been used to block nonspecific hybridization in place of Denhardt's solution and sonicated, denatured DNA (99). This shortened the prehybridiza-
tion time from at least 4 hr to less than 10 min. Sensitivity has also
been increased with dextran sulfate, which enhances the rate of hybridization and favors the formation of probe networks between partially overlapping sequences (68). This method is most advantageous when the probe is
larger than 250 bp and labeled by nick-translation. Polyethylene glycol
has been used as a substitute for dextran sulfate (4).

Dot Blots

Dot blots are an efficient alternative to Southern blots when large
populations are screened for the presence or absence of specific DNA sequences. For deletions, the probe hybridizes to one genotype but not to
the other; a population segregating for such a null allele can be analyzed
rapidly. For point mutations, a synthetic oligomer covering the DNA sequence to be analyzed is used and the stringency adjusted to allow hybridization only when the perfectly homologous sequence is present. This was
employed to detect the homozygous condition for the β-thalassemia allele at
the β-globin locus (78). Dot blots can also be combined with chromosome
sorting techniques to allow quick chromosomal localization of probes (64).
These probes can then be used to search for RFLPs associated with traits
determined by a specific chromosome.

RNA:DNA Mismatch Analysis

Variations in DNA sequences can also be detected via RNA:DNA mismatches. Recently, a powerful technique has been developed to detect

single base substitutions/deletions by ribonuclease cleavage at mismatches in [^{32}P]-RNA:DNA duplexes (73). A ^{32}P-labeled RNA probe is synthesized from a wild-type DNA template from the SP6 promoter of a transcription vector and hybridized to the denatured DNA to be tested; the resulting [^{32}P]-RNA:DNA hybrids are treated with RNase A. The location of the mismatches is determined by analyzing the size of the cleavage products after gel electrophoresis and autoradiography. If the DNA analyzed is identical to the wild-type DNA, a single band will be seen on the autoradiogram. A single base substitution will result in two RNA fragments. The ability to detect almost all possible single base substitutions/deletions with a single RNA probe is advantageous over RFLP analysis of DNA, which only detects large insertions/deletions and variations affecting the recognition sequence of the specific restriction endonuclease used. The [^{32}P]-RNA:DNA mismatch analysis method cannot be employed during the construction of a genetic map because of the large amount of DNA needed for each hybridization (3 to 6 µg of genomic DNA), which is not reused. As this method frequently detects polymorphism, however, it could be employed to analyze further crosses once a RFLP map has been established. It could also facilitate the detection of polymorphisms in regions of the genome with low levels of polymorphism, as well as indicate their nature in some cases.

Partial Digest Method

Another method to detect DNA variations in areas of the genome with infrequent polymorphism involves partial digests to increase the region surveyed with one probe. This "partial method" consists of making a 60% to 80% partial digestion of genomic DNA, Southern blotting, and probing with the sequence of interest. An uneven ladder of fragments is produced; RFLPs between individuals are seen as missing steps in the ladder. Restriction fragment length polymorphisms were detected at the insulin locus by this approach (96).

Polymerase Chain Reaction/Oligomer Restriction Method

The polymerase chain reaction/oligomer restriction (PCR/OR) method is a procedure that was originally developed for the detection of the sickle-cell mutation in humans (94). It is rapid and at least two orders of magnitude more sensitive than standard Southern-blotting procedures. A known polymorphic restriction site in the β-globin DNA sequence was specifically amplified using a synthetic oligonucleotide primer and DNA polymerase with repeated cycles of denaturation/amplification ("PCR" reaction). Solution hybridization of the amplified sequence with an end-labeled complementary probe was followed by digestion of the double-stranded product with the restriction endonuclease that detected the polymorphism ("OR" reaction). Polyacrylamide gel electrophoresis of the resulting oligomers, followed by autoradiography, revealed the polymorphism. The β^a (wild-type) and β^s (sickle-cell anemia) alleles could be distinguished with 1 µg of genomic DNA in less than 10 hr. Small amounts (0.5 ng) of low molecular weight, genomic DNA gave excellent results. This method is likely to be generally applicable for other genes, once they have been cloned and sequenced. It will also be valuable for diagnostic purposes, particularly if automated, and in cases where the target sequence is in low copy number (e.g., in early stages of viral or bacterial infections).

Theoretically, the PCR technique could be used to amplify any specific sequence (71,72) and could be coupled to other methods of oligomer hybridization. The starting amount of DNA needed for the [^{32}P]-RNA:DNA mismatch duplex analysis might be reduced if the target sequence is amplified with the PCR technique. Similarly, the stringency could be adjusted to allow hybridization of only perfectly matched oligomer primers; therefore, regeneration of the polymorphic restriction site or hybridization would rely on the extent of homology between the oligomer and the target sequence. An advantage of these methods over the OR reaction is that a well-defined polymorphic restriction enzyme site within the target sequence is not needed to detect polymorphism.

Pooled DNA Method

The use of pooled DNA samples has facilitated the detection of linkage between restriction fragments and complex disease-associated loci, such as insulin-dependent diabetes mellitus (DDM) and human leukocyte antigen (HLA) class II loci (6). The DNA samples from a population of individuals homozygous for the allele causing the disease were pooled and compared with pooled DNA samples of normal individuals. Specific complementary DNA (cDNA) clones representing genes likely to be involved in the disease development were used as probes. Only specific probe/enzyme combinations showing polymorphisms in intensity and/or banding pattern were further analyzed in segregating generations to test for linkage with the disease locus. This allowed the efficient use of probes and enzymes.

SOURCES OF PROBES

Genetic mapping with RFLPs requires the use of probes homologous to single-copy (single genes), low-copy (gene families), or tandemly repeated sequences. For identification purposes, higher copy number, dispersed sequences may also be useful. This section discusses the different sources and approaches used to obtain probes.

Isolation of Single- or Low-Copy Sequences from Random Genomic Clones

The presence of interspersed repetitive sequences in the genome of many eukaryotes requires the selection of single/low-copy DNA sequences from random clones of genomic DNA. The probability of an insert containing repeated DNA increases with its size; therefore, λ-bacteriophage libraries are a poor source of probes for RFLP analysis [except for organisms with a low proportion of repetitive DNA, such as many fungi and a few plants (e.g., Arabidopsis thaliana)], unless low-copy fragments are identified and subcloned. For eukaryotes with a high proportion of repetitive DNA, plasmid libraries containing short genomic DNA inserts (0.4 to 1.0 kb) are expected to be more efficient than λ libraries (10- to 23-kb inserts). One or more rounds of hybridization to plaques or colonies with ^{32}P-labeled total genomic DNA was generally sufficient to isolate single/low-copy sequences from some eukaryotes (51,57). Many clones carrying repetitive sequences, however, escaped detection in a single round of colony hybridization in maize (50). Dot blots of plasmid clones, hybridized to ^{32}P-labeled total genomic DNA, were more reliable than colony hybridizations for selecting low copy-number clones from lettuce (61). To increase efficiency, clones can be screened by colony hybridization prior to dot-blot analysis.

Single/low-copy sequences have been successfully selected from individual λ clones of a human library. Fragments produced by digestion of individual, randomly selected λ clones with one or two restriction endonucleases were separated by electrophoresis, transferred to a membrane, and hybridized to ^{32}P-labeled total genomic DNA (reverse genome blot). Single/low-copy fragments were identified by the lack of detectable hybridization, while fragments containing repeated sequences hybridized with varying intensities. Single/low-copy fragments were purified from the gel and used as probes on Southern blots to search for polymorphisms (36,47).

Whole cosmids or λ clones can be employed as probes if interspersed repetitive sequences are neutralized prior to hybridization (65). In humans, ^{32}P-labeled cosmid or λ clones were prehybridized with a large excess of nonradioactive total genomic DNA; therefore, regions homologous to repeated sequences were unable to hybridize. Only single/low-copy sequences remained single-stranded and free, subsequent to hybridization to membrane-bound DNA.

Chromosome-Specific Libraries

The chromosomal position of the character of interest is often known in humans and in plants when aneuploids are available. Chromosome-specific DNA clones can reduce the number of probes that need to be screened in order to obtain linkage with the character of interest. Several procedures have been developed to produce chromosome-specific probes for RFLP analysis in animals which might be applicable to plants.

Chromosome addition/substitution lines. Specific mouse-human chromosome addition lines have been constructed using somatic cell hybrids (47, 116). DNA from a human-Chinese hamster cell hybrid containing only human chromosome 11 was cloned into a λ vector (47). Since some repetitive DNA sequences are species-specific, and since a high proportion of the clones would carry repetitive sequences, ^{32}P-labeled total human genomic DNA was used to select clones containing human DNA. Reverse genome blots of digested clones then identified single/low-copy DNA fragments within each clone, which were subsequently used as probes to map their position on chromosome 11. Using a series of cell hybrids, each containing a different specific terminal deletion of chromosome 11, five sequences were mapped. Other repetitive sequences isolated from these clones were employed to select more clones specific to chromosome 11 (43). This approach might be applicable to plant species for which interspecific addition or substitution lines are available. A rye-specific repeated sequence family allowed rye chromosomes to be detected in wheat-rye substitution lines, using a rapid screening technique (squash blot) in which cell extracts are squashed directly on nitrocellulose filters (54). Also, four clones of repetitive DNA specific to wheat were isolated by reverse genome blots using ^{32}P-labeled rye DNA as probe (69).

Flow-sorted chromosomes. Another approach to obtain chromosome-specific probes is to construct λ clones from flow-sorted chromosomes. This technique has been successfully applied to chromosomes of mouse and humans (59,113). In humans, both normal and translocated metaphase chromosomes were separated. In mouse (2n=40), since the standard karyotype displays chromosomes of similar size, flow sorting generally resolved only five chromosomal peaks. A mouse karyotype, in which all chromosomes, except chromosomes 19 and X, were fused in a metacentric arrangement, allowed the construction of a library specific to the X chromosome (3). However, after elimination of recombinant phages containing repetitive sequences, only 25% to 30% of the tested sequences were X-specific. Sampling errors, contamination of the X-containing peak during flow sorting, and variation in the proportion of unique sequences among chromosomes have been advanced to explain the low cloning efficiency. Unequal distribution of the restriction endonuclease sites used for cloning also could have decreased the cloning efficiency of X-derived fragments. It is surprising that all the phages containing repetitive sequences were discarded, as they may have contained unique DNA sequences.

Chromosome-specific transcribed sequences have also been isolated from flow-sorted chromosome libraries. A λ-phage library, constructed from flow-sorted human X-chromosomes, was probed with ^{32}P-labeled pooled cDNAs from a hamster-human somatic cell hybrid line containing the X-chromosome as the only human chromosome (82). Only phages containing X-specific transcribed sequences hybridized; these probes are being used to construct a functional map of the human X-chromosome. Some plant species have karyotypes with distinct chromosomes; chromosome sorting techniques and the different approaches developed in humans to obtain chromosome-specific probes should be adaptable to these species.

Chromosome-specific repeated sequences. Chromosome-specific repeated sequences, particularly the α-satellite and the minisatellite, have been used to map regions of chromosomes in humans (47,63). The α-satellite is a 2-kb fragment which is tandemly repeated approximately 5,000 times and is mainly clustered at the centromeric region of the human X-chromosome. Therefore, the centromere of the X-chromosome can be mapped. Probing with the whole 2-kb sequence resulted in hybridization to some autosomal α-satellite families; a 250-bp subfragment, however, hybridized exclusively to the centromere of the X-chromosome and detected RFLPs (118). Another α-satellite sequence, specific for the centromeric region of chromosome 17, also detected RFLPs. Hypervariable minisatellites (10 to 15 bp) are dispersed in the human genome and exhibit substantial RFLPs; they are now employed for individual fingerprinting because of their large number of alleles, the multiple loci detected, and their high level of heterozygosity (55,121).

Microdissected chromosomes. Microdissection and microcloning of chromosomes were originally developed for polytene chromosomes of Drosophila (85), and since have been applied to mouse (40) and humans (11). In salivary glands of giant mutants of Drosophila, sequence amplification of euchromatin (as high as 2,000 copies) produces a characteristic banding pattern due to the parallel arrangement of the amplified sequences and localized condensation. Bands representing chromosome segments of 100 to 200 kb (depending on the size and density of the band) have been isolated by micromanipulation (85). Mammalian chromosomes do not provide the resolution possible with the polytene chromosome of dipteran insects; however, sections of specific chromosome arms of mouse and humans have been cloned following microdissection. This provided many prelocalized clones for fine gene mapping (11,40). In pea (Pisum sativum), many polytene prophase chromosomes can be obtained by culturing cotyledons in the presence of 2,4-dichlorophenoxyacetic acid (32). This technique may be applicable to other legumes and may provide material for microdissection and microcloning.

Random and Specific Complementary DNA Libraries

Random cDNA clones have been used extensively for RFLP analysis in animals and plants (e.g., Ref. 17; B.S. Landry, R.V. Kesseli, B. Farrara, and R.W. Michelmore, ms. in prep.). An advantage of cDNA clones over random genomic DNA clones is that clones containing repetitive sequences need not be screened out. In humans, from a limited study (ten single-copy and two multiple-copy cDNA clones), only clones representative of gene families revealed RFLPs (48). In tomato and lettuce, however, the majority of the polymorphic cDNA probes mapped to single loci (Ref. 16; B.S. Landry, R.V. Kesseli, B. Farrara, and R.W. Michelmore, ms. in prep.). At present, there is no evidence concerning whether or not the source of tissue from which the cDNA library is derived will bias the genomic distribution of the probes. The comparative efficiency with which cDNA and genomic DNA probes detect polymorphism has been studied in lettuce (B.S. Landry, R.V. Kesseli, H. Leung, and R.W. Michelmore, ms. in prep.). In this study, 123 genomic DNA clones, enriched for single/low-copy sequences, and 156 random cDNA clones were compared for their efficiency to detect RFLPs between four lines of lettuce in nine restriction endonuclease digests. Contrary to expectations, cDNA probes detected two and one-half times more polymorphism than was detected by the genomic DNA sequences. Genomic DNA clones were expected to detect more polymorphism than cDNA clones because of the absence of selection pressures maintaining the sequence integrity of nontranscribed DNA.

In some cases, genes responsible for a character of interest have already been cloned (46). Upon detection of RFLPs, these clones can be directly mapped and their identity confirmed. More frequently, however, only the physiological and/or biochemical processes involved in the trait and its inheritance are known. Complementary DNA libraries from specific tissues or organs involved in these processes will contain a high proportion of clones determining such a character. Specific groups of clones can be selected by probing expression libraries with labeled polyclonal antibodies or by differential hybridization to labeled cDNAs from tissues differentially expressing the trait. Restriction fragment length polymorphism mapping of these clones might identify genes responsible for the expression of the character. For example, a differential hybridization selection scheme was used in mouse to isolate cDNA clones specific to neuronal organs/tissues, and was also used to obtain brain-specific probes (18). These clones are now being utilized to identify genes involved in some of the known neurological disorders of mice. In Brassica sp., a cDNA clone encoding a glycoprotein that co-segregated with the self-incompatibility locus has been isolated from a cDNA library made from mature, incompatible stigma mRNAs (74). The identity of the cDNA clone corresponding to the S-locus was confirmed by RFLP co-segregation analysis.

APPLICATIONS OF RESTRICTION FRAGMENT LENGTH POLYMORPHISM ANALYSIS

Genetic Mapping

One of the first and most extensive applications of RFLPs in eukaryotes has been in the development of detailed linkage maps. In humans, this approach had been very productive (Tab. 1); RFLP mapping is now the most efficient way to map genes and has allowed many morphological and biochemical markers to be mapped. This technique has been extended to a wide variety of organisms (Tab. 2) and, theoretically, could be applied to any organism. In plants, RFLP markers in corn and tomato are rapidly expanding their already detailed genetic maps, which had been developed from morphological and isozyme polymorphisms (Tab. 1). The segregation analysis of RFLP markers is facilitated by: (a) the co-dominance of alleles (generally); (b) the extensive polymorphism available; (c) the minimal pleiotropic effect of individual markers; (d) the absence or limited influence of the

Tab. 1.   Comparison of number of RFLP markers to other genetic markers
           mapped in humans, maize, and tomato.

Markers	1982	1986
Humans		
Proteins and others	303[a]	950[b,c]
RFLPs	24[a]	410[c]
Maize		
Proteins and others	175[d]	282[e]
RFLPs	0	234[f,g]
Tomato		
Proteins and others	215[d]	240[h]
RFLPs	0	110[f] + 150[i,j]

Note: Numbers are approximate, since individual markers may be
mapped with varying degrees of accuracy.   RFLP markers are being
mapped at a rapid rate, therefore these figures will be underesti-
mates.

[a] Ref. 119.
[b] I.M. Cohen, Howard Hughes University, Connecticut, pers. comm.
This figure contains genes of known function, some of which were
mapped using RFLPs.
[c] V.A. McKusick, Johns Hopkins Hospital, Baltimore, Maryland, pers.
comm.
[d] Ref. 77.
[e] E. Coe, University of Missouri, Columbia, Missouri, pers. comm.
[f] T. Helentjaris, NPI, Salt Lake City, Utah, pers. comm.
[g] Other RFLP maps of corn are being developed but data are unavail-
able.
[h] M. Mutschler, Cornell University, Ithaca, New York, pers. comm.
[i] S.D. Tanksley, Cornell University, Ithaca, New York, pers. comm.
[j] Two independent sets of RFLP markers exist.   Since both sets
employed clones from leaf cDNA libraries, abundant mRNAs are expected to have resulted in markers in common.

environment; and (e) the availability of methods for linkage analysis (2,
13,19,104).   The number of probes necessary to saturate genomes of various
sizes in inbreeding or outbreeding species having different population
structures has been estimated (13,19,62).   For example, assuming a genome
size of 1,500 cM, 286 random RFLP markers would be necessary to cover the
genome every 20 cM (ρ = 0.9 and plus 25% to take chromosome ends into account).

     The construction of a linkage map using RFLPs has three phases: (a)
development of sources of probes; (b) identification of polymorphic probes;
and (c) segregation analysis.   The different types and sources of probes as
well as the different techniques used to detect polymorphisms have been
discussed in the previous sections.   When inbred lines are available, segregation analyses are preferably done on F_2 populations because of the
high information content per individual (2).   Testcrosses, backcrosses, and

Tab. 2.   Eukaryotes for which genetic maps are being developed using RFLP markers.

Common name	Species	Extent*	Reference(s)
Humans	Homo sapiens	1, 2	119
Mole-rat	Spalax ehrenbergi	2	76
Mouse	Mus sp.	2	3, 120
Rat	Rattus sp.	2	81
Pig	Sus scrofa	2	27
Sheep	Ovis aries	2	28
Fruit fly	Drosophila spp.	2	33
Nematode	Caenorhabditis elegans	2	30, 92
Ameba	Dictyostelium discoideum	2	117
Yeast	Saccharomyces cerevisiae	2	83
Tomato	Lycopersicon spp.	1, 2	17, 51, 110
Peppers	Capsicum spp.	1	17
Maize	Zea maydis	1, 2	51
Lettuce	Lactuca sativa	1	B.S. Landry et al., ms. in prep.
Pea	Pisum sativum	2	86, 87
Barley	Hordeum vulgare	2	93

*Key: 1, extensive mapping with random probes; 2, specific genes mapped.

recombinant inbred line populations can also be used in specific cases. Family analyses of F_1 progeny are generally used to construct linkage maps of heterozygous species. The polymorphisms detected between parental lines, however, need to be tested on small segregating populations to confirm segregation, prior to analyzing many progeny.

The choice of species and parental lines influences the frequency with which polymorphisms can be detected. In maize, frequent polymorphisms were detected even among commercial inbreds (50,91). In tomato, few RFLPs were found among commercial lines; a higher level of polymorphism was seen when Lycopersicon esculentum was compared to its wild relatives. The selection of genetically diverse parents is required for rapid development of a genetic map. This is facilitated by data on genetic distance. Data from morphological and isozyme markers have been used to select highly polymorphic crosses in maize (22), tomato (17), and lettuce (B.S. Landry, R.V. Kesseli, B. Farrara, and R.W. Michelmore, ms. in prep.) for RFLP mapping. Data on the frequency of RFLPs in turn provide more accurate estimates of the genetic distances between possible parental lines.

The efficiencies with which different restriction endonucleases detect polymorphism have been compared in some species. In humans, restriction endonucleases containing CpG dimer in their recognition sequence (e.g., MspI and TaqI) detected the majority of the polymorphism (10). In tomato, maize (50), and lettuce (B.S. Landry, R.V. Kesseli, H. Leung, and R.W. Michelmore, ms. in prep.), however, no more polymorphism was detected with restriction endonucleases containing CpG dimers than with other enzymes.

In lettuce, significant differences in efficiency were detected between restriction endonucleases, but were not correlated with the presence of CpG
dimers (B.S. Landry, R.V. Kesseli, H. Leung, and R.W. Michelmore, ms. in
prep.). Overall, enzymes recognizing four base pairs were less efficient
than enzymes recognizing six base pairs. The restriction endonucleases
BamHI, EcoRI, EcoRV, and HindIII detected acceptable levels of polymorphism
and consistently produced useful hybridization patterns.

Segregation analysis and construction of a linkage map are stepwise
processes which can be facilitated by the use of computer programs (104).
Chi-square tests for goodness-of-fit of the individual segregation ratios
are followed by two-way χ^2 contingency tests for independent assortment of
RFLP markers. Recombination frequencies and their standard errors for all
pairwise comparisons between loci are estimated using the maximum likeli-
hood method (2). Finally, map units (cM) are calculated using a mapping
function (58). The linkage map is deduced by the best fit to these values.

Genetic maps developed with RFLP markers can be related to specific
chromosomes using: (a) linkage with markers already assigned to chromosomes; (b) in humans, chromosome-specific hybridoma cell lines (47,116) or
sorted chromosomes (113); (c) in maize, monosomics and B-A chromosome
translocation stocks (38,49); (d) in wheat (97), tomato (90), and some
other species, aneuploids; and (e) in Drosophila, in situ hybridization to
polytene chromosomes (85).

Mapping of Quantitative Traits

Many agriculturally important traits are quantitatively inherited.
The inheritance of these characters can be analyzed biometrically to partition the combined effects of the loci into genetic (additive, dominant, and
epistatic) and residual (environmental and residual interactions) variances
(44,66). The biometrical approach is, however, unable to identify, characterize, and manipulate individual loci involved. Alternatively, statistical methods based on the normal distribution and three-point mapping can
locate genome regions or loci contributing to a quantitative trait (quantitative trait locus or QTL) (41,66,101,106,107). Morphological markers
(seed color, leaf morphology, etc.) have been used for limited mapping of
QTLs (95). Isozyme polymorphisms have also been used to map some QTLs in
tomato (leaf ratio, stigma exertion, fruit weight, and seed weight) (106)
and maize (ear number and grain yield) (103). The number of morphological
and isozyme markers that can segregate in a single cross is too low to obtain the close linkage required to identify the majority of the loci contributing to a quantitative trait. Segregation in a single cross of many
dispersed RFLP markers will allow the entire genome to be assayed for loci
contributing to quantitative traits (14,105). Four lines of tomato with
high soluble solids were selected from an interspecific cross followed by a
series of backcrosses between a donor parent with high soluble solids and a
recurrent parent with low soluble solids. Two RFLP loci identified fragments of chromosomes which were retained from the donor parent and which
were subsequently shown to be associated with QTLs determining high soluble
solids (79). In another study, 2-tridecadone (2-TD) has been identified as
the principal toxic factor responsible for insect resistance in tomato; a
minimum of three QTLs are involved, as three independent RFLP loci were
found associated with the accumulation of 2-TD (75). Restriction fragment
length polymorphism markers tightly linked to QTLs should allow indirect
selection of traits that are difficult or expensive to evaluate directly.
The RFLPs linked to QTLs could also identify specific chromosome segments

contributing to dominance or heterosis by analyzing an F_2 population from inbred lines. These chromosome segments could be accumulated in commercial inbreds to maximize their specific combining ability.

It will be more difficult to use RFLPs for QTL analysis in outbreeding than in inbreeding species (14). When sufficient RFLPs become available, however, they could aid in the identification of chromosome regions involved in QTLs and their transfer into breeding populations. Marker-assisted evaluation and selection for QTLs before reproductive maturity would increase the rate of genetic progress; this will be particularly important in programs where the generation time is long (e.g., trees).

Fingerprinting

Restriction fragment length polymorphisms can provide DNA fingerprints for identification of lines or individuals. Probes homologous to highly heterozygous loci and displaying multiple alleles are ideal for this purpose. Minisatellite DNAs, which are dispersed in the human genome, show extensive RFLPs (55). From the analysis of 79 individuals, a single mini-satellite locus displayed 77 different alleles and a high level of heterozygosity (97%) (121). Variants of the core sequence of these minisatellites provided somatically stable DNA fingerprints which were specific to individuals. A probe of a single minisatellite gave a theoretical probability of identity between two unrelated individuals as low as 3×10^{-11}; when two probes were considered, the probability became 5×10^{-19} (55). In plants, the number of single-copy RFLP markers necessary for fingerprinting of cultivars, protection of breeders' rights, and parentage identification for selfing and outcrossing species has been calculated (22,100). For example, in an inbreeding crop, when there are only two alleles at each RFLP locus, with each allele occurring with a frequency of 0.5 among 20 inbred lines, the probability of distinguishing each of the 20 lines is 0.99 if 20 probes are used; observations of frequent RFLPs in maize, however, suggested that fewer polymorphic probes would be necessary to obtain accurate identification of lines (14,38). For highly heterozygous, asexually propagated plants, a few markers would be sufficient. The use of polymorphic satellite DNA in plant identification could also be an efficient and reliable method for fingerprinting; RFLPs of such sequences, however, have not been studied (34,55). $[^{32}P]$-RNA:DNA mismatch analysis might also reduce the number of single/low-copy probes necessary for strain identification due to the high sensitivity of this method for detecting polymorphisms.

Genome Organization

Restriction fragment length polymorphism analysis is broadening the basic capability for genetic analysis, providing an opportunity for a more extensive investigation of genome organization. Previous molecular characterizations of genomes have relied on DNA reassociation kinetics (reviewed in Ref. 115). These experiments, however, gave only gross estimates of genome organization. Restriction fragment length polymorphism analyses can provide new insights into the organization and variation of specific components of a genome (37,39,53). Estimations of neutral mutation rate, genetic diversity, and phylogenetic relationship have been adapted for RFLP data (1,37,39,53). Some restriction endonucleases may not be distributed randomly, however, and phylogenetic relationships derived from RFLP data should be interpreted with caution (1). Also, using functionally related cDNAs as probes, functional maps of genomes can be constructed. Such maps will indicate whether genes which are expressed at the same developmental stage or under the same conditions are clustered. Restriction fragment length polymorphism analysis can also provide insights on the stability of gene order within and between species; such comparative gene mapping will generate information on genic and chromosomal evolution and on phylogenetic relationships among taxa.

The genomic organization and evolution of multigene families in a wide variety of organisms have been studied using RFLP analysis. The genomic distribution of members of the actin gene family was determined in Dictyostelium (117) and tomato (15) by this technique. The constant heavy chain of the human immunoglobulin genes was ordered within clusters by RFLP analysis (12). Also, frequent unequal crossing-over between repeated units was shown to cause deletions/duplications in the proline-rich proteins of the human salivary protein gene complex (8). Molecular characterization and RFLP mapping of the different clusters of chlorophyll a/b binding protein genes (cab) in tomato revealed seven functional genes and one truncated gene (84). The stability of individual cab genes can now be investigated within and between species, which may provide insights on the mechanisms of gene duplication. In pea, members of the cab and ribulose-1,5-bisphosphate carboxylase small subunit (rbcS) gene families are each tightly linked, reflecting either recent duplication events that have not yet undergone rearrangement or clustering maintained due to a common regulatory strategy (87).

Linkage disequilibrium and its causes have been studied with RFLPs in several genetic systems. Restriction fragment length polymorphism analysis revealed that within one cluster of the constant heavy-chain genes for human immunoglobulins, recombination frequency was not always correlated with physical distance (12). This demonstration of strong linkage disequilibrium between members of the same cluster has important implications to the evolution of this gene family and other multigene clusters. Nonrandom associations of polymorphic restriction sites have also been found in the human β-globin gene cluster, the human growth hormone gene cluster, and the HLA-D region (5,26). Studies on ribosomal DNA spacer length polymorphism in a population of barley maintained over 54 generations demonstrated selection for RFLP variants and associated loci (93).

Restriction fragment length polymorphism analysis has also been used to study genome organization of organelles. Maternal inheritance of the mitochondrial genome in humans was confirmed with RFLPs (42). Calculations of the average fraction of the restriction endonuclease sites that were polymorphic and rate of base pair substitutions in human mitochondrial DNA have indicated that the human species may have passed through a severe population constriction relatively recently (20). An extensive DNA polymorphism analysis of the human mitochondrial genome also provided evidence for co-evolution between specific nuclear and mitochondrial genes (23). The RFLP analysis of the maize mitochondrial genome indicated that dramatic rearrangements (duplications, deletions, and recombinations) have occurred during its evolution (98). In contrast, base substitutions account for most of the polymorphisms of animal mitochondrial genomes. Comparisons of restriction fragment patterns of chloroplast genomes of putative diploid wheat ancestors indicated the cytoplasmic origin of polyploid wheat species (109). Similar analyses on chloroplast DNA of Lycopersicon and Solanum spp. determined the maternal phylogenies of 15 accessions (80). These phylogenies were generally consistent with relationships based on morphology and crossability.

CONCLUSIONS AND FUTURE PROSPECTS

Restriction fragment length polymorphism mapping has become the most efficient way to construct detailed linkage maps. Extensive genetic maps of several plant species can be expected in the near future. Saturation of genomes with DNA markers will allow testing of hypotheses on genome organization and evolution. Identification and monitoring of genetic events within a single organism [transposition (9,122), gene activation (7), and clonal origin of tissues (35,114)] are becoming feasible. Characterization of RFLP loci tightly linked to QTLs will facilitate selection of traits that are difficult to assay directly and provide estimates of the number of loci involved. With the aid of computers, restriction mapping of the complete genome of Caenorhabditis elegans has been initiated using a set of overlapping cosmid clones. This approach should be applicable to any organism containing a low percentage of repetitive DNA (e.g., A. thaliana), if the large investment of time, labor, and funds is considered worthwhile.

Restriction fragment length polymorphism analysis in plants has, so far, only utilized a few of the available techniques. As reviewed earlier, techniques for preselecting probes, detecting low levels of polymorphism, fingerprinting with satellite sequences or with [^{32}P]-RNA:DNA mismatch analysis, and amplifying specific sequences by the PCR:OR method to increase the detection sensitivity are becoming routine in RFLP studies of humans and should be exploited for studies of plants. One of the primary limitations to application of RFLPs, however, is the extensive labor involved in analyzing sufficiently large populations. Machines for automated DNA isolation, electrophoresis, blotting, and hybridization are becoming available and will facilitate the handling of large numbers of DNA samples.

Recently, orthogonal-field-alteration gel electrophoresis (OFAGE) and field inversion gel electrophoresis (FIGE) have allowed separation of large DNA molecules, such as whole chromosomes of yeast (24,25), protozoans (52, 112), and trypanosomes (111). These techniques provide molecular karyotypes and allow the rapid determination of the chromosomal position of any DNA marker in organisms with no cytogenetic karyotype (24); they could therefore provide an effective substitute for chromosome-specific lines. Also, OFAGE or FIGE can be used in combination with restriction endonucleases which cut infrequently to separate large DNA fragments (21). This system might aid the cloning of genes linked to RFLPs. For example, tightly linked RFLP markers flanking a gene of interest (e.g., disease resistance gene) could be used to probe Southern blots of OFAGE gels; if both flanking markers hybridize to a single fragment, then the fragment should contain the gene of interest. DNA from the region of the gel containing this fragment could be cloned and then transformed into a host lacking the character of interest to test for functional complementation. One limitation of this approach may be that few restriction endonucleases have 8-bp recognition sequences. The use of different methylases in combination with the restriction endonuclease DpnI, however, generating different recognition sequences of 8, 10, and even 12 bp, may overcome this constraint (67).

Restriction fragment length polymorphism analyses of many organisms will generate large amounts of data and computer support will be necessary (60,70). For human RFLP studies, the Yale human gene mapping library is a network system which maintains several cross-referenced data sets relevant to mapping types of polymorphisms and cloning of human genes. Similar networks will be needed for other organisms to digest and disseminate the information harvested by RFLP analyses.

REFERENCES

1. Adams, J., and E.D. Rothman (1982) Estimation of phylogenetic relationships from DNA restriction patterns and selection of endonuclease
   sites. Proc. Natl. Acad. Sci., USA 79:3560-3564.
2. Allard, R.W. (1956) Formulas and tables to facilitate the calculation
   of recombination values in heredity. Hilgardia 24(10):235-278.
3. Amar, L., C.D. Arnaud, J. Cambrou, J.L. Guenet, and P.R. Avner (1985)
   Mapping the mouse X chromosome using random genomic probes and an interspecific mouse cross. EMBO J. 4:3695-3700.
4. Amasino, R.M. (1986) Acceleration of nucleic acid hybridization rate
   by polyethylene glycol. Analyt. Biochem. 152:304-307.
5. Antonarakis, S.E., C.D. Boehm, P.J.V. Giardina, and H.H. Kazazian, Jr.
   (1982) Nonrandom association of polymorphic restriction sites in the
   β-globin gene cluster. Proc. Natl. Acad. Sci., USA 79:137-141.
6. Arnheim, N., C. Strange, and H. Erlich (1985) Use of pooled DNA samples to detect linkage disequilibrium of polymorphic restriction fragments and human disease: Study of the HLA class II loci. Proc. Natl.
   Acad. Sci., USA 82:6970-6974.
7. Ascione, R., N. Sacchi, D.K. Watson, R.J. Fisher, S. Fujiwara, A.
   Seth, and T.S. Papas (1986) Oncogenes: Molecular probes for clinical
   application in malignant diseases. Gene Analyt. Techn. 3:25-39.
8. Azen, E., K.M. Lyons, T. McGonigal, N.L. Barret, L.S. Clements, N.
   Maeda, E.F. Vanin, D.M. Carlson, and O. Smithies (1984) Clones from
   the human gene complex coding for salivary proline-rich proteins.
   Proc. Natl. Acad. Sci., USA 81:5561-5565.
9. Baker, B., J. Schell, H. Lorz, and N. Federoff (1986) Transposition of
   the maize controlling element "Activator" in tobacco. Proc. Natl.
   Acad. Sci., USA 83:4844-4848.
10. Barker, D., M. Schafer, and R. White (1984) Restriction sites contain-
    ing CpG show a higher frequency of polymorphism in human DNA. Cell
    86:131-138.
11. Bates, G.P., J.S. Cavanna, N.J. Lench, S.D.M. Brown, and R. Williamson
    (1985) Regional microdissection and microcloning from the short arm of
    chromosome 2. Cytogenet. Cell Genet. 40:578.
12. Bech-Hansen, N.T., P.S. Linsley, and D.W. Cox (1983) Restriction frag-
    ment length polymorphisms associated with immunoglobulin C-gamma genes
    reveal linkage disequilibrium and genomic organization. Proc. Natl.
    Acad. Sci., USA 80:6952-6956.
13. Beckmann, J.S., and M. Soller (1983) Restriction fragment length poly-
    morphisms in genetic improvement: Methodologies, mapping and costs.
    Theor. Appl. Genet. 67:35-43.
14. Beckmann, J.S., and M. Soller (1986) Restriction fragment length poly-
    morphisms and genetic improvement of agricultural species. Euphytica
    35:111-124.
15. Bernatzky, R., and S.D. Tanksley (1986) Genetics of actin related se-
    quences in tomato. Theor. Appl. Genet. 72:314-321.
16. Bernatzky, R., and S.D. Tanksley (1986) Majority of random cDNA clones
    correspond to single loci in the tomato genome. Mol. Gen. Genet.
    203:8-14.
17. Bernatzky, R., and S.D. Tanksley (1986) Towards a saturated linkage
    map in tomato based on isozymes and random cDNA sequences. Genetics
    112:887-898.
18. Blatt, C., K. Mileham, M. Haas, M.N. Nesbitt, M.E. Harper, and M.I.
    Simon (1983) Chromosomal mapping of the mink cell focus-inducing and
    xenotropic env gene family in the mouse. Proc. Natl. Acad. Sci., USA
    80:6298-6302.

19. Botstein, D., R.L. White, M. Skolnick, and R.W. Davis (1980) Construction of a genetic linkage map in man using restriction fragment length polymorphisms. Am. J. Hum. Genet. 32:314-331.
20. Brown, W.M. (1980) Polymorphism in the mitochondrial DNA of humans as revealed by restriction endonuclease analysis. Proc. Natl. Acad. Sci., USA 77:3605-3609.
21. Brown, W.R.A., and A.P. Bird (1986) Long-range restriction mapping of mammalian genomic DNA. Nature 322:477-481.
22. Burr, B., S.V. Evola, F.A. Burr, and J.S. Beckmann (1983) The application of restriction fragment length polymorphism to plant breeding. In Genetic Engineering: Principles and Methods, Vol. 5, J.K. Setlow and A. Hollaender, eds. Plenum Press, New York, pp. 45-59.
23. Cann, R.L., W.M. Brown, and A.C. Wilson (1984) Polymorphic sites and the mechanism of evolution in human mitochondrial DNA. Genetics 106: 479-499.
24. Carle, G.F., and M.V. Olson (1985) An electrophoretic karyotype for yeast. Proc. Natl. Acad. Sci., USA 82:3756-3760.
25. Carle, G.F., M. Frank, and M.V. Olson (1986) Electrophoretic separations of large DNA molecules by periodic inversion of the electric field. Science 232:65-68.
26. Chakravarti, A., J.A. Philips, III, K.H. Mellits, K.H. Buetow, and P.H. Seeburg (1984) Patterns of polymorphism and linkage disequilibrium suggest independent origins of the human growth hormone gene cluster. Proc. Natl. Acad. Sci., USA 81:6085-6089.
27. Chardon, P., M. Kirszenbaum, C. Geffrotin, C. Renard, and D. Cohen (1985) Restriction fragment length polymorphism of the major histocompatibility complex of the pig. Immunogenetics 21:161-171.
28. Chardon, P., M. Kirszenbaum, P.R. Cullen, C. Geffrotin, C. Auffray, J.L. Strominger, D. Cohen, and M. Vaiman (1985) Analysis of the sheep MHC using HLA class I, II, and C4 cDNA probes. Immunogenetics 22:349-358.
29. Cheng, T.C., S.H. Orkin, S.E. Antonarakis, M.J. Potter, J.P. Sexton, A.F. Markam, P.J.V. Giardina, A. Li, and H.H. Kazazian, Jr. (1984) β-Thalassemia in Chinese: Use of in vivo RNA analysis and oligonucleotide hybridization in systematic characterization of molecular defects. Proc. Natl. Acad. Sci., USA 81:2821-2825.
30. Cox, G.N., S. Carr, J.M. Kramer, and D. Hirsh (1985) Genetic mapping of Caenorhabditis elegans collagen genes using DNA polymorphisms as phenotypic markers. Genetics 109:513-528.
31. Dahlberg, A.E., and E.J. Stellwag (1983) Electrophoretic transfer of DNA, RNA and protein onto diazobenzyloxymethyl paper. In Methods in Enzymology: Recombinant DNA, Part B, Vol. 100, R. Wu, L. Grossman, and K. Moldave, eds. Academic Press, Inc., New York, pp. 326-333.
32. Davis, D.R., and C.A. Cullis (1982) A simple plant polytene chromosome system, and its use for in situ hybridization. Plant Mol. Biol. 1: 301-304.
33. Davis, R.L., and N. Davidson (1984) Isolation of the Drosophila melanogaster dunce chromosomal region and recombinational mapping of dunce sequences with restriction site polymorphisms as genetic markers. Mol. Cell. Biol. 4:358-367.
34. Deumling, B. (1981) Sequence arrangement of a highly methylated satellite DNA of a plant, Scilla: A tandemly repeated inverted repeat. Proc. Natl. Acad. Sci., USA 78:338-342.
35. Dracopoli, N.C., A.N. Houghton, and L.J. Old (1985) Loss of polymorphic restriction fragments in malignant melanoma: Implications for tumor heterogeneity. Proc. Natl. Acad. Sci., USA 82:1470-1474.

36. Drayna, D., K. Davies, D. Hartley, J.L. Mandel, G. Camerino, R. Williamson, and R. White (1984) Genetic mapping of the human X chromosome by using restriction fragment length polymorphisms. Proc. Natl. Acad. Sci., USA 81:2836-2839.
37. Engels, W.R. (1981) Estimating genetic divergence and genetic variability with restriction endonucleases. Proc. Natl. Acad. Sci., USA 78:6329-6333.
38. Evola, S.V., F.A. Burr, and B. Burr (1986) The suitability of restriction fragment length polymorphisms as genetic markers in maize. Theor. Appl. Genet. 71:765-771.
39. Ewens, W.J., R.S. Spielman, and H. Harris (1981) Estimation of genetic variation at the DNA level from restriction endonuclease data. Proc. Natl. Acad. Sci., USA 78:3748-3750.
40. Fisher, E.M.C., J.S. Cavanna, and S.D.M. Brown (1985) Microdissection and microcloning of the mouse X chromosome. Proc. Natl. Acad. Sci., USA 82:5846-5849.
41. Gelderman, H. (1975) Investigations on inheritance of quantitative characters in animals by gene markers. I. Methods. Theor. Appl. Genet. 46:319-330.
42. Giles, R.E., H. Blanc, H.M. Cann, and D.C. Wallace (1980) Maternal inheritance of human mitochondrial DNA. Proc. Natl. Acad. Sci., USA 77:6715-6719.
43. Glaser, T., D. Gerhard, C. Payne, C. Jones, and D. Housman (1985) Three polymorphic DNA markers from chromosome 11. Cytogenet. Cell Genet. 40:643.
44. Griffing, B. (1956) A generalized treatment of the use of diallel crosses in quantitative inheritance. Heredity 10:31-50.
45. Grodzicker, T., J. Williams, P. Sharp, and J. Sambrook (1974) Physical mapping of temperature-sensitive mutations of adenoviruses. Cold Spring Harbor Symp. Quant. Biol. 39:439-446.
46. Gusella, J.F. (1986) DNA polymorphism and human disease. Ann. Rev. Biochem. 55:831-854.
47. Gusella, J.F., C. Keys, A. Varsanyi-Breiner, F.T. Kao, C. Jones, T.T. Puck, and D. Housman (1980) Isolation and localization of DNA segments from specific human chromosomes. Proc. Natl. Acad. Sci., USA 77:2829-2833.
48. Helentjaris, T., and R. Gesteland (1983) Evaluation of random cDNA clones as probes for human restriction fragment polymorphisms. Mol. Appl. Genet. 2:237-247.
49. Helentjaris, T., D.F. Weber, and S. Wright (1986) Use of monosomics to map cloned DNA fragments in maize. Proc. Natl. Acad. Sci., USA (in press).
50. Helentjaris, T., G. King, M. Slocum, C. Siedenstrang, and S. Wegman (1985) Restriction fragment polymorphisms as probes for plant diversity and their development as tools for applied plant breeding. Plant Mol. Biol. 5(2):109-118.
51. Helentjaris, T., M. Slocum, S. Wright, A. Schaefer, and J. Nienhuis (1986) Construction of linkage maps in maize and tomato using restriction fragment length polymorphism. Theor. Appl. Genet. (in press).
52. Holmes-Giannini, S., M. Schittini, J.S. Keithly, P.W. Warburton, C.R. Cantor, and L.H.T. Van der Ploeg (1986) Karyotype analysis of Leishmania species and its use in classification and clinical diagnosis. Science 232:762-765.
53. Hudson, R.R. (1982) Estimating genetic variability with restriction endonucleases. Genetics 100:711-782.

54. Hutchison, J., A. Abbott, M. O'Dell, and R.B. Flavell (1985) A rapid screening technique for the detection of repeated DNA sequences in plant tissues. Theor. Appl. Genet. 69:329-333.
55. Jeffreys, A.J., V. Wilson, and S.L. Thein (1985) Individual-specific "fingerprints" of human DNA. Nature 316:76-79.
56. Kan, Y.W., and A.M. Dozy (1978) Antenatal diagnosis of sickle-cell anaemia by DNA analysis of amniotic fluid cells. Lancet 2:910-912.
57. Kao, F.T., J.A. Hartz, M.L. Law, and J.N. Davidson (1982) Isolation and chromosomal localization of unique DNA sequences from a human genomic library. Proc. Natl. Acad. Sci., USA 79:865-869.
58. Kosambi, D.D. (1944) The estimation of map distance from recombination values. Ann. Eugen. 12:172-175.
59. Krumlauf, R., M. Jeanpierre, and B.D. Young (1982) Construction and characterization of genomic libraries from specific human chromosomes. Proc. Natl. Acad. Sci., USA 79:2971-2975.
60. Lalouel, J.M., T. Elsner, G.M. Lathrop, P. Callahan, A. Oliphant, R.L. White, D. Cohen, and J. Dausset (1985) The CEPH system of management of RFLP data. Cytogenet. Cell Genet. 40:676.
61. Landry, B.S., and R.W. Michelmore (1985) Selection of probes for restriction fragment length analysis from plant genomic clones. Plant Mol. Biol. Rep. 3(4):174-179.
62. Lange, K., and M. Boehnke (1982) How many polymorphic marker genes will it take to span the human genome? Am. J. Hum. Genet. 34:842-845.
63. Law, M.L., J.N. Davidson, and F.T. Kao (1982) Isolation of a human repetitive sequence and its application to regional chromosome mapping. Proc. Natl. Acad. Sci., USA 79:7390-7394.
64. Leonard, W.J., T.A. Donlon, R.V. Lebo, and W.C. Greene (1985) Localization of the gene encoding the human interleukin-2 receptor on chromosome 10. Science 228:1547-1549.
65. Litt, M., and R.L. White (1985) A highly polymorphic locus in human DNA revealed by cosmid-derived probes. Proc. Natl. Acad. Sci., USA 82:6206-6210.
66. Mather, K.M., and J.L. Jinks (1977) Introduction to Biometrical Genetics, Cornell University Press, New York, 231 pp.
67. McClelland, M., L.G. Kessler, and M. Bittner (1984) Site-specific cleavage of DNA at 8- and 10-base-pair sequences. Proc. Natl. Acad. Sci., USA 81:983-987.
68. Meinkoth, J., and G. Wahl (1984) Hybridization of nucleic acids immobilized on solid supports. Analyt. Biochem. 138:267-284.
69. Metzlaff, M., W. Troebner, F. Baldauf, R. Schegel, and J. Cullum (1986) Wheat specific repetitive sequences: Construction and characterization of four different genomic clones. Theor. Appl. Genet. 72:207-210.
70. Miller, J.A. (1984) Diagnostic DNA. Science News 126:104-107.
71. Mullis, K.B., and F.A. Faloona (1986) Specific synthesis of DNA in vitro via a polymerase catalyzed chain reaction. In Methods in Enzymology, R. Wu, L. Grossman, and K. Moldave, eds. Academic Press, Inc., New York (in press).
72. Mullis, K.B., F.A. Faloona, S. Scharf, R. Saiki, G. Horn, and H. Erlich (1986) Specific enzymatic amplification of DNA in vitro: The polymerase chain reaction. Cold Spring Harbor Symp. Quant. Biol. Vol. 51 (in press).
73. Myers, R., Z. Larin, and T. Maniatis (1985) Detection of single base substitutions by ribonuclease cleavage at mismatches in RNA:DNA duplexes. Science 230:1242-1246.

74. Nasrallah, J.B., T.H. Kao, M.L. Goldberg, and M.E. Nasrallah (1985) A cDNA clone encoding an S-locus-specific glycoprotein from Brassica oleracea. Nature 318:263-267.

75. Nienhuis, J., T. Helentjaris, M. Slocum, B. Ruggero, and A. Schaefer (1986) Restriction fragment length polymorphism analysis of loci associated with insect resistance in tomato. Crop Sci. (in press).

76. Nizetic, D., F. Figueroa, E. Nevo, and J. Klein (1985) Major histocompatibility complex of the mole-rat. Immunogenetics 22:55-67.

77. O'Brien, S.J., ed. (1984) Genetic Maps, Cold Spring Harbor Laboratory, Cold Spring Harbor, New York, 584 pp.

78. Orkin, S.H. (1983) The use of cloned DNA fragments to study human disease. In Genetic Engineering: Principles and Methods, Vol. 5, J.K. Setlow and A. Hollaender, eds. Plenum Press, New York, pp. 189-206.

79. Osborn, T.C., D.C. Alexander, and J.F. Fobes (1986) Identification of restriction fragment length polymorphism linked to genes controlling soluble solids content in tomato fruit. Theor. Appl. Genet. (submitted for publication).

80. Palmer, J.D., and D. Zamir (1982) Chloroplast DNA evolution and phylogenetic relationships in Lycopersicon. Proc. Natl. Acad. Sci., USA 79:5006-5010.

81. Palmer, M., P.J. Wettstein, and J.A. Frelinger (1983) Evidence for extensive polymorphism of class I genes in the rat major histocompatibility complex (RT1). Proc. Natl. Acad. Sci., USA 80:7616-7620.

82. Paulsen, K., G. Scherer, K.E. Davies, and H.H. Ropers (1985) The isolation of transcribed sequences from the human X chromosome. Cytogenet. Cell Genet. 40:721.

83. Petes, T.K., and D. Botstein (1977) Simple Mendelian inheritance of the reiterated ribosomal DNA of yeast. Proc. Natl. Acad. Sci., USA 74:5091-5095.

84. Pichersky, E., R. Bernatzky, S. Tanksley, R.W. Breidenbach, A.P. Kaush, and A.R. Cashmore (1985) Molecular characterization and genetic mapping of two clusters of genes encoding chlorophyll a/b binding proteins in Lycopersicon esculentum. Gene 40:247-258.

85. Pirrotta, V., H. Jackle, and J.E. Edstrom (1983) Microcloning of microdissected chromosome fragments. In Genetic Engineering: Principles and Methods, Vol. 5, J.K. Setlow and A. Hollaender, eds. Plenum Press, New York, pp. 1-17.

86. Polans, N.O., N.F. Weeden, and W.F. Thompson (1986) Distribution, inheritance and linkage relationships of ribosomal DNA spacer length variants in pea. Theor. Appl. Genet. 72:289-295.

87. Polans, N.O., N.F. Weeden, and W.F. Thompson (1985) Inheritance, organization, and mapping of rbcS and cab multigene families in pea. Proc. Natl. Acad. Sci., USA 82:5083-5087.

88. Potter, S., J. Newbold, C. Hutchison, III, and M. Edgell (1985) Specific cleavage analysis of mammalian mitochondrial DNA. Proc. Natl. Acad. Sci., USA 72:4496-4500.

89. Reed, K.C., and D.A. Mann (1985) Rapid transfer of DNA from agarose gels to nylon membranes. Nucl. Acids Res. 13:7207-7221.

90. Rick, C.M. (1975) The tomato. Handbook of Genetics 2:247-280.

91. Rivin, C.J., E.A. Zimmer, C.A. Cullis, V. Walbot, T. Huynh, and R.W. Davis (1983) Evaluation of genomic variability at the nucleic acid level. Plant Mol. Biol. Rep. 1:9-16.

92. Rose, A.M., D.L. Bouillie, E.P.M. Condido, K.A. Beckenbach, and D. Nelson (1982) The linkage mapping of cloned restriction fragment length differences in Caenorhabditis elegans. Mol. Gen. Genet. 188:286-291.

93. Saghai-Maroof, M.A., K.M. Soliman, R.A. Jorgensen, and R.W. Allard (1984) Ribosomal DNA spacer-length polymorphisms in barley: Mendelian inheritance, chromosomal location and population dynamics. Proc. Natl. Acad. Sci., USA 81:8014-8018.
94. Saiki, R.K., S. Scharf, F. Faloona, K.B. Mullis, G.T. Horn, H.A. Erlich, and N. Arnheim (1985) Enzymatic amplification of β-globin genomic sequences and restriction site analysis for diagnosis of sickle cell anemia. Science 230:1350-1354.
95. Sax, K. (1923) The association of size differences with seed-coat pattern and pigmentation in Phaseolus vulgaris. Genetics 8:552-560.
96. Schwartz, C.E., and M.H. Skolnick (1985) The use of partial digestion of genomic DNA to reveal informative RFLPs. Cytogenet. Cell Genet. 40:740.
97. Sears, E.R. (1954) The aneuploids of common wheat. Un. Missoury Res. Bull. 572:1-59.
98. Sederoff, R.R., C.S. Levings, III, D.H. Timothy, and W.W.L. Hu (1981) Evolution of DNA sequence organization in mitochondrial genomes of Zea. Proc. Natl. Acad. Sci., USA 78:5953-5957.
99. Singh, L., and K.W. Jones (1984) The use of heparin as a simple cost-effective means of controlling background in nucleic acid hybridization procedures. Nucl. Acids Res. 12(14):5627-5638.
100. Soller, M., and J.S. Beckmann (1983) Genetic polymorphism in varietal identification and genetic improvement. Theor. Appl. Genet. 67:25-33.
101. Soller, M., A. Genizi, and T. Brody (1976) On the power of experimental designs for the detection of linkage between marker loci and quantitative loci in crosses between inbred lines. Theor. Appl. Genet. 47:35-39.
102. Southern, E.M. (1975) Detection of specific sequences among DNA fragments separated by gel electrophoresis. J. Mol. Biol. 98:503-517.
103. Stuber, C.W., H.H. Goodman, and R.H. Moll (1982) Improvement of yield and ear number resulting from selection at allozyme loci in a maize population. Crop Sci. 22:737-740.
104. Suiter, K.A., J.F. Wendel, and J.S. Case (1983) Linkage-1: A pascal computer program for the detection and analysis of genetic linkage. J. Hered. 74:203-204.
105. Tanksley, S.D. (1983) Molecular markers in plant breeding. Plant Mol. Biol. Rep. 1:3-8.
106. Tanksley, S.D., H. Medina-Filho, and C.M. Rick (1982) Use of naturally-occurring enzyme variation to detect and map genes controlling quantitative traits in an interspecific backcross of tomato. Heredity 49:11-25.
107. Thoday, J.M. (1961) Location of polygenes. Nature 191:368-370.
108. Tsao, S., C. Brunk, and R. Pearlman (1981) Hybridizing dry agarose gels. Plant Mol. Biol. Newsletter 2(3):100-101.
109. Tsunewaki, K., and Y. Ogihara (1983) The molecular basis of genetic diversity among cytoplasms of Triticum and Aegilops species. II. On the origin of polyploid wheat cytoplasms as suggested by chloroplast DNA restriction fragment patterns. Genetics 104:155-171.
110. Vallejos, C.E., S.D. Tanksley, and R. Bernatzky (1986) Localization in the tomato genome of DNA restriction fragments containing sequences homologous to the rRNA (45S), the major chlorophyll a/b binding polypeptide and the ribulose bisphosphate carboxylase genes. Genetics 112:93-105.
111. Van der Ploeg, L.H.T., D.C. Schwartz, C.R. Cantor, and P. Borst (1984) Antigenic variation in Trypanosoma brucei analyzed by electrophoretic separation of chromosome-sized DNA molecules. Cell 37:77-84.

112. Van der Ploeg, L.H.T., M. Smits, T. Ponnudurai, A. Vermeulen, J.H.E. Th. Meuwissen, and G. Langsley (1985) Chromosome-sized DNA molecules of Plasmodium falciparum. Science 229:658-661.
113. Van Dilla, M.A., L.L. Deaven, K.L. Albrith, N.A. Allen, M.R. Aubuchon, M.F. Bartholdi, N.C. Brown, E.W. Campbell, A.V. Carrano, L.M. Clark, L.S. Cram, B.D. Crawford, J.C. Fuscoe, J.W. Gray, C.E. Hildebrand, P.J. Jackson, J.H. Jett, J.L. Longmire, C.R. Lozes, M.L. Luedemann, J.C. Martin, J.S. McNinch, L.J. Meincke, M.L. Mendelson, J. Meyne, R.K. Moyzis, A.C. Munk, J. Perlman, D.C. Peters, A.J. Silva, and B.J. Trask (1986) Human chromosome-specific DNA libraries: Construction and availability. Bio/Technology 4:537-552.
114. Vogelstein, B., E.R. Fearon, S.R. Hamilton, and A.P. Feinberg (1985) Use of restriction fragment length polymorphisms to determine the clonal origin of human tumors. Science 227:642-645.
115. Walbot, V., and R. Golberg (1979) Plant genome organization and its relationship to classical plant genetics. In Nucleic Acids in Plants, T. Hall and J. Davies, eds. CRC Press, Inc., Boca Raton, Florida, pp. 3-40.
116. Watkins, P.C., R.E. Tanzi, K.T. Gibbons, J.V. Tricoli, G. Landes, R. Eddy, T.B. Shows, and J.F. Gusella (1985) Isolation of polymorphic DNA segments from human chromosome 21. Nucl. Acids Res. 13:6075-6089.
117. Welker, D.L., K.P. Hirth, P. Romans, A. Noegel, R.A. Firtel, and K.L. Williams (1986) The use of restriction fragment length polymorphisms and DNA duplications to study the organization of the actin multigene family in Dictyostelium discoideum. Genetics 112:27-42.
118. Willard, H.F. (1985) Polymorphic alpha satellite repeated DNA at the centromere of the X chromosome. Cytogenet. Cell Genet. 40:778.
119. Willard, H.F., M.H. Skolnick, P.L. Pearson, and J.L. Mandel (1985) Human gene mapping by recombinant DNA techniques. Cytogenet. Cell Genet. 40:360-489.
120. Winoto, A., M. Steinmetz, and L. Hood (1983) Genetic mapping in the major histocompatibility complex by restriction enzyme site polymorphism: Most mouse class I genes map to the Tla complex. Proc. Natl. Acad. Sci., USA 80:3425-3429.
121. Wong, Z., V. Wilson, A.J. Jeffreys, and S.L. Thein (1986) Cloning a selected fragment from a human DNA fingerprint: Isolation of an extremely polymorphic minisatellite. Nucl. Acids Res. 14(11):4605-4616.
122. Yoder, J., F. Belzile, K. Alpert, J. Palys, and R.W. Michelmore (1986) Mobilization of the maize transposable element Ac in tomato. Tomato Biotechnology Symposium, Alan R. Liss, Inc., New York (in press).

PLANT GENE STRUCTURE AND FUNCTION

AN ANALYSIS OF CHROMATIN STRUCTURE AND GENE REGULATION

Robert J. Ferl, Anna-Lisa Paul,
Mohammed Ashraf, and Scott Bollinger

Department of Botany
University of Florida
Gainesville, Florida   32611

SUMMARY

We present here a compilation of our studies aimed at describing the architecture of the maize alcohol dehydrogenase genes (Adh). Specifically, we have sought a structural description of these genes at levels beyond primary sequence; i.e., the association of the DNA with nuclear proteins to form chromatin and the conformation of the DNA itself. The basic definition of chromatin is quite broad and refers to the nuclear DNA together with its associated histones and nonhistone chromosomal proteins in the complex structural array that packages and organizes the eukaryotic genome within the nucleus. What we hope to accomplish by elucidating the structural aspects of the Adh genes is an understanding of the mechanics involved in organizing these genes within the chromatin array, the structural changes involved in preparing the gene for transcriptional activation, and the identification of those sequences in the promoters of these genes that are responsible for regulating transcriptional activity.

We have chosen the maize Adh gene system for analysis for several reasons. First, both Adh1 and Adh2 are genetically well-characterized genes that have been cloned and sequenced (5,6,18,37). Second, both genes are transcriptionally induced by anaerobic stress, providing a convenient laboratory mechanism for controlling the transcriptional state of the genes (14). Third, while similarly (though not identically) responsive to anaerobic stress, there is almost no sequence homology between the 5' flanking regions of the genes (5,6). These two genes, therefore, provide an interesting system to search for similarities and contrasts in their chromatin structure and to elucidate the roles that chromatin structure might play in their coordinate regulation.

INTRODUCTION: GENERAL ASPECTS OF CHROMATIN STRUCTURE

The eukaryotic genome depends on several orders of condensation to package the DNA to a manageable level in the nucleus. The first order of condensation has been likened to "beads on string," where the DNA strand wraps around histone octamers to form nucleosomes, generating the 10-nm fiber. The second-order structure is generated by winding this 10-nm fiber into a shallow supercoil (solenoid), which is about 30 nm thick. The final order of structure consists of further supercoiling and condensation into the typical metaphase chromosome (46).

While the second and third orders of condensation do the most to package the genome, the first-order structure has recently received much attention relative to the regulation of gene expression. Changes in the transcriptional state of a gene are often associated with changes in the organization of nucleosomes in the region of the gene. Activation of a gene will often alter the packing state of the nucleosomes to create "open" areas along its length, especially around the promoter (46,47). It is thought that these "open" regions play a vital role in gene regulation, either by providing access to the gene for transcriptional machinery or by functioning as some other indicator of the transcriptional state of the gene. This is supported by two observations. First, "open" regions of chromatin are present in many genes only when the genes are transcriptionally active. Second, transcription factors have been found associated with these regions (8,33,43). Other special structural features of chromatin, such as nonhistone proteins and regions of Z-DNA, have been associated with "open" chromatin as well. These components may play a role in generating and maintaining regions of "open" chromatin (8,21).

Open regions of genes have been characterized predominantly by the degree of access afforded to the nuclease DNase I, which is a nonspecific endonuclease, digesting (for the most part) any unprotected piece of DNA. It can be used to identify open regions, since the DNA will be less protected from nuclease digestion where the nucleosome packaging is more relaxed. Active genes seem to be generally more sensitive to DNase I than inactive genes (17,46). In addition, regions just 5' to the start of transcription can be even more sensitive to DNase I digestion than the region of the coding sequences of the gene (16,22,38,41,48,49). These regions are generally referred to as hypersensitive sites and usually encompass 50 to 200 base pairs of DNA (43).

The DNase I hypersensitive sites that are present at or near the active promoter are likely to be associated with sequences that play a role in regulating that gene, although the exact function and structural nature of such sites are unclear. As mentioned, hypersensitive sites are often associated with nonhistone proteins. That is, a correlation is established, but no necessary connection, as with the 5' region of the human β-interferon and several other genes (22,43,51). There is at least one example, however, where a protein actually confers nuclease hypersensitivity to the gene. The addition of nuclear extract and histones to a plasmid carrying the chicken β-A globin gene in vitro creates a hypersensitive site in the promoter of the gene (8).

The relationship between hypersensitive sites and transcriptional activity is conveniently studied in genes that can be induced experimentally. Such systems allow for direct comparison of the same gene in both its inactive and active state. A number of animal genes have been examined in this way. The _Drosophila_ glue protein gene _Sgs4_ is developmentally induced. In this case, cells expressing the gene can be experimentally selected (39). The chicken ovalbumin gene can be induced hormonally (22), and both the mouse metallothionein-1 gene (38) and the _Drosophila_ heat shock protein gene (48) are induced by stress (cadmium and heat, respectively).

Plant genes have not been as extensively characterized with respect to nuclease hypersensitivity. The phaseolin gene codes for a major seed protein in _Phaseolus_. When chromatin from phaseolin-synthesizing tissue was tested, the entire phaseolin gene was generally more sensitive to DNase I digestion, but no specific hypersensitive sites have been detected (29).

MAIZE ALCOHOL DEHYDROGENASE GENES

We have found DNase I hypersensitive sites in the maize alcohol dehydrogenase genes. The _Adh1_ and _Adh2_ genes are found on separate chromosomes but code for proteins similar enough to form functional heterodimers (15). This suggests that they owe their origin to gene duplication (37), which is supported by the existence of similarities in coding sequence homology and shared antigenic determinants of the proteins (5,6,15). The 5' and 3' flanking sequences of both these genes have diverged completely except for an apparent 8-bp consensus sequence in the promoter region (5). It will be interesting to investigate the similarities and differences in the control mechanism of these two genes.

The _Adh1_ and _Adh2_ genes are induced by anaerobic stress (14). Increased _Adh1_ mRNA levels can be detected after 2 hr of anaerobiosis, and a detectable increase in the level of the protein is observed after 3 hr (5, 6,11,18). These data suggest that induction is mediated through transcriptional control. Therefore, any changes in chromatin structure upon induction are likely to reflect modifications that facilitate the transcriptional activation of the gene.

The first indication that there is a general modulation of chromatin associated with anaerobiosis came from electron micrographs of root nuclei from normal and hypoxic seedlings. The chromatin from anaerobically stressed plants showed a dramatic increase in condensation over nonstressed plants (1). At the molecular level, in situ digestion of nuclei from seedling roots with restriction endonucleases shows an anaerobically induced increase in accessibility to enzymes at the sites closest to the transcription start site in _Adh1_ (10). We have recently employed DNase I to give a more comprehensive view of chromatin modulation around the _Adh_ promoters.

DNase I Hypersensitive Sites of Maize Adh1

There are two types of DNase I hypersensitive sites seen in the 5' region of _Adh1_: constitutive and anaerobically induced sites (34). These two classes of sites are grouped into two distinct regions. Figure 1 shows representative lanes from an autoradiograph of DNA resulting from in situ digestions of nuclei from cell suspensions (44). The constitutive region is further upstream than the induced region, ranging from positions -160 to -700. There are three major (numbered 3, 4, and 5) and three minor hypersensitive sites within this region that are open to DNase I digestion regardless of the transcriptional state of the gene (Fig. 1). The constitutive hypersensitive sites are found in nuclei from both uninduced and induced cells. The region of distinct anaerobic response ranges from -35 to -150. The two hypersensitive sites within this region are seen only after anaerobic induction of the cells.

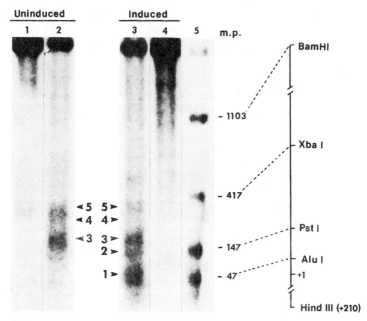

Fig. 1.   The DNase I hypersensitive sites in maize Adhl. Four representa-
           tive lanes of an autoradiograph showing the five major hypersen-
           sitive sites in the maize Adhl 5' region are given for uninduced
           (inactive gene) and induced (active gene) cells. Lanes 1 and 4
           are controls with no exogenous DNase I. Lanes 2 and 3 are from
           reactions with DNase I added to a concentration of 0.2 µg/ml and
           0.1 µg/ml, respectively. The bands are numbered in the space be-
           tween lanes 2 and 3. Their positions can be compared to internal
           markers in lane 5, with the map positions (m.p.) relative to the
           start of transcription corresponding to each marker band at
           right. Methods: After in situ digestions with DNase I of nuclei
           from uninduced and anaerobically induced cells, the DNA was puri-
           fied, digested to completion with HindIII, and electrophoresed
           on 2% agarose. The resulting gel was blotted to Genescreen (NEN-
           Research Products, Boston, Massachusetts) and probed with a
           cloned fragment homologous to an area 3' to the promoter (+210 to
           approximately +10) in order to visualize the bands.

        The relative openness of these two regions is shown by densitometric
scans of the DNase I data. A composite of scans encompassing a wide range
of DNase I concentrations on nuclei from both uninduced and induced cells
was used to generate the surface plots shown in Fig. 2. These graphs represent the dynamic effects of DNase I on intact chromatin. Raised areas
along the surface of the graphs correspond to areas of DNase I hypersensitivity; the higher the peak, the greater the degree of digestion. Three of
the major sites are labeled (refer to Fig. 1 for positions). For the most
part, sites that are less prominent are masked by the background. Each
line in the plane of migration represents a different concentration of
DNase I. The thin lines more or less perpendicular to these lines connect
corresponding points from each DNase I concentration. In the uninduced
set, the bands corresponding to the constitutive hypersensitive sites are
intensified as the concentration of DNase I increases. After induction, a

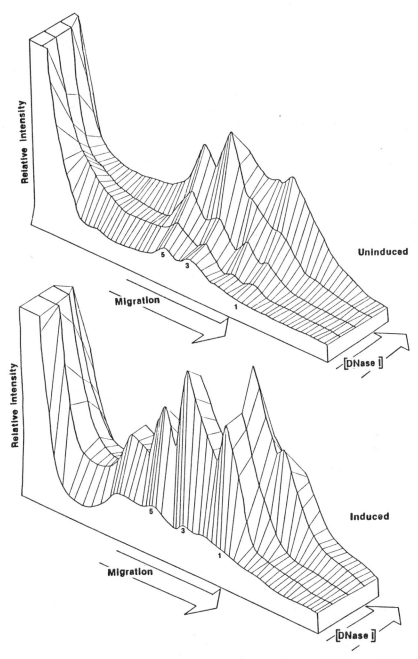

Fig. 2.   Densitometrically generated surface plots of DNase I hypersensitivity. The lines in the plane of migration represent each lane of increasing concentration of DNase I. The higher the peak, the higher the intensity of the corresponding band on the autoradiogram.

second hypersensitive area appears within the anaerobic response region (band 1). At first, all bands are of about equal intensity. However, as the DNase I concentration increases, the bands within the constitutive region diminish as those in the anaerobic response region intensify.

In situ digestions of nuclei with restriction enzymes having sites in the hypersensitive regions were also used to quantitate the degree of openness. The AluI site at -47 and the PstI site at -147 fall within DNase I generated bands 1 and 2, respectively. When nuclei were isolated from induced cells, the AluI site was three times more accessible to digestion by AluI, and the PstI site was over twice as accessible to digestion by PstI compared to nuclei from aerobic cells. Restriction sites further upstream in the constitutive hypersensitive region (XbaI and another AluI) showed less difference in accessibility to restriction endonucleases with changes in the transcriptional activity of the gene. The marked difference seen in the intensities of bands corresponding to the inducible DNase I hypersensitive sites is therefore supported by the accessibility of restriction sites in this region.

Several genes show division of hypersensitive sites into constitutive and inducible regions. For example, there are two genes in chicken that show this arrangement. The hypersensitive sites in the chicken lysozyme gene from oviduct are mixed in their distribution (16). Two constitutive sites center around -100 and -2400, with an inducible site between them at -1900. The vitellogenin gene from chicken has constitutive regions to the 3' side and within the protein coding region of the gene. Hypersensitive sites also appear just 5' to the transcription start site after induction (2). In the immediate-early gene of the human cytomegalovirus, the constitutive hypersensitive region is the hypersensitive region closer to the start of transcription (-175 to -525), with the inducible region ranging further upstream (-650 to -975) (30).

There are sequences that have been associated with DNase I hypersensitive sites, but it is unclear whether the enzyme prefers the actual sequence or a chromatin conformation influenced by the sequence. For example, the sequence GNNAAGNANNAT seems to coincide with regions of the simian virus 40 (SV40) promoter hypersensitive to DNase I digestion (21). There is also a core consensus sequence (TAAAGC) in Drosophila that is found in the DNase I hypersensitive sites of a number of genes (39). The Drosophila core consensus sequence is found in maize Adhl at position -510 within the constitutive hypersensitive region.

Structural Oddities in the DNA of the Adhl Promoter Region

We have examined the Adhl promoter for non-B form DNA structures that might play a role in regulation, perhaps as part of the overall chromatin structure or as specific regulatory sequences. Basically, we have looked for those regions of the promoter that adopt a non-B form structure when placed under supercoiled tension in vitro. These structures can be recognized by their hypersensitivity to the nuclease S1 or by their reaction with certain chemical probes (7).

There are two regions of the promoter that have been so identified: a Z-DNA tract at position -330 to -314 from the start of transcription and a tract of extreme homopurine/homopyrimidine asymmetry centered at position -65 (12).

The region from -330 to -314 (CACACACGCGCGCGCTCC) was characterized as to its ability to form Z-DNA in vitro by several criteria. The borders of the tract are hypersensitive to S1 nuclease (12). The T and C residues near the borders are hypersensitive to osmium tetroxide and hydroxylamine, respectively. The G residues within the Z region are hypersensitive to diethylpyrocarbonate (R.J. Ferl, unpubl. results). All of these features are diagnostic for Z-DNA (19,40). It should be noted that the occurrence of this segment as Z-DNA in vivo has not yet been demonstrated.

There is evidence that regions of Z-DNA influence DNase I digestion in chromatin. One example of this is the viral control element in the minichromosome of SV40 where two hypersensitive sites flank a region of Z-DNA (49). It was suggested that the hypersensitive sites are at least partially generated by the presence of Z-DNA binding proteins, which may then form a particle that can be recognized by transcription factors. In Adh1, the Z-DNA region at -330 to -314 is near or within the first major hypersensitive site in the constitutive region.

The asymmetric homopurine/homopyrimidine tract at -65 is structurally similar to many of the S1 hypersensitive sites that have been found in the 5' flanking regions of many nonplant genes (3,4,9,13,20,25,26,27,28,31,36, 42,45). The reason why these sites are hypersensitive to S1 nuclease under supercoil tension is somewhat enigmatic, and several models have been proposed, from triple helices to non-Z-left-handed DNA. Whatever the exact structural perturbation is in these tracts, it is known that homopurine/homopyrimidine tracts serve as energy sinks to relieve supercoil tension. These tracts therefore have features potentially related to the issue of chromatin structure. First, it is known that such stretches of DNA do not package well into nucleosomes (7). In Adh1, the fact that the major inducible DNase I hypersensitive site lies over this region is very intriguing. Second, in at least one case, the β-interferon gene, a homopurine/homopyrimidine tract has been shown to bind a transcription factor (50).

Models for the Regulation of Adh1

There are two related models that are suggested by the organization of hypersensitive sites into constitutive and inducible regions, as diagrammed in Fig. 3. In the first model, the signal to the gene that there is a need

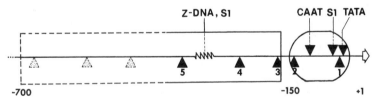

Fig. 3.   Model of the 5' region of Adh1. The rectangle encloses the constitutive hypersensitive region, whereas the anaerobic response region is defined by an oval. Arrowheads below the line show positions of hypersensitive sites within these regions, and arrows above the line point out sequences or areas of interest. The dotted portion of the constitutive region contains minor hypersensitive sites which do not respond to increasing concentrations of DNase I with an increase in intensity.

for activation is initially routed through the constitutive region. This region may bind a factor that causes a change downstream in the anaerobic response region, thus exposing the core promoter for transcription. In the second model, the constitutive region acts merely as a guide or portal to facilitate access to the more TATA-proximal elements of the promoter. In this case, the inducible hypersensitive area identifies an anaerobic response region that would have to be acted on directly by some factor(s) in order to recognize the signal that initiates the transcriptional process.

Both variations of this model predict that the major events that are involved in the recognition of anaerobiosis and the initiation of transcription take place in the "anaerobic response region" between positions -40 and -150. This idea has been recently supported by in vivo protein fingerprinting experiments which have identified the binding of factors to this region (R.J. Ferl, unpubl. results).

The DNase I Hypersensitive Sites of Maize Adh2

As diagrammed in Fig. 4, the promoter region of Adh2 shows three constitutive DNase I hypersensitive sites in chromatin (M. Ashraf, V. Vasil, I.K. Vasil, and R.J. Ferl, ms. in prep.). The three sites lie 5' to the coding region, between -25 and -400. The sites have been mapped in chromatin of nuclei from induced and uninduced roots, shoots, and suspension culture cells. There is no difference in the number or position of the hypersensitive sites in any of these tissues. However, the susceptibility of these hypersensitive sites to DNase I digestion increases with anaerobiosis. Several studies have indicated the existence of constitutive DNase I hypersensitive sites in the chromatin of the promoters of inducible genes, e.g., the heat shock genes of Drosophila (hsp22, hsp23, hsp26, and hsp28) (23), the rat preproinsulin II gene (49), and the ADHII gene of Saccharomyces cerevisiae (41). In these examples, as well as in maize Adh2, the presence of DNase I hypersensitive sites is not correlated with gene activity but only with potential for activation. Gene activity is, however, correlated with the degree of hypersensitivity.

It is interesting to correlate DNase I hypersensitive sites with the possible regulatory functions of the underlying DNA (Ref. 5; S.E. Bollinger and R.J. Ferl, ms. in prep.). The TATA box lies within the DNase I hypersensitive site 1 (Fig. 4). The Adh genes possess a potential "anaerobic consensus sequence" (CACCTCCC) 5' to the genes (-200 in Adh1 and -145 in Adh2) (5). This sequence is flanked by DNase I hypersensitive sites in both Adh genes (sites 2 and 3 of Fig. 3; sites 1 and 2 of Fig. 4).

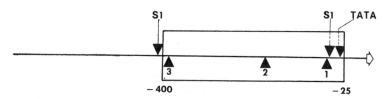

Fig. 4.   Model of the 5' region of Adh2. All hypersensitive sites are of
           a constitutive nature and are found in the region defined by the
           rectangle. Arrowheads below the line show positions of hypersensitive sites, and arrows above the line point out sequences of
           interest.

Structural Oddities in the DNA of the Adh2 Promoter Region

The Adh2 promoter region was mapped using S1 nuclease to look for non-B form DNA that may play a role in regulation (S.E. Bollinger and R.J. Ferl, ms. in prep.). Two supercoil-dependent S1 hypersensitive sites were observed. The first S1 hypersensitive site is located at -30, directly over the TATA box. It is a candidate for slippage loopout structure formation. The sequence contains short, direct repeats separated by a nonrepeated region. Under supercoiled stress, the duplicate regions might slide to pair with each other, forming two single-strand loops which can then act as substrates for S1 nuclease. Analysis of the adenovirus late promoter also shows a possible slippage area in the TATA region (50). A similar slippage in the 5' region of the Drosophila heat shock genes has also been seen (26).

The second S1 hypersensitive site maps to -400 and is characterized by a high concentration of homopolymeric T and A regions. The AT-rich segments are capable of non-B form potential when flanked by short regions of GC-rich DNA. Areas of homopolymeric dA/dT that are at least 4 bp long can cause bending at the junctions of the A-T regions (24) that might serve as substrate for S1 nuclease.

Model for the Regulation of Adh2

Unpublished results from several laboratories suggest that Adh2 is induced under less severe hypoxia than Adh1. The presence of constitutive hypersensitive sites in the Adh2 promoter indicates that the critical regions of the promoter chromatin are constantly open for the transcription signal to some degree. The more sensitive hypoxic response of Adh2 might therefore be facilitated, since the areas essential for the start of transcription are readily available.

ACKNOWLEDGEMENTS

The authors express appreciation to L. Curt Hannah and Bill Gurley for helpful discussion and review of this manuscript. This work was supported by Grants 83-CRCR-1-1271 and 86-CRCR-1-1997 from the U.S. Department of Agriculture Competitive Grants Program to R.J.F.

REFERENCES

1. Aldrich, H.C., D. Akin, M. Hils, and R.J. Ferl (1985) Ultrastructural correlations of anaerobic stress. Tissue and Cell 17:341-348.
2. Burch, J.B.E., and H. Weintraub (1983) Temporal order of chromatin structural changes associated with the activation of the major chicken vitellogenin gene. Cell 33:65-76.
3. Cantor, C. (1981) DNA choreography. Cell 25:293-295.
4. Cantor, C., and A. Efstratiadis (1984) Possible structures of homopurine-homopyrimidine S1 hypersensitive sites. Nucl. Acids Res. 12:8059-8072.
5. Dennis, E.S., M.M. Sachs, W.L. Gerlach, E.J. Finnegan, and W.K. Peacock (1985) Molecular analysis of the alcohol dehydrogenase-2 (Adh2) gene of maize. Nucl. Acids Res. 13:727-743.

6. Dennis, E.S., W.L. Gerlach, A.J. Pryor, A. Bennetzen, A. Ingils, D. Llewellyn, M.M. Sachs, R.J. Ferl, and W.J. Peacock (1984) Molecular analysis of the alcohol dehydrogenase (Adh1) gene of maize. Nucl. Acids Res. 12:3983-3989.

7. Elgin, S.C.R. (1984) Anatomy of hypersensitive sites. Nature (London) 309:213-214.

8. Emerson, B.M., and G. Felsenfeld (1984) Specific factor conferring nuclease hypersensitivity of the 5' end of the adult beta-globin gene. Proc. Natl. Acad. Sci., USA 81:95-99.

9. Evans, T., E. Schon, G. Gora-Maslak, J. Patterson, and A. Efstratiadis (1984) S1 hypersensitive sites in eukaryotic promoter regions. Nucl. Acids Res. 12:8043-8058.

10. Ferl, R.J. (1985) Modulation of chromatin structure in the regulation of the maize Adh1 gene. Mol. Gen. Genet. 200:207-210.

11. Ferl, R., M. Brennen, and D. Schwartz (1981) In vitro translation of maize ADH: Evidence for the anaerobic induction of mRNA. Biochem. Genet. 18:681-691.

12. Ferl, R.J., H. Nick, and B. Laughner (1986) S1 nuclease features of the maize alcohol dehydrogenase-1 gene promoter. Plant Mol. Biol. (submitted for publication).

13. Finer, M.H., E.J.B. Fodor, H. Boedtker, and P. Doty (1984) Endonuclease S1 sensitive site in chicken pro-a2(I) collagen 5' flanking gene region. Proc. Natl. Acad. Sci., USA 81:1659-1663.

14. Freeling, M. (1973) Simultaneous induction by anaerobiosis or 2,4-D of multiple enzymes specified by two unlinked genes: Differential Adh1 Adh2 expression in maize. Mol. Gen. Genet. 127:215-227.

15. Freeling, M. (1974) Dimerization of multiple maize ADH studied in vivo and in vitro. Biochem. Genet. 12:407-417.

16. Fritton, H.P., T. Igo-Kemenes, J. Nowock, U. Strech-Jurk, M. Thiesen, and A.E. Sippel (1984) Alternative sets of DNase I hypersensitive sites characterize the various functional states of the chicken lysozyme gene. Nature (London) 311:163-165.

17. Garel, A., and R. Axel (1976) Selective digestion of transcriptionally active ovalbumin genes from oviduct nuclei. Proc. Natl. Acad. Sci., USA 73:3966-3970.

18. Gerlach, W.L., A.J. Pryor, E.S. Dennis, R.J. Ferl, M.M. Sachs, and W.J. Peacock (1982) cDNA cloning and induction of the alcohol dehydrogenase gene (Adh1) of maize. Proc. Natl. Acad. Sci., USA 79:2981-2985.

19. Glikin, G.H., G. Gargiulo, L. Rena-Descalzi, and A. Worcel (1983) Escherichia coli single-strand binding protein stabilizes specific denatured sites in superhelical DNA. Nature (London) 303:770-774.

20. Johnson, B., and A. Rich (1985) Chemical probes of DNA conformation: Detection of Z-DNA at nucleotide resolution. Cell 42:713-724.

21. Jongstra, J., T.R. Reudelhuber, P. Oudet, C. Benoist, C.-B. Chae, J.M. Jeltsch, D.J. Mathis, and P. Chambon (1984) Induction of altered chromatin structures by Simian Virus 40 enhancer promoter elements. Nature (London) 307:708-714.

22. Kaye, J.S., S. Pratt-Kaye, M. Bellard, G. Dretzen, F. Bellard, and P. Chambon (1986) Steroid hormone dependence of four DNase I-hypersensitive regions located within the 7000-bp 5'-flanking segment of the ovalbumin gene. EMBO J. 5:277-285.

23. Keene, M.A., V. Corces, K. Lowenhaupt, and S.C.R. Elgin (1981) DNase I hypersensitive sites in Drosophila chromatin occur at the 5' ends of regions of transcription. Proc. Natl. Acad. Sci., USA 78:143-146.

24. Koo, H.-S., H.-M. Wu, and D.M. Crother (1986) DNA bending at adenine-thymine tracts. Nature (London) 320:501-506.
25. Larsen, A., and H. Weintraub (1982) An altered conformation detected by S1 nuclease occurs at specific regions in active chick globin chromatin. Cell 29:609-622.
26. Mace, H.A.F., H.R.B. Pelham, and A. Travers (1983) Association of an S1 nuclease sensitive structure with short direct repeats 5' of Drosophila heat shock genes. Nature (London) 304:555-557.
27. Margot, J.B., and R.C. Hardison (1985) DNase-1 and nuclease S1 sensitivity of the rabbit B1 globin gene in nuclei and in supercoiled plasmids. J. Mol. Biol. 184:195-210.
28. McKeon, C., A. Schmidt, and B. deCrombrugghe (1984) A sequence conserved in both the chicken and mouse a2(I) collagen promoter contains sites sensitive to S1 nuclease. J. Biol. Chem. 259:6636-6640.
29. Murray, M.G., and W.C. Kennard (1984) Altered chromatin conformation of higher plant gene phaseolin. Biochemistry 23:4225-4232.
30. Nelson, J.A., and M. Groudine (1986) Transcriptional regulation of the human cytomegalovirus major immediate-early gene is associated with induction of DNase I-hypersensitive sites. Mol. Cell. Biol. 6:452-461.
31. Nickol, J.M., and G. Felsenfeld (1983) DNA conformation at the 5' end of the chicken adult B-globin gene. Cell 35:467-477.
32. Nordheim, A., and A. Rich (1983) Negatively supercoiled Simian Virus 40 DNA contains Z-DNA segments within the transcriptional enhancer region. Nature (London) 303:674-679.
33. Parker, C.S., and J. Topol (1984) A Drosophila RNA polymerase II transcription factor contains a promoter-region-specific DNA binding activity. Cell 36:357-369.
34. Paul, A.-L., V. Vasil, I.K. Vasil, and R.J. Ferl (1986) Constitutive and anaerobically induced DNase I hypersensitive sites in the 5' region of the maize Adh1 gene. Proc. Natl. Acad. Sci., USA (in press).
35. Pospelov, V.A., G.H. Klobeck, and G.H. Zachau (1984) Correlation between DNase I hypersensitive sites and putative regulatory sequences in human immunoglobulin genes of the K light chain type. Nucl. Acids Res. 12:7007-7021.
36. Schon, E., T. Evans, J. Welsh, and A. Efstratiadis (1983) Conformation of promoter DNA: Fine mapping of S1 hypersensitive sites. Cell 35:837-848.
37. Schwartz, D. (1966) The genetic control of alcohol dehydrogenase in maize: Gene duplication and repression. Proc. Natl. Acad. Sci., USA 56:1431-1436.
38. Senear, A.W., and R.D. Palmiter (1983) Expression of mouse metallothionein-1 gene alters the nuclease hypersensitivity of its 5' regulatory region. Cold Spring Harbor Symp. Quant. Biol. 47:539-547.
39. Shermoen, A.W., and S.K. Beckendorf (1982) A complex of interacting DNase I-hypersensitive sites near the Drosophila glue protein gene Sgs4. Cell 29:601-607.
40. Singleton, C., M. Kilpatrick, and R. Wells (1984) S1 nuclease recognizes DNA conformational junction between left-handed helical (dT-dG)n.(dC-dA)n and contiguous right-handed sequences. J. Biol. Chem. 259:1963-1967.
41. Sledziewski, A., and E.T. Young (1982) Chromatin conformational changes accompany transcriptional activation of a glucose-repressed gene in Saccharomyces cerevisiae. Proc. Natl. Acad. Sci., USA 79:253-256.

42. Sunter, G., K.W. Buck, and R.H.A. Coutts (1985) S1-sensitive sites in the supercoiled double stranded form of tomato golden mosaic virus DNA component B: Identification of regions of potential alternative secondary structure and regulatory function. Nucl. Acids Res. 13:4645-4659.

43. Thomas, G.H., E. Siegfried, and S.C.R. Elgin (1985) DNase I hypersensitive sites: A structural feature of chromatin associated with gene expression. In Chromosomal Proteins and Gene Expression, G. Reeck, G. Goodwin, and P. Puigdomench, eds. Plenum Press, New York, pp. 77-101.

44. Vasil, V., and I.K. Vasil (1986) Plant regeneration from friable embryogenic callus and cell suspension cultures of Zea mays. J. Plant Physiol. 124:399-408.

45. Weintraub, H. (1985) High resolution mapping of S1 and DNase I hypersensitive sites in chromatin. Mol. Cell. Biol. 5:1538-1539.

46. Weintraub, H., and H. Groudine (1976) Chromosome subunits in active genes have an altered conformation. Science 193:848-856.

47. Weisbrod, S. (1982) Active chromatin. Nature (London) 297:289-295.

48. Wu, C. (1980) The 5' ends of Drosophila heat shock genes in chromatin are hypersensitive to DNase I. Nature (London) 286:854-860.

49. Wu, C., and W. Gilbert (1981) Tissue specific exposure of chromatin structure at the 5' terminus of the rat preproinsulin II gene. Proc. Natl. Acad. Sci., USA 78:1577-1580.

50. Yu, Y.-T., and J.L. Manley (1986) Structure and function of the S1 nuclease sensitive site in the adenovirus late promoter. Cell 45:743-751.

51. Zinn, K., and T. Maniatis (1986) Detection of factors that interact with the human B-interferon regulatory region in vivo by DNase I footprinting. Cell 45:611-618.

THE SMALL SUBUNIT GENES OF PETUNIA:

A WELL-CHARACTERIZED PLANT MULTIGENE FAMILY

Caroline Dean, Pamela Dunsmuir,
and John Bedbrook

Advanced Genetic Sciences
Oakland, California 94608

INTRODUCTION

Many key proteins in both plants and animals are specified by multi-gene families. The evolutionary significance of multigeny appears to be several-fold. On the one hand, gene dosage may be necessary to meet requirements of copious expression over short developmental times. An example of this is the deposition of seed storage proteins during the latter phase of seed maturation; multigene families for such plant proteins have been described (13,17). A second evolutionary basis for multigene families seems to be the requirement for multiple peptides with similar, yet distinct, functions. In plants, the chlorophyll a/b binding proteins of the light-harvesting complex represent such an example (11). A requirement for the expression of identical products in different tissues is yet a third basis for multigeny. In Drosophila, the actin genes (12) show a tissue-specific expression of this type. Tissue-specific expression of specific actin genes in soybean may be inferred from the results of Hightower and Meagher (15). Finally, individual genes in multigene families may be required at different stages of development. Although this has been shown to be true in animal systems, e.g., the actin genes in Drosophila, such a demonstration has not yet been made in higher plants.

In this chapter we address the multigene family specifying the small subunit of ribulose bisphosphate carboxylase (RuBPCase), which is the primary enzyme of the carbon fixation pathway in the chloroplasts of C3 plants and can account for 50% of the protein in leaf cells (8). Ribulose bisphosphate carboxylase is composed of two subunits, eight of each assembling to give one molecule of the enzyme. The large subunit [molecular weight (Mr) 55,000] is encoded by chloroplast DNA (6) and synthesized in the organelle. The small subunit, rbcS (Mr 14,000), is nuclear-encoded and synthesized as a high molecular weight precursor in the cytoplasm (16). The rbcS precursor protein is transported into the chloroplasts and processed to the mature subunit by post-translational mechanisms (5,14). RbcS expression is light-dependent (1,19). It has been demonstrated that there are multiple copies of the rbcS gene in the nuclear DNA of most plant species, including petunia, pea, wheat, soybean, and Lemna (2,3,4,7,11,20).

We describe here our knowledge of the structure and expression of the multiple genes for rbcS in Petunia. Our data to date indicate that the multigeny is not related to specific requirements for differing rbcS peptides, or to a requirement for tissue-specific expression. Our current conclusion is that the multigenic nature of the rbcS genes is an evolutionary accident. Whatever the specific function for the multiple genes is, they provide an excellent experimental system for assessing the role of various sequences in the quantitative aspects of gene expression.

LINKAGE AND HOMOLOGY ANALYSIS DIVIDES THE EIGHT SMALL
SUBUNIT GENES OF PETUNIA INTO THREE GROUPS

Hybridization of rbcS complementary DNA (cDNA) clones (11a) to petunia genomic DNA indicated that the petunia genome has a minimum of eight genes (9). Molecular cloning of genomic DNA (9) confirmed the existence of eight rbcS genes in Petunia as well as two partial gene fragments. Figure 1 illustrates portions of the Petunia chromosomes that contain these rbcS genes and gene fragments. Hybridization experiments with different cDNA clones coupled with thermal elution analysis, as well as hybridization experiments with probes derived from the 3' untranslated region of different rbcS genes, divide the eight rbcS genes into three groups. These groups are called subfamilies and are depicted in Fig. 1. The subfamily that is designated 51 contains six genes, five of which are tightly linked on a single Petunia chromosome. The 117 subfamily and the 71 subfamily each has a single gene which is separated from any other rbcS gene by at least 8 kb.

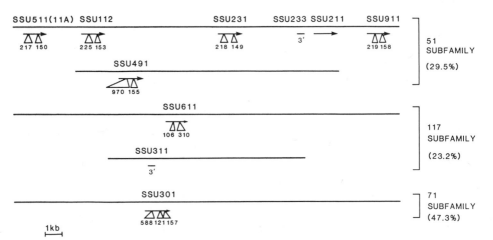

Fig. 1.   Schematic representation of the arrangement of the eight rbcS genes in Petunia. The position of the genes in Petunia nuclear DNA is indicated with arrows, which also indicate the direction of transcription. The division of the genes into subfamilies is summarized, and the contribution of each subfamily to the total rbcS mRNA expression in leaf tissue is given as a percentage in brackets. Introns are drawn as triangles below the genes and their size in base pairs is given. The genomic positions of the two 3' gene fragments are indicated.

THE DIFFERENT rbcS GENES OF PETUNIA SPECIFY NEAR IDENTICAL PEPTIDES

The rbcS polypeptide can be divided into two parts: the transit peptide which is cleaved off during, or subsequent to, entry into chloroplasts, and the mature rbcS subunit which is the peptide found in the enzyme. In seven of the rbcS genes, the transit peptide constitutes 57 amino
acids at the N terminus, and in one gene the transit peptide is 58 amino
acids; the mature peptide is 123 amino acids in every case. Figure 2 gives
the amino acid sequences determined from the nucleotide sequences of six of
the Petunia genes, including the genes of the 117 and the 71 subfamilies
and four of the six genes of the 51 subfamily.

Although there is considerable divergence in amino sequence between
genes in the transit peptide, the mature rbcS peptide predicted for each
gene is highly conserved. There are no amino acid differences within the
four 51 subfamily genes shown, and only one difference between these genes
and the genes of the 117 and 71 subfamilies. There are two differences between SSU611, the representative of the 117 subfamily, and SSU301, the representative of the 71 subfamily. These amino acid changes are all located
at or very close to the C terminus. It is unlikely that these changes result in functionally distinct peptides, since interspecific comparison of
rbcS genes shows the C terminus to be a region which is poorly conserved
(18).

THE EIGHT rbcS GENES OF PETUNIA ARE EXPRESSED AT DIFFERENT LEVELS

We measured the pool size of mRNA corresponding to the various rbcS
genes. These measurements were determined by three methods: (a) quantitative hybridization via gene-specific probes, (b) cDNA cloning frequency of
the various RNAs, and (c) primer extension analysis. Table 1 summarizes
that data from our analysis. The rbcS gene SSU301 shows the highest levels
of steady-state RNA and accounts for approximately 47% of rbcS mRNA; gene
611 accounts for approximately 23%; the genes of the 51 subfamily collectively account for the remaining 30% of the mRNA. Genes SSU511 and SSU231
are not distinguished by our analysis and together account for 15.2% of the
rbcS mRNA pool. The expression of SSU911 is not detected by our measurements; gene SSU491 accounts for 7%, gene SSU112 for 5.4%, and gene SSU211
for 1.9% of the mRNA. These results show that there is considerable variation in the level of expression of the various rbcS genes.

TISSUE-SPECIFIC EXPRESSION OF THE PETUNIA rbcS GENES

Figure 3 illustrates the results of typical experiments in which the
relative steady-state levels of rbcS mRNA were measured in various plant
organs. Each organ contains several different cell types, so this analysis
gives an average value of rbcS expression in the different cell types of
one organ.

A cDNA probe, pSSU51, was used in the analysis. This probe hybridizes
to all eight Petunia rbcS genes. If the level of expression in light-grown
leaf tissue is given a value of 100%, then the relative value is 4.2% in
sepals, 3% in petals, 2.3% in stems, 0.25% in stigma/anthers, and 0.2% in
roots. The level of rbcS mRNA from leaf tissue from plants grown in the
dark for seven days was 1% that in light-grown plants.

```
       1
SSU301 MET ALA SER SER VAL ILE SER SER     ALA ALA VAL ALA THR ARG THR ASN VAL ALA GLN ALA SER MET
SSU611 --- --- --- --- --- --- --- ---     --- --- --- --- --- SER SER --- ALA VAL --- --- --- ---
SSU491 --- --- --- --- --- MET --- ---     --- --- --- --- --- ASN --- --- ALA --- --- --- --- ---
SSU231 --- --- --- --- --- MET --- ---     --- --- --- --- --- SER --- --- ALA --- --- --- --- ---
SSU112 --- --- --- --- --- MET --- --- SER --- --- --- --- --- SER --- --- ALA --- --- --- --- ---
SSU911 --- --- --- --- --- MET --- ---     --- --- --- --- --- SER --- --- ALA --- --- --- --- ---


       23
SSU301 VAL ALA PRO PHE ASN GLY LEU LYS SER ALA VAL SER PHE PRO VAL SER ARG LYS GLN ASN LEU ASP ILE
SSU611 --- --- --- --- THR --- --- --- --- SER ALA --- --- --- THR LYS --- ASN --- --- --- --- ---
SSU491 --- --- --- --- THR --- --- --- --- ALA --- --- --- --- THR --- --- --- --- --- --- --- ---
SSU231 --- --- --- --- THR --- --- --- --- ALA --- --- --- --- --- --- --- --- --- --- --- --- ---
SSU112 --- --- --- --- THR --- --- --- --- ALA --- --- --- --- --- --- --- --- --- --- --- --- ---
SSU911 --- --- --- --- THR --- --- --- --- ALA --- --- --- --- --- --- --- --- --- --- --- --- ---


       46                                         1
SSU301 THR SER ILE ALA SER ASN GLY GLY ARG VAL GLN CYS MET GLN VAL TRP PRO PRO TYR GLY LYS LYS LYS
SSU611 --- --- LEU --- --- --- --- --- --- --- SER --- --- --- --- --- --- --- --- --- --- --- ---
SSU491 --- --- --- --- --- --- --- --- --- --- --- --- --- --- --- --- --- --- --- --- --- --- ---
SSU231 --- --- --- --- --- --- --- --- --- --- --- --- --- --- --- --- --- --- --- --- --- --- ---
SSU112 --- --- --- --- --- --- --- --- --- --- --- --- --- --- --- --- --- --- --- --- --- --- ---
SSU911 --- --- --- --- --- --- --- --- --- --- --- --- --- --- --- --- --- --- --- --- --- --- ---


       12
SSU301 TYR GLU THR LEU SER TYR LEU PRO ASP LEU THR ASP GLU GLN LEU LEU LYS GLU ILE GLU TYR LEU LEU
SSU611 --- --- --- --- --- --- --- --- --- --- --- --- --- --- --- --- --- --- --- --- --- --- ---
SSU491 --- --- --- --- --- --- --- --- --- --- --- --- --- --- --- --- --- --- --- --- --- --- ---
SSU231 --- --- --- --- --- --- --- --- --- --- --- --- --- --- --- --- --- --- --- --- --- --- ---
SSU112 --- --- --- --- --- --- --- --- --- --- --- --- --- --- --- --- --- --- --- --- --- --- ---
SSU911 --- --- --- --- --- --- --- --- --- --- --- --- --- --- --- --- --- --- --- --- --- --- ---


       35
SSU301 ASN LYS GLY TRP VAL PRO CYS LEU GLU PHE GLU THR GLU HIS GLY PHE VAL TYR ARG GLU TYR HIS ALA
SSU611 --- --- --- --- --- --- --- --- --- --- --- --- --- --- --- --- --- --- --- --- --- --- ---
SSU491 --- --- --- --- --- --- --- --- --- --- --- --- --- --- --- --- --- --- --- --- --- --- ---
SSU231 --- --- --- --- --- --- --- --- --- --- --- --- --- --- --- --- --- --- --- --- --- --- ---
SSU112 --- --- --- --- --- --- --- --- --- --- --- --- --- --- --- --- --- --- --- --- --- --- ---
SSU911 --- --- --- --- --- --- --- --- --- --- --- --- --- --- --- --- --- --- --- --- --- --- ---


       58
SSU301 SER PRO GLY TYR TYR ASP GLY ARG TYR TRP THR MET TRP LYS LEU PRO MET PHE GLY CYS THR ASP ALA
SSU611 --- --- --- --- --- --- --- --- --- --- --- --- --- --- --- --- --- --- --- --- --- --- ---
SSU491 --- --- --- --- --- --- --- --- --- --- --- --- --- --- --- --- --- --- --- --- --- --- ---
SSU231 --- --- --- --- --- --- --- --- --- --- --- --- --- --- --- --- --- --- --- --- --- --- ---
SSU112 --- --- --- --- --- --- --- --- --- --- --- --- --- --- --- --- --- --- --- --- --- --- ---
SSU911 --- --- --- --- --- --- --- --- --- --- --- --- --- --- --- --- --- --- --- --- --- --- ---


       81
SSU301 THR GLN VAL LEU GLY GLU LEU GLN GLU ALA LYS LYS ALA TYR PRO ASN ALA TRP ILE ARG ILE ILE GLY
SSU611 --- --- --- --- --- --- --- --- --- --- --- --- --- --- --- --- --- --- --- --- --- --- ---
SSU491 --- --- --- --- --- --- --- --- --- --- --- --- --- --- --- --- --- --- --- --- --- --- ---
SSU231 --- --- --- --- --- --- --- --- --- --- --- --- --- --- --- --- --- --- --- --- --- --- ---
SSU112 --- --- --- --- --- --- --- --- --- --- --- --- --- --- --- --- --- --- --- --- --- --- ---
SSU911 --- --- --- --- --- --- --- --- --- --- --- --- --- --- --- --- --- --- --- --- --- --- ---


       104
SSU301 PHE ASP ASN VAL ARG GLN VAL GLN CYS ILE SER PHE ILE ALA TYR LYS PRO PRO GLY PHE
SSU611 --- --- --- --- --- --- --- --- --- --- --- --- --- --- --- --- --- --- GLU --- TYR
SSU491 --- --- --- --- --- --- --- --- --- --- --- --- --- --- --- --- --- --- --- --- TYR
SSU231 --- --- --- --- --- --- --- --- --- --- --- --- --- --- --- --- --- --- --- --- TYR
SSU112 --- --- --- --- --- --- --- --- --- --- --- --- --- --- --- --- --- --- --- --- TYR
SSU911 --- --- --- --- --- --- --- --- --- --- --- --- --- --- --- --- --- --- --- --- TYR
```

Fig. 2.   The predicted amino acid sequence of the coding regions of six
           Petunia rbcS genes.   The amino acid sequence of the different
           genes is given as a comparison to the sequence predicted by gene
           SSU301.   Only amino acid replacements are shown.   A space has
           been placed into the amino acid sequence of all the genes except
           SSU112, to accommodate the extra amino acid in the transit pep-
           tide of this gene.

This analysis was extended to test for the relative expression of five
individual rbcS genes in the various organs.   Table 2 summarizes the results of this analysis and shows that although the absolute numbers vary,
the relative ranking of the five genes tested is the same in all organs.
That is, gene SSU301, which is the most abundantly expressed gene in the
leaf, is also the most abundantly expressed gene in sepals, stigma/anthers,
petals, and stem; gene SSU611, which is the second most abundantly expressed gene in leaf, is also the second most abundantly expressed gene in
these various organs.

Tab. 1.   Relative expression of rbcS genes in *Petunia* leaf tissue.

rbcS gene	A[1] Hybridization to RNA		B[2] Number of cDNA clones	C[3] Relative expression of each gene (%)
SSU301	1	1		47.3
SSU611	1	0.48	73	23.2
SSU491	0.145	0.18	23	7
SSU112	)0.15	)0.16	17	5.4
SSU911	)	)	0	ND
SSU511			)48	)15.2
SSU231			)	)
SSU211			6	1.9

[1]Relative hybridization of the four rbcS 3' tail probes to *Petunia* leaf
RNA.   The two columns summarize results from two different RNA preparations.   The gene showing the strongest hybridization signal is given a
value of 1.   The expression of the other rbcS genes is presented as a
fraction of this.   Genes SSU112 and SSU911 both hybridize to the same
probe, and the results are given collectively.
[2]The number of cDNA clones isolated corresponding to each rbcS gene.   The
division of 54 cDNA clones hybridizing to pSSU51 (a cDNA clone defining
a gene subfamily) into those corresponding to the genes SSU231, SSU211,
or SSU511 was based on the relative numbers of these three genes in the
18 cDNA clones sequenced.   The same is true for the division of the 17
cDNA clones hybridizing to the 3' tail probe 91A (10).
[3]The relative contribution of each rbcS gene in the total rbcS expression
in leaf tissue (calculated from the data in columns A and B).   ND = Not
detected.

64   C. DEAN ET AL.

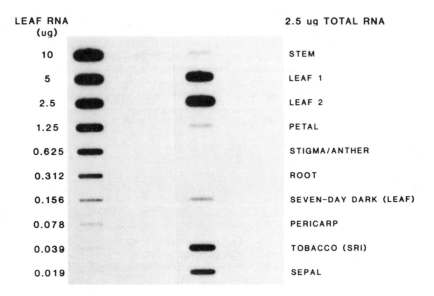

Fig. 3.   Slot blot analysis of rbcS expression in the different organs of
           the Petunia plant. Total RNA was extracted from the different
           organs of the Petunia plant and applied to a slot blot as de-
           scribed in Ref. 10. The slot blot was hybridized with a Petunia
           rbcS cDNA clone, pSSU51, which had been labeled using T₄ polymer-
           ase (10). Alkali-hydrolyzed RNA was used as a control to ensure
           that only RNA was contributing to the hybridization signal.

     In summary, although there is considerable variation in the level of
expression of the different rbcS genes and, collectively, these genes are
expressed at considerably differing levels in different organs, there is no
evidence from our analysis that there are specific rbcS genes which are
more efficiently expressed in one organ type relative to any other rbcS
gene.

THE rbcS GENE AS A MULTIGENE FAMILY

     To date, our analysis has not revealed any specific evolutionary sig-
nificance to the existence of multiple genes for rbcS in higher plants. It
is not possible to argue that the multiple genes are required in a dosage-
effect manner, since one of the eight genes accounts for nearly 50% of the
total expression. Furthermore, it is not possible to attribute specific
distinct functions to the different rbcS genes, since they all encode an
essentially identical peptide. Finally, as discussed above, there is no
evidence to indicate that the different genes are particularly important
for expression in differing organs. We have not yet looked for differential expression of the rbcS genes during development.

     Although our analysis has not revealed a biological purpose for mul-
tigeny for the rbcS protein, it does provide us with an excellent system
for an analysis of quantitative aspects of gene expression in plants. We
are now using this system to ask what sequences are responsible for the

Tab. 2.   Relative expression of small subunit genes in different organs of
          Petunia.

rbcS gene	Organ							
	Leaf		Stigma/Anther		Petal		Stem	
SSU301	1	(1)	1	(1)	1	(1)	1	(1)
SSU611	0.5	(0.44)	0.63	(0.15)	0.27	(0.56)	0.22	(0.17)
SSU491	0.14	(0.18)	0.08	(0.15)	0.02	(0.06)	0.03	(0.04)
SSU112	0.15	(0.15)	0.08	(0.15)	0.01	(0.02)	0.03	(0.02)
SSU911								

The relative hybridization of the four rbcS 3' tail probes to RNA isolated from
different organs of Petunia is summarized.   The gene showing the strongest
hybridization signal is given a value of 1.   The expression of the other rbcS
genes is presented as a fraction of this.   The numbers in parentheses show
results from a second experiment. In each experiment, alkali-hydrolyzed RNA was
used as a control to ensure that only RNA was contributing to the hybridization
signal.   The expression of the two rbcS genes SSU112 and SSU911 is given collectively, since the 3' tail probe 91A hybridizes transcripts of both genes.

relative levels of expression of the different rbcS genes. We have published a complete sequence analysis of the promoter regions of the rbcS
genes (10), and we are now analyzing expression of the Petunia genes after
their introduction into tobacco.

ANALYSIS OF PETUNIA rbcS GENE EXPRESSION IN TOBACCO:
A SYSTEM FOR ANALYSIS OF THE BASIS OF QUANTITATIVE SIGNALS

      Our present research on the rbcS gene family is focused on understand-
ing the basis of the differing levels of expression of the various rbcS
genes.   To do this, we plan to study the expression of isolated Petunia
genes and modified forms of these genes in tobacco. For this system to be
useful, the following criteria need to be met. First, the expression of
the Petunia genes needs to be detectable without confusion resulting from
background contamination from the endogenous tobacco rbcS genes.   Second,
relative expression levels observed for the different rbcS genes in Petunia
need to be mimicked when the genes are individually introduced into tobacco.   Third, the level of expression observed in Petunia should be attain-
able when a specific gene is introduced into tobacco.

      The results of experiments addressing these issues are illustrated in
Fig. 4.   In these experiments the level of expression of two different
Petunia genes is quantitated in multiple, independent tobacco plants transformed with either of the two Petunia genes. Quantitation of RNA pools is
by primer extension analysis. Figure 4A shows the level of expression of
the Petunia rbcS gene SSU301 in six independent transformants, as well as
the detection of this gene product in untransformed tobacco and petunia.

      It is seen that tobacco plants transformed with the SSU301 gene show
significant levels of expression of this gene.   Untransformed tobacco shows
no background with this primer.   The level of expression of the SSU301 gene

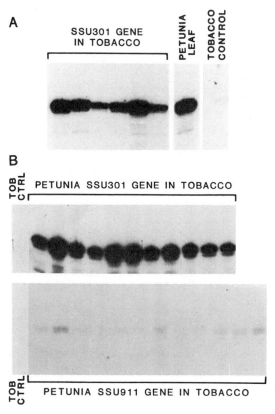

Fig. 4.   Primer extension analysis of tobacco transformants carrying the
           Petunia rbcS genes SSU301 and SSU911.   (A) Comparison of the lev-
           el of expression of SSU301 in different tobacco transformants
           compared to that in Petunia leaf tissue.   (B) Comparison of the
           level of expression of SSU301 and SSU911 in leaf tissue of dif-
           ferent tobacco transformants.   The oligonucleotides used in the
           analysis were complementary to a region in the transit peptide
           which is divergent between the different rbcS genes.   The extend-
           ed fragments (up to the 5' end of the mRNA's) were 161 and 126
           for the SSU301 and SSU911 genes, respectively.

in independent transformants is somewhat variable, but in two cases it is
comparable to the level of expression observed in Petunia.   Figure 4B compares the level of expression of the Petunia rbcS gene SSU301 in tobacco
with the level of expression of the Petunia rbcS gene SSU911 in tobacco.
In all eleven SSU301 transformants there are high levels of expression, and
in all twelve SSU911 transformants there are very low levels of expression.
These results indicate that the quantitative aspects of Petunia rbcS genes
observed in Petunia are reflected when the individual genes are introduced
into tobacco.   The results also suggest that we have a suitable system for
analysis of the determinants of quantitative differences in the level of
expression of the different Petunia rbcS genes.

REFERENCES

1. Bedbrook, J.R., S. Smith, and R.J. Ellis (1980) Molecular cloning and sequencing of cDNA encoding the precursor to the small subunit of chloroplast ribose-1,5-bisphosphate carboxylase. <u>Nature</u> 287:692-697.

2. Berry-Lowe, S.L., T.D. McKnight, D.M. Shah, and R.B. Meagher (1982) The nucleotide sequence, expression and evolution of one member of a multigene family encoding the small subunit of ribulose bisphosphate carboxylase. <u>J. Mol. Appl. Genet.</u> 1:483-498.

3. Broglie, R., G. Coruzzi, G. Lamppa, B. Keither, and N. Chua (1983) Structural analysis of nuclear genes encoding for the precursor to the small subunit of wheat. <u>Bio/Technology</u> 1:55-61.

4. Cashmore, A.R. (1983) Nuclear genes encoding the small subunit of ribulose-1,5-bisphosphate carboxylase. In <u>Genetic Engineering of Plants</u>, T. Kosuge, C.P. Meredith, and A. Hollaender, eds. Plenum Press, New York, pp. 29-38.

5. Chua, N., and G.W. Schmidt (1978) Post-translational transport into intact chloroplasts of a precursor to the small subunit of ribulose-1,5-bisphosphate carboxylase. <u>Proc. Natl. Acad. Sci., USA</u> 75:6110-6114.

6. Coen, D.M., J.R. Bedbrook, L. Bogorad, and A. Rich (1977) Maize chloroplast DNA fragment encoding the large subunit of ribulose bisphosphate carboxylase. <u>Proc. Natl. Acad. Sci., USA</u> 74:5487-5491.

7. Coruzzi, G., R. Broglie, C. Edwards, and N.H. Chua (1984) Tissue-specific and light-regulated expression of pea nuclear genes encoding the small subunit of ribulose-1,5-bisphosphate carboxylase. <u>EMBO J.</u> 3:1671-1679.

8. Dean, C., and R.M. Leach (1982) Genome expression during normal leaf development I. Cellular and chloroplast numbers and DNA, RNA, and protein levels in tissues of different ages within a seven-day-old wheat leaf. <u>Plant Physiol.</u> 69:904-910.

9. Dean, C., P. van den Elzen, S. Tamaki, P. Dunsmuir, and J.R. Bedbrook (1985) Linkage and homology analysis divides the eight genes for the small subunit of petunia ribulose-1,5-bisphosphate carboxylase into three gene families. <u>Proc. Natl. Acad. Sci., USA</u> 82:4964-4968.

10. Dean, C., P. van den Elzen, S. Tamaki, P. Dunsmuir, and J. Bedbrook (1985) Differential expression of the eight genes of the petunia ribulose bisphosphate carboxylase small subunit multi-gene family. <u>EMBO J.</u> 4:3055-3061.

11. Dunsmuir, P. (1985) The petunia chlorophyll a/b binding protein genes: A comparison of <u>Cab</u> genes from different gene families. <u>Nucl. Acids Res.</u> 13:2503-2518.

11a. Dunsmuir, P., S. Smith, and J.R. Bedbrook (1983) A number of different nuclear genes for the small subunit of RuBPCase are transcribed in petunia. <u>Nucl. Acids Res.</u> 11:4177-4183.

12. Fyerberg, E.A., J.W. Mahaffey, B.J. Bond, and N. Davidson (1983) Transcripts of the six drosophila actin genes accumulate in a stage and tissue-specific manner. <u>Cell</u> 33:115-123.

13. Goldberg, B., R. Fischer, J. Harada, D. Jofuku, and J. Okamuro (1983) Organization of soybean seed protein genes and their flanking regions. In <u>Structure and Function of Plant Genomes</u>, O. Ciferri and L. Dure, eds. Plenum Press, New York, pp. 37-46.

14. Highfield, P.E., and R.J. Ellis (1978) Synthesis and transport of the small subunit of chloroplast ribulose bisphosphate carboxylase. <u>Nature</u> 271:424-429.

15. Hightower, R.C., and R.B. Meagher (1985) Divergence and differential expression of soybean actin genes. <u>EMBO J.</u> 4:1-8.

16. Kawashima, N., and S.G. Wildman (1972) Studies on fraction I protein IV. Mode of inheritance of primary structure in relation to whether chloroplast or nuclear DNA contains the code for a chloroplast protein. Biochim. Biophys. Acta 262:42-49.
17. Larkins, B., K. Pedersen, M. Marks, D. Wilson, and P. Argos (1983) Structure and expression of zein genes in maize endosperm. In Structure and Function of Plant Genomes, O. Ciferri and L. Dure, eds. Plenum Press, New York, pp. 73-84.
18. Mazur, B.J., and C.F. Chi (1985) Sequence of a genomic DNA clone for the small subunit of ribulose-bisphosphate carboxylase-oxygenase. Nucl. Acids Res. 13:2373-2386.
19. Smith, S.M., and R.J. Ellis (1981) Light stimulated accumulation of transcripts of nuclear and chloroplast genes for ribulose bisphosphate carboxylase. J. Mol. Appl. Genet. 1:127-137.
20. Wimpee, C.F., W.J. Stiekema, and E.M. Tobin (1983) Sequence heterogeneity in the RuBP carboxylase small subunit gene family of Lemna gibba. In Plant Molecular Biology (UCLA Symposium on Molecular and Cellular Biology, New Series, Vol. 12), R.B. Goldberg, ed. A.R. Liss, Inc., New York, pp. 391-401.

MAIZE MITOCHONDRIAL GENES AND CYTOPLASMIC MALE STERILITY

V.K. Eckenrode and C.S. Levings, III

Department of Genetics
North Carolina State University
Raleigh, North Carolina 27695-7614

INTRODUCTION

Plants are termed "male-steriles" when they do not produce viable pollen. The specific mechanisms causing male sterility in plants vary from species to species and can be affected by the environment, nuclear genes, and cytoplasmically inherited genes. When the male-sterile trait is inherited in a non-Mendelian fashion, it is designated cytoplasmic male sterility (CMS). Cytoplasmic male sterility occurs in many higher plants. Laser and Lersten (65) have cataloged at least 140 plant species in which the trait is observed. Since the CMS trait normally does not affect female fertility, male-sterile plants are able to set seed when provided viable pollen. This seed is the product of cross-pollination. In hybrid seed production, the male parent often carries a nuclear restorer gene(s) that suppresses the CMS trait and restores fertility to the hybrid.

Plant breeders have taken advantage of the CMS trait in the production of hybrid seed. In hybrid seed production, CMS lines can eliminate the costly and tedious procedure of hand-emasculation. For example, CMS is used commercially in production of hybrid seed for faba bean, maize, petunia, sorghum, sugar beet, and sunflower (54,68). In fact, CMS is essential in the production of hybrid seed of sorghum, which has small, self-fertile flowers.

One source of CMS in maize, cms-T, is preferentially susceptible to attack by Bipolaris maydis, race T, the causative agent in southern corn leaf blight. Cms-T was widely used to produce hybrid maize seed in the 1960s. By 1970, approximately 85% of the hybrid corn in the U.S. carried this cytoplasm (68). A severe outbreak of southern corn leaf blight in 1970 caused the industry to abandon the use of cms-T and to become aware of the dangers of such a high degree of cytoplasmic uniformity (68,113).

We will focus on maize because much more is known about CMS in maize than in other species. Cytoplasmic male sterility in maize has recently been reviewed by Hanson and Conde (54), Laughnan and Gabay-Laughnan (67), Levings (72), and Pring and Lonsdale (95).

DESCRIPTION OF CYTOPLASMIC MALE STERILITY IN MAIZE

The CMS trait in maize was first described by Rhoades (97,98). Subsequently, Duvick (38) and Beckett (5) cataloged a number of maize CMS sources. In general, these sources fall into one of three groups: the Texas or T-cytoplasmic group (cms-T), the USDA or S-cytoplasmic group (cms-S), or the Charrua or C-cytoplasmic group (cms-C). These groups are distinguished from each other by their pattern of fertility restoration in response to different restorer genes in inbred tester lines (5). Some variability in the fertility restoration reaction also exists within male-sterile groups (5,49).

Cms-T is restored to fertility by Rf1 and Rf2. The gene Rf1 is located on chromosome 3 (39), and Rf2 is located on chromosome 9 (103). Both genes are dominant and both are required by the plant for fertility restoration. Since the mode of restoration of cms-T is sporophytic, in a cms-T plant heterozygous for both Rf1 and Rf2 (Rf1/rf1, Rf2/rf2), all pollen grains are fertile despite the fact that only one-quarter of the individual pollen grains have the Rf1, Rf2 genotype.

Cms-S is restored by Rf3, which is located on chromosome 2 (66). Rf3 is a dominant gene and its mode of restoration is gametophytic (17). That is, each pollen grain must possess the Rf3 allele for fertility to be restored. If a plant is heterozygous for the Rf3 gene (Rf3/rf3), only one-half of the pollen grains will be viable.

Cms-C is restored in a sporophytic manner. There is a disagreement as to whether restoration is effected by the single dominant gene Rf4 (63), or by two or more genes (67).

Abundant evidence suggests that the CMS trait in maize is due to a mitochondrial gene(s) (72). Although 75% to 80% of the restriction fragments are shared by mitochondrial DNA (mtDNA) from all four cytoplasmic groups (N, cms-C, cms-S, cms-T) (74), each group is easily identifiable based on specific restriction fragments. Because there is a correlation of group assignments based on restriction patterns with the assignments based on genetic identification, restriction patterns of mtDNA provide a useful means for identifying the various cytoplasms (73,94). There are, however, minor differences in restriction patterns within the N group (28) and within each of the male-sterile cytoplasms (28,94,96). It is not known if these variations in restriction patterns correlate with the genetic variations sometimes observed in response to tester stocks. Both types of variation indicate that variability exists within each cytoplasmic group. In contrast to the situation with mitochondria, the restriction fragment patterns of chloroplast DNA from each of the four groups are nearly indistinguishable (94). These results suggest that the variations in mtDNA arrangement among the four cytoplasms may be related to the CMS trait.

Additional differences among the four cytoplasms have been shown by comparisons of in vitro translational products from isolated mitochondria (42,43). Leaver and co-workers distinguish 18 to 20 polypeptides when these translational products are separated on one-dimensional polyacrylamide gels (68), and 30 to 50 polypeptides with two-dimensional gels (52). In comparison, Attardi and co-workers have identified by two-dimensional gel electrophoresis 26 polypeptides synthesized by isolated HeLa cell mitochondria, whereas only 13 polypeptide-encoding genes have been identified (Tab. 1). This suggests that the number of maize mitochondrial

Tab. 1. Mitochondrial genes and their products.

Mitochondrial gene/product	mtDNA size:	Animal 14–18 kb	Other Yeast/Fungi 19–108 kb	Plant 200–2,500 kb
Ribosomal RNAs				
Large subunit		16S	21S	26S
Small subunit		12S	15S	18S
5S		–	–	+
Transfer RNAs		22	23–25	∿30 (5)
Cytochrome c oxidase				
Subunit I		+	+	+
Subunit II		+	+	+
Subunit III		+	+	+
Ubiquinol cytochrome c reductase				
Apocytochrome b		+	+	+
F_o–ATPase complex				
Subunit 6		+	+	+
Subunit 8		+	+	+
Subunit 9		–	+/–	+
F_1–ATPase complex				
Subunit alpha		–	–	+
Ribosomal protein				
VarI/S5		–	+	?
S13		–	–	+
NADH–ubiquinone oxidoreductase				
Number of subunits		6	–/6	?
RNA processing enzymes				
Intron 2 CoB maturase		–	+	?
Intron 4 CoB maturase		–	+	?
9S RNA		?	+	?
Unassigned reading frames		1	≤14	?

polypeptides may be over-estimated when determined by this technique. Variations in polypeptide patterns are identified among mitochondria from each of the three male-sterile and normal cytoplasms; variation is not observed in polypeptide patterns within the groups (43). Eight new minor polypeptides (apparent molecular weight of 58,000 to 84,000) are detected in mitochondria from cms-S mitochondria. In mitochondria from cms-C, a polypeptide of 17,500 Da is synthesized and one of 15,500 Da is missing in contrast with normal cytoplasm. It is not known whether these two polypeptides are related. Similarly, in cms-T mitochondria, a unique polypeptide of 13,000 Da is synthesized and one of 21,000 Da is absent. Interestingly, in the presence of Rf1 and Rf2, a specific reduction in the amount of the 13,000-Da polypeptide synthesized by cms-T mitochondria is observed (41). This indicates that nuclear genes can have an effect on the expression of a particular mitochondrial gene.

Further evidence supporting the notion that mitochondria are linked to the male-sterile trait comes from cytological investigation of microsporogenesis. The development of anther tissue has been studied by electron microscopy in all four maize cytoplasms. Duvick (38) has noted that the cytological and chemical evidence indicates that aborted pollen grains in male-sterile cytoplasms appear to have starved to death. Warmke and Lee (69,112) have shown that mitochondrial replication increases rapidly during microsporogenesis; they suggest that a malfunction at this particularly stressful time might contribute to the male-sterile lesion. In cms-T plants, mitochondria of the tapetum, the innermost anther cell wall layer, are observed to undergo ultrastructural changes immediately after meiosis, beginning at the tetrad stage (27,69,111). Mitochondria in the microspores change shortly thereafter (111,112). Similar structural changes do not occur in the mitochondria of normal maize. Structural changes are not observed in the mitochondria of cms-C or cms-S plants until pollen abortion (27,70,71). Abnormalities are noted in the tapetal cells of cms-C plants, but only with the pollen grains themselves in cms-S plants. This is consistent with the sporophytic mode of restoration in cms-T and cms-C plants, and the gametophytic mode in cms-S plants. In support, approximately one-half of the pollen grains develop normally and the other half abort late in microsporogenesis in cms-S plants heterozygous for the restorer gene (Rf3/rf3) (53). Although these studies describe events leading to pollen abortion, they provide little insight into the mechanism of pollen abortion.

Maize plants containing the T-cytoplasm are susceptible to the fungal pathogen B. maydis, race T, and its toxin (T-toxin); fertiles and other male-sterile cytoplasms are not susceptible (68). The toxin preferentially binds to mitochondria isolated from cms-T lines (84). The T-toxin increases the permeability of the inner mitochondrial membrane to NAD^+, inhibits respiration dependent on NAD^+-linked substrates (82), uncouples oxidative phosphorylation (6), and induces mitochondrial swelling (84). Mitochondria from normal maize, other male-sterile lines (84), and from cms-T revertants (15,46) are not affected by the toxin.

Using tissue culture techniques, several unsuccessful attempts have been made to separate toxin sensitivity from the CMS trait (54). These failures suggest that the two traits may be due to a single gene or to linked loci. When calli from toxin-sensitive cms-T plants are grown in the presence of T-toxin, toxin-resistant callus cultures are recovered (14,45). When these calli are regenerated to whole plants, the toxin-resistant plants are also male-fertile (14,45). Similar experiments performed without toxin selection also result in male-fertile, toxin-resistant plants (15,108). Genetic analysis has shown that these changes are due to cytoplasmic, and not nuclear, genes. Restriction analysis has demonstrated rearrangements in the mtDNA of the revertant plants (47,62,108). The mtDNA alteration most consistently associated with the reversion event is the loss of a 6.6-kb XhoI fragment (108). This evidence indicates a connection between mitochondria and CMS.

ORGANIZATION OF THE MITOCHONDRIAL GENOME

Whereas animal and fungal genes are partitioned between the nuclear and mitochondrial genomes, plant genes are partitioned among three genomes: the nuclear, the mitochondrial, and the chloroplast genomes. As outlined previously, substantial evidence suggests that CMS in maize is due to a mutation in the mtDNA and not the chloroplast DNA (72). Modern molecular techniques have allowed researchers to characterize the organization, informational content, and expression of plant mtDNAs.

The mtDNA of all eukaryotic cells encodes the same basic set of structural RNAs and proteins (Tab. 1). Structural RNAs include three rRNAs and a complete set of tRNAs required for mitochondrial protein synthesis. The protein-coding genes contribute polypeptides to the complexes essential for respiration and ATP synthesis. In addition, yeast and fungi mitochondria encode a ribosome-associated protein (19,64), and yeast encodes a gene product associated with RNA processing (83,109). Only a few plant mitochondrial genes have been isolated that do not occur in either animal or fungal mtDNAs. Despite this basic functional conservation, there is considerable variety in the size, organization, and expression of mtDNA from the different kingdoms.

Animal mtDNAs are the smallest and are organized very economically as a single circular species ranging in size from 14 to 18 kb (51). Genes on the animal mitochondrial genome contain no introns and are tightly packed with few or no noncoding nucleotides separating individual genes (1). There appears to be a primary full-length transcript from each strand from which individual RNAs are processed with the aid of functional tRNA genes located at the 3' termini of the genes (2,18).

Fungal mtDNAs are organized in circles up to nine times larger than mammalian mtDNAs, from 19 to 108 kb in size (51). Interestingly, they encode the same basic set of genes as smaller animal mitochondrial genomes. However, fungal genes may contain introns and may be separated from each other by AT-rich spacers. The introns and the spacers account for the additional mtDNA in yeast. There are a minimum of 27 transcriptional initiation sites on yeast mtDNA (23). Multigenic transcripts are processed, although processing signals apparently do not involve tRNAs, as they do in animal mitochondria. A conserved dodecamer occurs at the 3' termini of protein-coding genes and is thought to be involved in processing the transcripts into mature forms (87). Most tRNA genes in yeast mtDNA are clustered and must also be processed (37). A special 9S mtRNA is required for processing these transcripts into mature tRNA species (83,89,109). In Neurospora crassa, GC-rich palindromes flanking known genes are suggested as processing signals for multigenic transcripts containing rRNA and tRNA genes (114). In comparison with yeast and similar to the situation in mammals, a few tRNA genes have been identified that flank protein-coding genes and may be used as processing signals in Neurospora and Torulopsis glabrata mitochondria (12,18,24).

Plant mtDNAs are much larger and more complex in arrangement than those of other organisms. Plant mitochondrial genomes range in size from 200 to 2,500 kb (51). Within the cucurbit family, there is a significant eight-fold variation in the size of mtDNAs; they range from 330 kb for watermelon to 2,500 kb for muskmelon (110). Less than 10% of these mtDNAs are repetitive (110). A few plant mitochondrial genes have been identified that are not members of the basic set of genes encoded in animal and fungal mtDNA (Tab. 1). However, the additional genes are not enough to account for the large plant mitochondrial genomes.

Plant mtDNAs often consist of a complex assortment of circular molecules of different sizes and numbers. This is unlike animal and fungal mtDNAs, which are usually organized in a single circular molecule. The completion of the physical maps of the mtDNAs of Brassica campestris (218 kb; Ref. 90) and male-fertile (normal, N) maize (570 kb; Ref. 77) has provided insight into the organization of plant mtDNAs. Both genomes are arranged in a single large circle, called the master chromosome. Within each master chromosome there are repeated sequences with a reiteration frequency of two. Brassica has one such pair; the repeats are separated by 135 and 83 kb around the circle. Recombination between the two repeats produces two smaller circles of 135 and 83 kb. Similarly, recombination between the two smaller circles reproduces the master chromosome. The relative molarities of these three circles apparently depend on the rates of inter- and intramolecular recombination.

At 570 kb, the normal maize mitochondrial genome is more than twice as large as the Brassica genome and contains six pairs of repeats, approximately 1, 2, 3, 10, 12, and 14 kb in size (77). Five of these repeats (1, 2, 3, 12, and 14 kb) have been implicated in recombinational events (77). A larger variety of circular DNA molecules can therefore be produced in maize mitochondria than in Brassica. This situation accounts for the circular molecules of various sizes observed from maize mitochondria by electron microscopy (76). Similar to Brassica, the rates of inter- and intramolecular recombination among each of the various pairs of repeats affect the relative abundance of the various circles. The most abundant circles in maize mitochondria are 67, 503, 250, and 253 kb in size (95). A number of the genes encoded by normal maize mtDNA have recently been located on the map of the master chromosome (31). From this analysis, it is evident that both strands of maize mtDNA are transcribed, and that coding sequences are not clustered. Polypeptide-encoding genes have been located both adjacent to and within repeats that participate in recombinational events. The possible effect of different molecular environments on the transcription of particular genes is not yet known (31).

PLANT MITOCHONDRIAL GENES

To date, 18 plant genes belonging to the basic set of mitochondrially encoded genes have been identified (Tab. 1). Mitochondria conduct their own protein synthesis and possess all components necessary for protein synthesis. Similar to mitochondrial genomes from animals and fungi, plant mtDNAs encode both rRNAs and tRNAs. The genes encoding the small subunit (18S) rRNA from maize (21), wheat (105), and Oenothera (13) and the large subunit (26S) rRNA from maize (29) and Oenothera (78) have been sequenced. The encoded rRNAs show greater sequence and secondary structure similarities to bacterial and chloroplast rRNAs than to cytoplasmic rRNAs or to mammalian and fungal mitochondrial rRNAs (13,21,29,78,105). In addition, plant mitochondrial ribosomes possess a 5S rRNA species that is absent in fungal and animal mitochondrial ribosomes, but is present in bacterial, chloroplast, and cytoplasmic ribosomes. The 5S rRNA gene is encoded in plant mitochondria and has been sequenced from maize (20) and wheat (104). Similar to the 18S and 26S rRNAs, the 5S rRNA shows greater homology to its bacterial and chloroplast counterparts than to its cytoplasmic counterpart.

Mitochondrial genes encoding initiator methionine tRNA from wheat (50) and Oenothera (48), two maize methionine tRNAs, probably initiator and elongator (91), maize aspartate tRNA (92), and lupine glycine tRNA (4) have been sequenced. In maize and wheat mitochondria, the phenylalanine tRNA gene has been located but not sequenced (80). Only two tRNAs from plant mitochondria have been sequenced: phenylalanine and tyrosine (79), both from bean. These tRNA studies extend the similarities of the plant mitochondrial protein-synthesizing apparatus with bacteria and chloroplast to include tRNAs. The possibility of two maize methionine tRNA genes suggests that plant mitochondria may have a codon recognition pattern similar to the bacteria. Animal (3) and yeast (107) mitochondria have an expanded codon recognition pattern and require fewer (22 to 25) tRNA genes.

Since there is no evidence that mRNAs are imported into plant mitochondria, it is presumed that all mRNAs translated in mitochondria are products of mitochondrial transcription. The protein-coding genes sequenced from plant mitochondria include cytochrome c oxidase subunit I (COI) from maize (57), cytochrome c oxidase subunit II (COII) from maize (44), Oenothera (55), rice (61), wheat (8), and pea (85), apocytochrome b (cob) from maize (30) and Oenothera (102), F_0-ATPase subunit 6 (atp6) from maize (34), F_0-ATPase subunit 9 (atp9) from maize (36), F_1-ATPase subunit alpha (atp-alpha) from maize (11,58), and the ribosomal protein gene S13 (S13) from maize and tobacco (7). Hiesel and Brennicke (56) have recently identified an Oenothera mtDNA sequence with low homology (26%) to the F_0-ATPase subunit 8 (atp8) sequence of yeast. This preliminary evidence suggests that atp8 is encoded by a plant mitochondrial gene. Hauswirth and co-workers (pers. comm.) have indicated that they located the cytochrome c oxidase subunit III (COIII) gene in maize using a beef heart mitochondrial gene probe. With the exception of the six subunits of the NADH-ubiquinone oxidoreductase enzyme complex that have recently been identified, all proteins encoded by both animal and fungal mitochondria have now been identified in at least one plant mtDNA. Identification of these genes has been based on open reading frames starting with an initiator methionine codon, transcription products, and/or sequence homologies with genes from other organisms. The organization and expression of maize mitochondrial genes have recently been more thoroughly reviewed by Eckenrode and Levings (40).

The mitochondrial location of two of these seven genes is unique to plants. In animals and fungi, the atp-alpha polypeptide is encoded in the nucleus (86). Mitochondrial synthesis has been demonstrated for this polypeptide not only in maize (52), but also in Vicia faba (9), sweet potato (60), sugar beet, wheat, and tobacco (10). Interestingly, the mitochondria of the unicellular heterotroph Prototheca zopfii have recently been shown to synthesize an atp-alpha polypeptide (33). The mitochondrial location of the S13 ribosomal protein gene is also unique to some plant mitochondria (7). Although a ribosomal protein gene is encoded in the mitochondria of yeast (var1; Ref. 19) and Neurospora (S5; Ref. 64), no ribosome-associated protein is encoded by animal mitochondria. The location of the S13 gene differs in higher plants, because it is apparently encoded by the mitochondria of maize, tobacco, and wheat, but not of bean or pea (7).

The products of six open reading frames from mammalian mitochondria have recently been identified as belonging to the NADH-ubiquinone oxidoreductase enzyme complex (22,81). They are designated ND1, ND2, ND3, ND4, ND4L, and ND5. Homologous reading frames have been identified in Xenopus laevis (99), Drosophila (25,26,32), and Neurospora crassa (59). Homologies to Aspergillus to ND1 and ND4 (16) and to ND3 and ND5 (100) have been reported. The mtDNA of <u>Chlamydomonas reinhardtii</u> contains a gene with amino acid homology to <u>ND2</u> (93). Homologies to <u>ND1</u> have also been detected in the mtDNAs from maize (7,100) and tobacco (7). The sequences homologous to <u>ND1</u> in both the maize and tobacco mtDNAs do not contain the entire <u>ND1</u> open reading frame. Whether these plant mtDNAs contain only a fragment of the <u>ND1</u> gene or the gene is intact but is split by introns remains to be determined.

THE CYTOPLASMIC MALE STERILITY GENE

We have reviewed the current knowledge of mitochondrial genes because it is often assumed that the CMS trait is due to a mutation affecting one of the basic sets of mitochondrial gene products. Even though this relationship has not yet been confirmed, it remains a viable hypothesis. The mitochondrial-encoded polypeptides involved in electron transport, ATP synthesis, and protein translation seem to function normally in most of the tissues and organs of male-sterile plants. In maize, CMS plants are as vigorous and productive as normal plants when provided pollen. It is only in those tissues involved in pollen formation that the lesion for CMS is manifested. Until we learn more about pollen development and the tissues involved, it may be difficult to establish a causative relationship between a mitochondrial gene mutation and male sterility.

Cytoplasmic male sterility has been studied most extensively in the maize T cytoplasm. Recent investigations have identified a mtDNA sequence that is believed to encode the gene responsible for the CMS trait. Surprisingly, the gene does not code for one of the basic set of mitochondrial polypeptides; instead, it codes for a polypeptide unique to <u>cms</u>-T mitochondria. The origin of this gene is also unusual; it has apparently arisen by intramolecular recombinational events involving other mitochondrial gene sequences.

A mtDNA sequence has been identified, designated TURF 2H3, that is uniquely and abundantly transcribed in <u>cms</u>-T mitochondria (35). TURF 2H3 is a chimeric sequence in that it contains portions of the flanking and/or coding regions of other maize mitochondrial genes and a chloroplast gene. It includes a part of the 5' flanking region of the ATPase subunit 6 gene and part of the 3' flanking and coding region of the 26S rRNA gene of the mitochondrial genome. The sequence also contains a portion of the chloroplast gene, tRNA-Arg. An analysis of TURF 2H3 indicates seven recombinational sites that could have been generated by intramolecular and intergenomic recombination.

Sequence analysis of TURF 2H3 has identified two long open reading frames, called ORF13 and ORF25, which encode polypeptides of 12,961 Da and 24,675 Da, respectively. Databank searches have failed to detect any protein with significant homology to ORF13 or ORF25. The putative ORF25 protein is hydrophilic in nature and may be a matrix protein. The N-terminal region of ORF13 is hydrophobic and the C-terminal region is hydrophilic. Thus, ORF13 could be an inner membrane protein.

Hybridization studies have detected the ORF25 sequence in the mitochondrial genomes of N, <u>cms</u>-C, and <u>cms</u>-S maize and wheat, rice, tobacco, pea, and bean. These results suggest that the ORF25 sequence codes for a gene common to plant mitochondria. In contrast, the ORF13 sequence is unique to the mitochondrial genome of <u>cms</u>-T maize; it is not found in the mitochondrial genomes of wheat, rice, tobacco, pea, bean, and other maize cytoplasms. This is not unexpected since the ORF13 sequence is composed chiefly of rearranged sequences.

Both ORF13 and ORF25 are transcribed, but ORF13 is only transcribed in cms-T mitochondria. This is expected, of course, because the ORF13 DNA sequence is not found in other maize mitochondrial genomes. The exclusive occurrence of the ORF13 gene sequence and transcript in cms-T parallels the discovery of a 13,000-Da polypeptide in T-cytoplasm only (41). In vitro translational studies with mitochondria from cms-T have revealed a novel 13,000-Da polypeptide that is absent in N, cms-C, and cms-S maize. These results suggest that the 13,000-Da protein is encoded by the ORF13 sequence.

A relationship between ORF13 and CMS is also indicated by a contrast in restored and nonrestored cms-T lines (35). The male-sterile phenotype (pollen abortion) is suppressed by two nuclear restorer genes, Rf1 and Rf2. A comparison of restored and nonrestored cms-T lines shows that the TURF 2H3 transcripts are uniquely altered by the restorer genes Rf1 and Rf2. It is not yet known whether the transcriptional modifications are due to changes in transcriptional initiation or processing events. In vitro translational studies with mitochondria have also revealed differences between restored and nonrestored cms-T (41). Levels of the 13,000-Da protein are greatly reduced when cms-T is restored to male fertility by the nuclear restorer genes Rf1 and Rf2. Significantly, the 13,000-Da polypeptide and the transcripts associated with ORF13 are both affected by the same restorer genes that suppress male sterility in cms-T.

It is meaningful that ORF13 is located on a 6.6-kb XhoI fragment, because this same size fragment is lost in the reversion of cms-T from male sterility to fertility (108). In plants regenerated from callus culture, reversion from male sterility to male fertility and from disease suscepti-bility to disease resistance often occurs (14,46). The disappearance of a 6.6-kb XhoI fragment in mtDNA digests is very frequently correlated with reversion, whereas plants that remain male-sterile and disease-susceptible after culture and regeneration do not lose the 6.6-kb XhoI fragment. Since this specific base change has been observed in 15 of 16 revertants, it has been proposed to be associated with fertility reversion (108).

In contrast with cms-T, very little progress has been made in under-standing the molecular basis of male sterility in cms-C and cms-S. In mitochondria from cms-S lines, there are two plasmid-like molecules, S-1 and S-2, in addition to the mitochondrial genome. The nucleotide sequences have been determined for S-1 (88) and S-2 (75), and, together, these two molecules contain four large open reading frames. Transcription has been demonstrated from the two open reading frames of S-2 (101,106), but no function has been assigned to any of the open reading frames of the S plas-mids. It has been proposed that they code for proteins important in the replication or maintenance of S-1 and S-2 (75). As yet, there is no sub-stantial evidence directly linking S-1 and S-2 to the CMS trait.

CONCLUSIONS

Only in cms-T is the molecular basis of CMS beginning to come into focus. Circumstantial evidence now implicates ORF13 as the mtDNA sequence responsible for the male sterility trait of cms-T. Studies of ORF13 have

revealed two interesting features. Intramolecular recombination has contributed significantly to the origin of the ORF13 sequence, and ORF13 is
not a mutation of a basic mitochondrial gene. In fact, the sequence analysis suggests that ORF13 has arisen by fortuitous rearrangements which have
generated an open reading frame preceded by a functional mitochondrial promoter. Although the origin of ORF13 seems bizarre, the mechanism by which
the ORF gene product is able to suppress viable pollen formation may be
even more unusual.

REFERENCES

1. Anderson, S., A.T. Bankier, B.G. Barrell, M.H.L. de Bruijn, A.R. Coulson, J. Drouin, I.C. Eperon, D.P. Nierlick, B.A. Roe, F. Sanger, P.H.
Schreier, A.J.H. Smith, R. Staden, and I.G. Young (1981) Sequence and
organization of the human mitochondrial genome. Nature 290:457-465.
2. Attardi, G., P. Cantatore, A. Chomyn, S. Crews, R. Gelfand, C. Merkel,
J. Montoya, and D. Ojala (1982) A comprehensive view of mitochondrial
gene expression in human cells. In Mitochondrial Genes, P. Slonimski,
P. Borst, and G. Attardi, eds. Cold Spring Harbor Laboratory, Cold
Spring Harbor, New York, pp. 51-71.
3. Barrell, B.G., S. Anderson, A.T. Bankier, M.H.L. de Bruijn, E. Chen,
A.R. Coulson, J. Drouin, I.C. Eperon, D.P. Nierlich, B.A. Roe, F.
Sanger, P.H. Schreier, A.J.H. Smith, R. Staden, and I.G. Young (1980)
Different pattern of codon recognition by mammalian mitochondrial
tRNAs. Proc. Natl. Acad. Sci., USA 77:3164-3166.
4. Bartnik, E., and P. Borsuk (1986) A glycine tRNA gene from lupine
mitochondria. Nucl. Acids Res. 14:2407.
5. Beckett, J.B. (1971) Classification of male-sterile cytoplasms in
maize (Zea mays L.). Crop Sci. 11:724-727.
6. Bednarski, M.A., S. Izawa, and R.P. Scheffer (1977) Reversible effects
of toxin from H. maydis race T on oxidative phosphorylation by mitochondria from maize. Plant Physiol. 59:540-545.
7. Bland, M.M., C.S. Levings, III, and D.F. Matzinger (1986) The tobacco
mitochondrial ATPase subunit 9 gene is closely linked to an open reading frame for a ribosomal protein. Mol. Gen. Genet. 204:8-16.
8. Bonen, L., P.H. Boer, and M.W. Gray (1984) The wheat cytochrome oxidase subunit II gene has an intron insert and three radical amino acid
changes relative to maize. EMBO J. 3:2531-2536.
9. Boutry, M., M. Briquet, and A. Goffeau (1983) The alpha subunit of a
plant mitochondrial F₁-ATPase is translated in mitochondria. J. Biol.
Chem. 258:8524-8526.
10. Boutry, M., A.-M. Farber, M. Charbonnier, and M. Briquet (1984) Micro-
analysis of plant mitochondrial protein synthesis products: Detection
of variant polypeptides associated with cytoplasmic male sterility.
Plant Mol. Biol. 3:445-452.
11. Braun, C.J., and C.S. Levings, III (1985) Nucleotide sequence of the
F₁-ATPase alpha subunit gene from maize mitochondria. Plant Physiol.
79:571-577.
12. Breitenberger, C.A., K.S. Browning, B. Alzner-DeWeerd, and U.L. Raj-
Bhandary (1985) RNA processing in Neurospora crassa mitochondria: Use
of transfer RNA sequences as signals. EMBO J. 4:185-195.
13. Brennicke, A., S. Moller, and P.A. Blanz (1985) The 18S and 5S ribosomal RNA genes in Oenothera mitochondria: Sequence rearrangements in
the 18S and 5S rRNA genes of higher plants. Mol. Gen. Genet. 198:404-
410.

14. Brettell, R.I.S., B.V.D. Goddard, and D.S. Ingram (1979) Selection of Tms-cytoplasm maize tissue cultures resistant to Drechslera maydis T-toxin. Maydica 24:203-213.
15. Brettell, R.I.S., E. Thomas, and D.S. Ingram (1980) Reversion of Texas male-sterile cytoplasm maize in culture to give fertile, T-toxin resistant plants. Theor. Appl. Genet. 58:55-58.
16. Brown, T.A., R.W. Davies, J.A. Ray, R.B. Waring, and C. Scazzocchio (1983) The mitochondrial genome of Aspergillus nidulans contains reading frames homologous to the human URFs 1 and 4. EMBO J. 2:427-435.
17. Buchert, J.G. (1961) The stage of genome-plasmon interaction in the restoration of fertility to cytoplasmically pollen-sterile maize. Proc. Natl. Acad. Sci., USA 47:1436-1440.
18. Burger, G., M.H. Citterich, M.A. Nelson, S. Werner, and G. Macino (1985) RNA processing in Neurospora crassa mitochondria: Transfer RNAs punctuate a large precursor transcript. EMBO J. 4:197-204.
19. Butow, R.A., P.S. Perlman, and L.I. Grossman (1985) The unusual varl gene of yeast mitochondrial DNA. Science 228:1496-1501.
20. Chao, S., R.R. Sederoff, and C.S. Levings, III (1983) Partial sequence analysis of the 5S to 18S rRNA gene region of the maize mitochondrial genome. Plant Physiol. 71:190-193.
21. Chao, S., R. Sederoff, and C.S. Levings, III (1984) Nucleotide sequence and evolution of the 18S ribosomal RNA gene in maize mitochondria. Nucl. Acids Res. 12:6629-6644.
22. Chomyn, A., P. Mariottini, M.W.J. Cleeter, C.I. Ragan, A. Matsuno-Yagi, Y. Hatefi, R.F. Doolittle, and G. Attardi (1985) Six unidentified reading frames of human mitochondrial DNA encode components of the respiratory-chain NADH dehydrogenase. Nature 314:592-597.
23. Christianson, T., and M. Rabinowitz (1983) Identification of multiple transcriptional initiation sites on the yeast mitochondrial genome by in vitro capping with guanyltransferase. J. Biol. Chem. 258:14025-14033.
24. Clark-Walker, G.D., C.R. McArthur, and K.S. Sriprakash (1985) Location of transcriptional control signals and transfer RNA sequences in Torulopsis glabrata mitochondrial DNA. EMBO J. 4:465-473.
25. Clary, D.O., and D.R. Wolstenholme (1983) Genes for cytochrome c oxidase subunit I, URF2, and three tRNAs in Drosophila mitochondrial DNA. Nucl. Acids Res. 11:6859-6872.
26. Clary, D.O., J.A. Wahleithner, and D.R. Wolstenholme (1984) Sequence and arrangement of the genes for cytochrome b, URF1, URF4L, URF4, URF5, URF6 and five tRNAs in Drosophila mitochondrial DNA. Nucl. Acids Res. 12:3747-3762.
27. Colhoun, C.W., and M.W. Steer (1981) Microsporogenesis and the mechanism of cytoplasmic male sterility in maize. Ann. Bot. 48:417-424.
28. Conde, M.F., D.R. Pring, and C.S. Levings, III (1979) Maternal inheritance of organelle DNA's in Zea mays-Zea perennis reciprocal crosses. J. Heredity 70:2-4.
29. Dale, R.M.K., N. Mendu, H. Ginsburg, and J.C. Kridl (1984) Sequence analysis of the maize mitochondrial 26S rRNA gene and flanking regions. Plasmid 11:141-150.
30. Dawson, A.J., V.P. Jones, and C.J. Leaver (1984) The apocytochrome b gene in maize mitochondria does not contain introns and is preceded by a potential ribosome binding site. EMBO J. 3:2107-2113.
31. Dawson, A.J., T.P. Hodge, P.G. Isaac, C.J. Leaver, and D.M. Lonsdale (1986) Location of the genes for cytochrome oxidase subunits I and II, apocytochrome b, alpha-subunit of the F_1ATPase and the ribosomal RNA genes on the mitochondrial genome of maize (Zea mays L.). Curr, Genet. 10:561-564.

32. de Bruijn, M.H.L. (1983) Drosophila melanogaster mitochondrial DNA, a novel organization and genetic code. Nature 304:234-241.

33. Deters, D.W., and M.W. Ewing (1985) The alpha subunit of the mito- chondrial ATP synthetase is mitochondrially made in the unicellular heterotroph Prototheca zopfii. Curr. Genet. 10:125-131.

34. Dewey, R.E., C.S. Levings, III, and D.H. Timothy (1985) Nucleotide se- quence of ATPase subunit 6 gene of maize mitochondria. Plant Physiol. 79:914-919.

35. Dewey, R.E., C.S. Levings, III, and D.H. Timothy (1986) Novel recombi- nations in the maize mitochondrial genome produce a unique transcrip- tional unit in the Texas male-sterile cytoplasm. Cell 44:439-449.

36. Dewey, R.E., A.M. Schuster, C.S. Levings, III, and D.H. Timothy (1985) Nucleotide sequence of F_0-ATPase proteolipid (subunit 9) gene of maize mitochondria. Proc. Natl. Acad. Sci., USA 82:1015-1019.

37. Dujon, B. (1983) Mitochondrial genes, mutants and maps: A review. In Mitochondria 1983: Nucleo-Mitochondrial Interactions, R.J. Schweyen, K. Wolf, and F. Kaudewitz, eds. Walter de Gruyter, New York, pp. 1-24.

38. Duvick, D.N. (1965) Cytoplasmic pollen sterility in corn. Adv. Genet. 13:1-56.

39. Duvick, D.N., R.J. Snyder, and E.G. Anderson (1961) The chromosomal location of Rf_1, a restorer gene for cytoplasmic pollen sterile maize. Genetics 46:1245-1252.

40. Eckenrode, V.K., and C.S. Levings, III (1986) Maize mitochondrial genes. In Vitro Cell Dev. Biol. 22:169-176.

41. Forde, B.G., and C.J. Leaver (1980) Nuclear and cytoplasmic genes con- trolling synthesis of variant mitochondrial polypeptides in male- sterile maize. Proc. Natl. Acad. Sci., USA 77:418-422.

42. Forde, B.G., R.J.C. Oliver, and C.J. Leaver (1978) Variation in mito- chondrial translation products associated with male-sterile cytoplasms in maize. Proc. Natl. Acad. Sci., USA 75:3841-3845.

43. Forde, B.G., R.J.C. Oliver, C.J. Leaver, R.E. Gunn, and R.J. Kemble (1980) Classification of normal and male-sterile cytoplasm maize. I. Electrophoretic analysis of variation in mitochondrially synthe- sized proteins. Genetics 95:443-450.

44. Fox, T.D., and C.J. Leaver (1981) The Zea mays mitochondrial gene cod- ing cytochrome oxidase subunit II has an intervening sequence and does not contain TGA codons. Cell 26:315-323.

45. Gengenbach, B.G., and C.E. Green (1975) Selection of T-cytoplasm maize callus cultures resistant to Helminthosporium maydis race T pathotox- in. Crop Sci. 15:645-649.

46. Gengenbach, B.G., C.E. Green, and C.M. Donovan (1977) Inheritance of selected pathotoxin resistance in maize plants regenerated from cell cultures. Proc. Natl. Acad. Sci., USA 74:5113-5117.

47. Gengenbach, B.G., J.A. Connelly, D.R. Pring, and M.F. Conde (1981) Mitochondrial DNA variation in maize plants regenerated during tissue culture selection. Theor. Appl. Genet. 59:161-167.

48. Gottschalk, M., and A. Brennicke (1985) Initiator methionine tRNA gene in Oenothera mitochondria. Curr. Genet. 9:165-168.

49. Gracen, V.E., and C.O. Grogan (1974) Diversity and suitability for hy- brid production of different sources of cytoplasmic male sterility in maize. Agron. J. 66:654-657.

50. Gray, M.W., and D.F. Spencer (1983) Wheat mitochondrial DNA encodes a eubacteria-like initiator methionine transfer RNA. FEBS Lett. 161: 323-327.

51. Grivell, L.A. (1983) Mitochondrial gene expression 1983. In Mitochondria 1983: Nucleo-Mitochondrial Interactions, R.J. Schweyen, K. Wolf, and F. Kaudewitz, eds. Walter de Gruyter, New York, pp. 25-45.
52. Hack, E., and C.J. Leaver (1983) The alpha-subunit of the maize F_1-ATPase is synthesized in the mitochondrion. EMBO J. 2:1783-1789.
53. Hall, C.E. (1979) Microsporogenesis in male-fertile and S-type cytoplasmic male-sterile maize. Ph.D. dissertation, University of Illinois, Urbana, Illinois, 82 pp.
54. Hanson, M.R., and M.F. Conde (1985) Functioning and variation of cytoplasmic genomes: Lessons from cytoplasmic-nuclear interactions affecting male fertility in plants. Int. Rev. Cytol. 94:213-267.
55. Hiesel, R., and A. Brennicke (1983) Cytochrome oxidase subunit II gene in mitochondria of Oenothera has no intron. EMBO J. 2:2173-2178.
56. Hiesel, R., and A. Brennicke (1985) Overlapping reading frames in Oenothera mitochondria. FEBS Lett. 193:164-168.
57. Isaac, P.G., V.P. Jones, and C.J. Leaver (1985) The maize cytochrome c oxidase subunit I gene: Sequence, expression and rearrangement in cytoplasmic male sterile plants. EMBO J. 4:1617-1623.
58. Isaac, P.G., A. Brennicke, S.M. Dunbar, and C.J. Leaver (1985) The mitochondrial genome of fertile maize (Zea mays L.) contains two copies of the gene encoding the alpha-subunit of the F_1-ATPase. Curr. Genet. 10:321-328.
59. Ise, W., H. Haiker, and H. Weiss (1985) Mitochondrial translation of subunits of the rotenone-sensitive NADH:ubiquinone reductase in Neurospora crassa. EMBO J. 4:2075-2080.
60. Iwasaki, Y., and T. Asahi (1985) Intracellular sites of the synthesis of sweet potato mitochondrial F_1ATPase subunits. Plant Mol. Biol. 5:339-346.
61. Kao, T.-H., E. Moon, and R. Wu (1984) Cytochrome oxidase subunit II gene of rice has an insertion sequence within the intron. Nucl. Acids Res. 12:7305-7315.
62. Kemble, R.J., R.B. Flavell, and R.I.S. Brettell (1982) Mitochondrial DNA analysis of fertile and sterile maize plants derived from tissue culture with the Texas male sterile cytoplasm. Theor. Appl. Genet. 62:213-217.
63. Kheyr-Pour, A., V.E. Gracen, and H.L. Everett (1981) Genetics of fertility restoration in the C-group of cytoplasmic male sterility in maize. Genetics 98:379-388.
64. Lambowitz, A.M., R.J. LaPolla, and R.A. Collins (1979) Mitochondrial ribosome assembly in Neurospora: Two-dimensional gel electrophoretic analysis of mitochondrial ribosomal proteins. J. Cell Biol. 82:17-31.
65. Laser, K.D., and N.R. Lersten (1972) Anatomy and cytology of microsporogenesis in cytoplasmic male sterile angiosperms. Bot. Rev. 38: 425-454.
66. Laughnan, J.R., and S.J. Gabay (1975) An episomal basis for instability of S male sterility in maize and some implications for plant breeding. In Genetics and the Biogenesis of Cell Organelles, C.W. Birky, Jr., P.S. Perlman, and T.J. Byers, eds. Ohio State University Press, Columbus, Ohio, pp. 330-349.
67. Laughnan, J.R., and S. Gabay-Laughnan (1983) Cytoplasmic male sterility in maize. Ann. Rev. Genet. 17:27-48.
68. Leaver, C.J., and M.W. Gray (1982) Mitochondrial genome organization and expression in higher plants. Ann. Rev. Plant Physiol. 33:373-402.
69. Lee, S.-L.J., and H.E. Warmke (1979) Organelle size and number in fertile and T-cytoplasmic male-sterile corn. Am. J. Bot. 66:141-148.

70. Lee, S.-L.J., E.D. Earle, and V.E. Gracen (1980) The cytology of pollen abortion in S-cytoplasmic male-sterile corn anthers. Am. J. Bot. 67:237-245.
71. Lee, S.-L.J., V.E. Gracen, and E.D. Earle (1979) The cytology of pollen abortion in C-cytoplasmic male-sterile corn anthers. Am. J. Bot. 66:656-667.
72. Levings, III, C.S. (1983) The plant mitochondrial genome and its mutants. Cell 32:659-661.
73. Levings, III, C.S., and D.R. Pring (1976) Restriction endonuclease analysis of mitochondrial DNA from normal and Texas cytoplasmic male-sterile maize. Science 193:158-160.
74. Levings, III, C.S., and D.R. Pring (1979) Mitochondrial DNA of higher plants and genetic engineering. In Genetic Engineering: Principles and Methods, Vol. 1, J.K. Setlow and A. Hollaender, eds. Plenum Press, New York, pp. 205-222.
75. Levings, III, C.S., and R.R. Sederoff (1983) Nucleotide sequence of the S-2 mitochondrial DNA from the S cytoplasm of maize. Proc. Natl. Acad. Sci., USA 80:4055-4059.
76. Levings, III, C.S., D.M. Shah, W.W.L. Hu, D.R. Pring, and D.H. Timothy (1979) Molecular heterogeneity among mitochondrial DNAs from different maize cytoplasms. In Extrachromosomal DNA (ICN-UCLA Symp. Mol. Cell Biol., Vol. 15), D.J. Cummings, P. Borst, I.G. Dawid, S.M. Weissman, and C.F. Fox, eds. Academic Press, Inc., New York, pp. 63-73.
77. Lonsdale, D.M., T.P. Hodge, and C.M.-R. Fauron (1984) The physical map and organization of the mitochondrial genome from the fertile cytoplasm of maize. Nucl. Acids Res. 12:9249-9261.
78. Manna, E., and A. Brennicke (1985) Primary and secondary structure of 26S ribosomal RNA of Oenothera mitochondria. Curr. Genet. 9:505-515.
79. Marechal, L., P. Guillemaut, and J.-H. Weil (1985) Sequences of two bean mitochondria tRNAs[Tyr] which differ in the level of post-transcriptional modification and have a prokaryotic-like large extra-loop. Plant Mol. Biol. 5:347-351.
80. Marechal, L., P. Guillemaut, J.-M. Grienenberger, G. Jeannin, and J.-H. Weil (1985) Structure of bean mitochondrial genomes of maize and wheat. FEBS Lett. 184:289-293.
81. Mariottini, P., A. Chomyn, M. Riley, B. Cottrell, R.F. Doolittle, and G. Attardi (1986) Identification of the polypeptides encoded in the unassigned reading frames 2, 4, 4L, and 5 of human mitochondrial DNA. Proc. Natl. Acad. Sci., USA 83:1563-1567.
82. Matthews, D.E., P. Gregory, and V.E. Gracen (1979) Helminthosporium maydis race T toxin induces leakage of NAD^+ from T cytoplasm corn mitochondria. Plant Physiol. 63:1149-1153.
83. Miller, D.L., and N.C. Martin (1983) Characterization of the yeast mitochondrial locus necessary for tRNA biosynthesis: DNA sequence analysis and identification of a new transcript. Cell 34:911-917.
84. Miller, R.J., and D.E. Koeppe (1971) Southern corn leaf blight: Susceptible and resistant mitochondria. Science 173:67-69.
85. Moon, E., T.-H. Kao, and R. Wu (1985) Pea cytochrome oxidase subunit II gene has no intron and generates two mRNA transcripts with different 5'-termini. Nucl. Acids Res. 13:3195-3212.
86. Neuport, W., and B. Schatz (1981) How proteins are transported into mitochondria. Trends Biochem. Sci. (Pers. Ed.) 6:1-4.
87. Osinga, K.A., E. De Vries, B. Van der Horst, and H.F. Tabak (1984) Processing of yeast mitochondrial messenger RNAs at a conserved dodecamer sequence. EMBO J. 3:829-834.

88. Paillard, M., R.R. Sederoff, and C.S. Levings, III (1985) Nucleotide sequence of the S-1 mitochondrial DNA from the S cytoplasm of maize. EMBO J. 4:1125-1128.
89. Palleschi, C., S. Francisci, E. Zennaro, and L. Frontali (1984) Expression of the clustered mitochondrial tRNA genes in Saccharomyces cerevisiae: Transcription and processing of transcripts. EMBO J. 3:1389-1395.
90. Palmer, J.D., and C.R. Shields (1984) Tripartite structure of the Brassica campestris mitochondrial genome. Nature 307:437-440.
91. Parks, T.D., W.G. Dougherty, C.S. Levings, III, and D.H. Timothy (1984) Identification of two methionine transfer RNA genes in the maize mitochondrial genome. Plant Physiol. 76:1079-1082.
92. Parks, T.D., W.G. Dougherty, C.S. Levings, III, and D.H. Timothy (1985) Identification of an aspartate transfer RNA gene in maize mitochondrial DNA. Curr. Genet. 9:517-519.
93. Pratje, E., S. Schnierer, and B. Dujon (1984) Mitochondrial DNA of Chlamydomonas reinhardtii: The DNA sequence of a region showing homology with mammalian URF2. Curr. Genet. 9:75-82.
94. Pring, D.R., and C.S. Levings, III (1978) Heterogeneity of maize cytoplasmic genomes among male-sterile cytoplasms. Genetics 89:121-136.
95. Pring, D.R., and D.M. Lonsdale (1985) Molecular biology of higher plant mitochondrial DNA. Int. Rev. Cytol. 97:1-46.
96. Pring, D.R., M.F. Conde, and C.S. Levings, III (1980) DNA heterogeneity within the C group of maize male-sterile cytoplasms. Crop Sci. 20:159-162.
97. Rhoades, M.M. (1931) Cytoplasmic inheritance of male sterility in Zea mays. Science 73:340-341.
98. Rhoades, M.M. (1933) The cytoplasmic inheritance of male sterility in Zea mays. J. Genet. 27:71-93.
99. Roe, B.A., D.-P. Ma, R.K. Wilson, and J.F.-H. Wong (1985) The complete nucleotide sequence of the Xenopus leavis mitochondrial genome. J. Biol. Chem. 260:9759-9774.
100. Scazzocchio, C., T.A. Brown, R.B. Waring, J.A. Ray, and R.W. Davies (1983) Organisation of the Aspergillus nidulans mitochondrial genome. In Mitochondria 1983: Nucleo-Mitochondrial Interactions, R.J. Schweyen, K. Wolf, and F. Kaudewitz, eds. Walter de Gruyter, New York, pp. 303-312.
101. Schardl, C.L., and D.M. Lonsdale (1984) Linearization of maize mitochondrial chromosomes by recombination with linear episomes. Nature 310:292-296.
102. Schuster, W., and A. Brennicke (1985) TGA-termination codon in the apocytochrome b gene from Oenothera mitochondria. Curr. Genet. 9:157-163.
103. Snyder, R.J., and D.N. Duvick (1969) Chromosomal location of Rf_2, a restorer gene for cytoplasmic pollen sterile maize. Crop Sci. 9:156-157.
104. Spencer, D.F., L. Bonen, and M.W. Gray (1981) Primary sequence of wheat mitochondrial 5S ribosomal ribonucleic acid: Functional and evolutionary implications. Biochemistry 20:4022-4029.
105. Spencer, D.F., M.N. Schnare, and M.W. Gray (1984) Pronounced structural similarities between the small subunit ribosomal RNA genes of wheat mitochondria and Escherichia coli. Proc. Natl. Acad. Sci., USA 81:493-497.
106. Traynor, P.L., and C.S. Levings, III (1986) Transcription of the S-2 maize mitochondrial plasmid. Plant Mol. Biol. (in press).
107. Tzagoloff, A. (1982) Mitochondria, Plenum Press, New York, 342 pp.

108. Umbeck, P.F., and B.G. Gengenbach (1983) Reversion of male-sterile T-cytoplasm maize to male fertility in tissue culture. Crop Sci. 23:584-588.
109. Underbrink-Lyon, K., D.L. Miller, N.A. Ross, H. Fukuhara, and N.C. Martin (1983) Characterization of a yeast mitochondrial locus necessary to tRNA biosynthesis: Deletion mapping and restriction mapping studies. Mol. Gen. Genet. 191:512-518.
110. Ward, B.L., R.S. Anderson, and A.J. Bendich (1981) The mitochondrial genome is large and variable in a family of plants (Cucurbitaceae). Cell 25:793-803.
111. Warmke, H.E., and S.-L.J. Lee (1977) Mitochondrial degeneration in Texas cytoplasmic male-sterile corn anthers. J. Hered. 68:213-222.
112. Warmke, H.E., and S.-L.J. Lee (1978) Pollen abortion in T-cytoplasmic male-sterile corn (Zea mays): A suggested mechanism. Science 200: 561-563.
113. Wheeler, J.E., and A.O. Martinez (1974) Mitochondria and cytoplasmic male sterility as related to southern corn leaf blight. PANS 20:403-408.
114. Yin, S., J. Burke, D.D. Chang, K.S. Browning, J.E. Heckman, B. Alzner-DeWeerd, M.J. Potter, and U.L. RajBhandary (1982) Neurospora crassa mitochondrial tRNAs and rRNAs: Structure, gene organization, and DNA sequences. In Mitochondrial Genes, P. Slonimski, P. Borst, and G. Attardi, eds. Cold Spring Harbor Laboratory, Cold Spring Harbor, New York, pp. 361-373.

REGULATION OF GENE EXPRESSION

PLANT RNA POLYMERASES: STRUCTURES, REGULATION, AND GENES

Tom J. Guilfoyle and Margaret A. Dietrich

Department of Biochemistry
University of Missouri
Columbia, Missouri 65211

INTRODUCTION

Plants, like other eukaryotes, have three distinct classes of nuclear DNA-dependent RNA polymerases (9,10,21,26). In addition, they possess RNA polymerases unique to the chloroplast and mitochondrial organelles. Within the nucleus, genomic DNA is transcribed by RNA polymerases I (or A), II (or B), and III (or C), and each class of enzyme carries out a unique transcriptional role. RNA polymerase I is localized in the nucleolus and transcribes ribosomal DNA (rDNA) cistrons into precursor ribosomal RNA (rRNA) containing species of 25S, 18S, and 5.8S rRNAs. RNA polymerase II is localized in the nucleoplasm and produces precursors to mRNAs and some small nuclear RNAs. RNA polymerase III is also localized in the nucleoplasm and transcribes 5S rRNA, tRNA, and some small nuclear RNA genes. While RNA polymerases II and III are localized in the nucleoplasm in situ, both enzymes are subject to extensive leaching from nuclei during cell disruption and are largely recovered in the cytoplasm fraction of cell extracts (9,10).

Each class of plant nuclear RNA polymerase exhibits a characteristic inhibition profile when exposed to the fungal toxin, α-amanitin (10,21,26). RNA polymerase I is refractory to the toxin at concentrations as high as 2 mg/ml. RNA polymerase II is half-maximally inhibited at 0.05 µg/ml and fully inhibited at 1 µg/ml of α-amanitin. In contrast, RNA polymerase III displays two types of inhibition profiles, depending on the species of plant tested. In the first case (e.g., wheat), the class III enzyme is half-maximally inhibited at about 5 µg/ml, and in the second case (e.g., cauliflower), half-maximal inhibition is achieved at about 1 to 2 mg/ml of fungal toxin.

Enzymes representing each of the three classes of nuclear RNA polymerases have been purified to homogeneity from a number of different plants, and these enzymes have been characterized and compared to one another in terms of subunit structures, related and common subunit polypeptides, transcriptional properties, and regulation. More recently, genes encoding certain of the RNA polymerase subunit polypeptides have been isolated and characterized. It is the object of this chapter to summarize part of this research on plant nuclear RNA polymerases.

MOLECULAR STRUCTURES OF PLANT RNA POLYMERASES

Aggregate Molecular Weights and General Subunit Structures

Nuclear RNA polymerases are composed of multiple polypeptides which result in enzymes possessing aggregate molecular weights in the range of 400 to 750. Enzymes in each class of nuclear RNA polymerase are composed of two large subunits, each in excess of 100 kDa (Tab. 1), similar to the β' and β subunits of the Escherichia coli enzyme. In addition to the two largest subunits, 5 to 13 polypeptides with molecular weights less than 100 are associated with the purified enzymes. Whether all of the polypeptides associated with a purified enzyme are authentic subunits required for enzymatic function is not known; however, those putative subunit polypeptides listed in Tab. 1 are present in the RNA polymerases at unit stoichiometries, except for a 25- to 27-kDa polypeptide of basic charge which is present at a stoichiometry of two for each of the nuclear enzymes, and are only dissociated from the enzymes by treatment with strong denaturing agents (e.g., sodium dodecyl sulfate or urea).

Tab. 1.   Subunit structures of plant RNA polymerases I, II, and III.

Cauliflower I	Cauliflower II	Cauliflower III	Wheat I	Wheat II	Wheat III	Soybean I	Soybean II
				220			215 (a)
190			200			195	
	180						
		150			150		
	140			140			138 (b)
125		130	125		130	120	
					94		
		70					
		50			55		
	40			42/40		45	42 (c)
38		45/38	38		38		
					30		
					28		
25	25	25		27/25	25	27	27 (d)
		24	24		24.5		
		23					
	22			21	20.5		22 (e)
19	19	19	20	20	20	19	19 (f)
		17.8			19.5		
17.5	17.5	17.5	17.8	17.8	17.8	17.6	17.6 (g)
	17		17		17		17 (h)
	16.2			16.3			16.2 (i)
	16			16			16.1 (j)
	14			14			14 (k)

Note: Molecular weights are given in kDa. Letters in parentheses refer to subunit nomenclature used in the text.

Comparative Structural Analysis of RNA Polymerase II

RNA polymerase II represents about 80% to 90% of the total nuclear RNA polymerase present in a plant cell (10). Because of its prevalence and amenability to purification, this class of enzyme has been subjected to extensive structural analysis. The subunit structure is highly conserved between monocotyledonous and dicotyledonous plants (Fig. 1). For each polypeptide present in wheat RNA polymerase II, there is an analogous polypeptide in the class II enzyme of soybean. Each contains a largest subunit of 220 kDa (subunit a) and a minor degradation product from this subunit of 180 kDa. The second largest subunit is 140 kDa (subunit b) in each case. The third subunit is 42 kDa (subunit c) in soybean, while in wheat this subunit is composed of a doublet of 42 and 40 kDa, which sums to a stoichiometry of one. The fourth subunit is 27 kDa (subunit d) in soybean, is basic in charge, and is present at a stoichiometry of two. Subunit d in

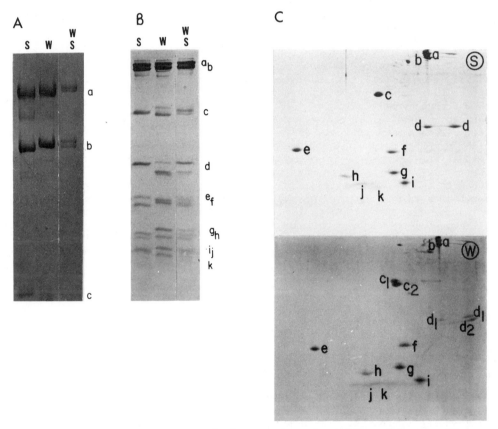

Fig. 1.   Subunit structures of wheat and soybean RNA polymerase II enzymes. Enzymes were purified and subjected to one- or two-dimensional gel electrophoresis as described previously (19). Gels were stained with Coomassie brilliant blue R. (A) Five percent polyacrylamide gel; (B) 15% polyacrylamide gel; (C) 15% two-dimensional polyacrylamide gels. Symbols: W, wheat; S, soybean; WS, wheat plus soybean. Lower case letters refer to analogous polypeptides in the enzymes from wheat and soybean (see Tab. 1).

wheat is again a doublet composed of two basic polypeptides of 27 and 25 kDa, which sum to a stoichiometry of two. Each enzyme also contains two distinct polypeptides in the molecular weight range of 19 to 22 (subunits e and f), and one of these is highly acidic in charge (subunit f; Fig. 1C). In addition, each enzyme contains two distinct polypeptides of about 17 kDa (subunits g and h), two unique polypeptides of about 16 kDa (subunits i and j), and a smallest polypeptide of about 14 kDa (subunit k). Polypeptides corresponding to subunits a through k have also been identified in rye, maize, cauliflower, turnip, alfalfa, bush bean, and pea (Ref. 12, 18, and 19; T. Guilfoyle, unpubl. results).

In addition to the evidence described above for analogous polypeptides in class II enzymes from different plant species, antibodies raised against individual subunits from one species have been shown to cross-react only with the analogous subunit of similar size and charge in another species (12). These antibody studies also suggest that the smaller subunits do not arise from the larger subunits, since little or no cross-reactivity is observed among subunits of different size.

Related and Common Subunits

Although the two largest subunits of RNA polymerases I, II, and III differ in size (Tab. 1) and cross-react weakly when probed with specific antibodies (12), certain of the smaller subunits are identical in size and show strong cross-reactivity (12). In general, at least three of the small subunits appear to be common to the three classes of nuclear RNA polymerase. These common subunits are subunits d, f, and g, which are associated with the RNA polymerase II enzymes described above. Antibodies raised against RNA polymerase II react with all the polypeptides associated with the class II enzyme (Fig. 2A), but react strongly only with those common subunits in the class I (Fig. 2B) or III enzyme (data not shown; Ref. 12). Antibodies raised against the individual subunits of RNA polymerase II react much more strongly with the common subunits in RNA polymerases I and III compared to reactions of subunits unique to each enzyme class (12). In addition to the three subunits common to RNA polymerases I, II, and III, RNA polymerases I and III have a 38- to 40-kDa polypeptide in common and possibly a second common polypeptide of about 17 kDa (10,12,24). It has been suggested that the common polypeptides form a core complex which is required for a common enzymatic function in the three classes of enzyme (24).

Heterogeneity of Subunits within a Class of RNA Polymerase

Some heterogeneity within a given class of RNA polymerase has been reported (9,10,26). This heterogeneity within a class of enzyme is displayed upon chromatography, sedimentation, or nondenaturing polyacrylamide gel electrophoresis of purified enzymes, and in some cases, appears to result from modification or addition of single polypeptides associated with a specific class of enzyme. The best studied case is RNA polymerase II, where three subclasses of enzyme (i.e., RNA polymerases II_o, II_a, and II_b) have been distinguished. The subunit structures of these subclasses of enzyme differ in only the size of the largest subunit, which is 240, 220, and 180 kDa for II_o, II_a, and II_b, respectively (10,21,26). Class II_a and II_b enzymes from soybean are shown in Fig. 3. In situ, possibly only the largest form of the enzyme exists, and smaller subforms of the enzyme appear to result from proteolysis of the carboxyl terminus of the largest subunit (13). There is some evidence which indicates that only the undegraded forms of

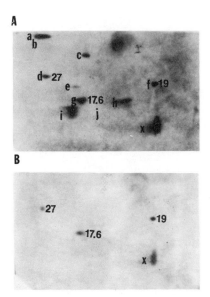

Fig. 2.   Common subunits in soybean RNA polymerases I and II. RNA polym-
           erases were purified to homogeneity (8) and subjected to two-
           dimensional polyacrylamide gel electrophoresis. Polypeptides
           were blotted from gels to diazobenzyloxymethyl-paper, and blots
           were probed with antibody raised against soybean RNA polymerase
           II followed by reaction with ^{125}I-labeled protein A (12). Common
           polypeptides are indicated in kDa. Reactive polypeptides are in-
           dicated by letters (see Tab. 1); "x" is an unidentified antigen
           common to RNA polymerases I, II, and III (10). (A) RNA polymer-
           ase II; (B) RNA polymerase I.

RNA polymerase II and forms that received only very limited proteolysis
(i.e., II_o and possibly II_a, but not II_b) can carry out accurate initiation
of transcription in vitro (5). It is interesting that the largest subunit
of the enzyme can be phosphorylated in vivo when the large polypeptide is
220 to 240 kDa, while the 180-kDa degradation product lacks a phosphorylated moiety (Fig. 4). This suggests that phosphorylation of the largest subunit of the RNA polymerase II is limited to a 40- to 60-kDa portion at the
carboxyl terminus of the molecule.

SPECIFICITY OF TRANSCRIPTION

     As alluded to at the beginning of this chapter, each class of nuclear
RNA polymerase has a specific transcriptional role. This can be demonstrated with isolated nuclei where RNA chains, which were initiated in
vivo, are propagated in vitro, and the purified nuclear transcripts are hybridized to specific DNA probes. Since the α-amanitin inhibition profile
for a class of RNA polymerase is an invariant characteristic of the enzyme,
a concentration series of α-amanitin can be included in the in vitro transcription cocktails and used to discriminate among in vitro transcripts
produced by RNA polymerases I, II, and III. Using this experimental strategy, it can be demonstrated that rRNA synthesis is resistant to α-amanitin
inhibition, mRNA synthesis is half-maximally inhibited at about 0.05 μg/ml

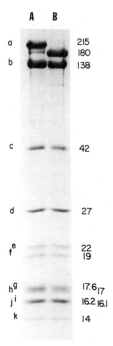

Fig. 3.   Subunit structures of soybean RNA polymerases II$_a$ (A) and II$_b$
           (B). Purified enzymes were subjected to electrophoresis on 10%
           to 16% exponential gradient SDS polyacrylamide gels and stained
           with Coomassie brilliant blue R (11). Subunits are labeled with
           lower case letters (see Tab. 1), and are indicated in kDa.

of the toxin, and 5S rRNA and tRNA syntheses are half-maximally inhibited
at about 5 μg/ml of α-amanitin (Fig. 5). These results strongly suggest
that RNA polymerases I, II, and III play transcriptional roles in the synthesis of rRNA, mRNA, and 5S rRNA plus tRNA, respectively.

     Results with soluble transcription systems, most of them derived from
animal tissue culture cells, have substantiated the proposed transcriptional roles for RNA polymerases I, II, and III. With these soluble systems it
has been demonstrated that, in the presence of specific ancillary protein-
aceous factors, RNA polymerases I and II can accurately initiate transcription on cloned rRNA and mRNA genes (7,22), respectively, and RNA polymerase
III can accurately transcribe cloned 5S rRNA and tRNA genes (3,27) which
contain appropriate promoter elements. These in vitro experiments, along
with in vivo transfection experiments, have proven invaluable in identifying those sequences that constitute a promoter and/or terminator for animal
RNA polymerases I, II, and III. Unfortunately, to date, soluble in vitro
transcription systems have not been effectively produced from plant
sources, and, therefore, the analysis of promoter elements for genes transcribed by plant nuclear RNA polymerases has been necessarily limited to in
vivo approaches, namely transformations with the T-DNA of Agrobacterium
tumefaciens or direct DNA uptake with isolated protoplasts.

     One plant source which may hold some promise for the development of
soluble in vitro transcription systems is isolated nuclei from wheat germ.

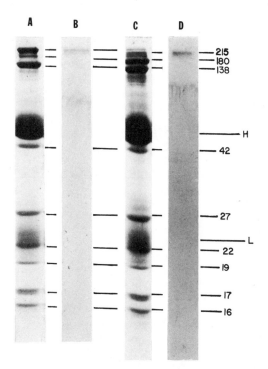

Fig. 4.   Phosphorylation of the 220–kDa subunit of soybean RNA polymerase
          II.   Soybean cells were labeled in vivo with ^{32}P, and partially
          purified enzymes were immunoprecipitated with antibody raised
          against soybean RNA polymerase II (11).   Coomassie blue-stained,
          10% to 16% gradient SDS polyacrylamide gels of immunoprecipitated
          RNA polymerases II$_a$ and II$_b$ are shown in lanes A and C, respec-
          tively.   Autoradiograms of these gels are shown in adjacent lanes
          B and D, respectively.   Subunits are indicated in kDa.   Notations
          H and L signify the heavy and light chains of IgG.

In this nuclear system, at least 5S rRNA genes and possibly tRNA genes appear to be transcribed accurately by both endogenous and exogenous sources
of wheat RNA polymerase III (Fig. 6; Ref. 14).   There is additional evidence that wheat chromatin, depleted of endogenous RNA polymerase III, can
serve as a template for the accurate transcription of 5S rRNA genes by added wheat RNA polymerase III (J. Suzich and T. Guilfoyle, unpubl. results).
This suggests that all of the accessory factors (in addition to RNA polymerase III) are retained in the isolated nuclei and on the purified chromatin, and that these nuclear or chromatin sources might serve as a starting
point for the identification of factors that allow RNA polymerase III (and
possibly I and II) to accurately initiate transcription on purified genes.

REGULATION OF RNA POLYMERASES

     Nuclear RNA polymerase activities are dramatically modulated upward or
downward during a wide variety of growth and developmental transitions (9,
10,11,26).   Changes in RNA polymerase activities do not appear to involve
observable changes in RNA polymerase subunit structures, although covalent

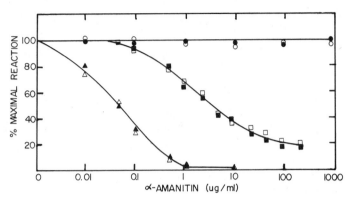

Fig. 5.   Alpha-amanitin inhibition profiles for 25S + 18S rRNA (o), mRNA
           (Δ), and 5S rRNA + tRNA (□) syntheses and for wheat RNA polymer-
           ases I (●), II (▲), and III (■).   RNA synthesis was carried out
           in vitro with isolated nuclei from soybean plumules (for 25S +
           18S rRNA and mRNA) or wheat embryos (for 5S rRNA + tRNA).   For
           detection of products, purified in vitro ^{32}P-labeled RNAs were
           hybridized to cloned soybean rDNA or auxin-responsive mRNA (cDNA)
           probes, or total RNAs were analyzed on 10% polyacrylamide gels to
           detect 5S rRNA and tRNAs.   Wheat RNA polymerases, which were
           purified to homogeneity (12), were assayed with template of de-
           natured calf thymus DNA.   Alpha-amanitin was added to the in
           vitro transcription cocktails at the concentrations indicated,
           and reactions were carried out for 30 min.

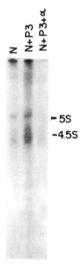

Fig. 6.   Exogenous purified wheat RNA polymerase III that is added to
           wheat embryo nuclei results in increased synthesis of 5S rRNA and
           pre-tRNAs.   Nuclei were incubated without (N) or with (N+P3) ex-
           ogenous RNA polymerase III, or they were incubated with exogenous
           RNA polymerase III and 100 μg/ml of α-amanitin (N+P3+α).   Auto-
           radiograms of radioactive small RNAs resolved on 10% polyacryla-
           mide gels are shown.

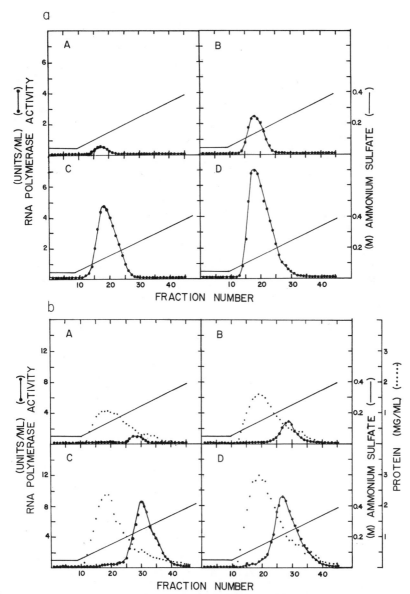

Fig. 7.   Increases in amounts of RNA polymerases I and II induced by auxin
           treatment of soybean hypocotyls. One-kilogram amounts of hypo-
           cotyls excised from soybean seedlings which had been treated for
           0 hr (A), 12 hr (B), 24 hr (C), or 48 hr (D) were homogenized and
           subjected to centrifugation at 10,000 X g (8). The solubilized
           pellets, containing nucleolar chromatin and the bulk of RNA
           polymerase I activity, and the supernatants, containing the bulk
           of RNA polymerase II activity, were chromatographed on DEAE-
           cellulose columns. Individual fractions were assayed for RNA
           polymerase activity. (a) Elution profiles for RNA polymerase I;
           (b) elution profiles for RNA polymerase II.

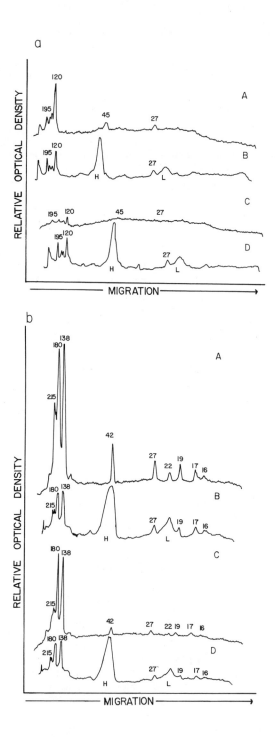

Fig. 8.   Incorporation of [^{35}S]methionine into RNA polymerase I and II
           subunits before and after auxin treatment. Rootless soybean
           seedlings were labeled with [^{35}S]methionine for 24 hr in the
           presence or absence of the synthetic auxin 2,4-dichlorophenoxy-
           acetic acid (2,4-D) (8). Partially purified enzymes were immuno-
           precipitated with antibody raised against RNA polymerase I or II.
           Immunoprecipitates were subjected to SDS polyacrylamide gel elec-
           trophoresis, and gels were stained (B and D) or autoradiographed
           (A and C). Notations H and L signify the heavy and light chains
           of IgG. Densitometric scans of gels and autoradiograms of RNA
           polymerases I and II are shown in panels a and b, respectively.
           Scans A and B are RNA polymerases from auxin-treated hypocotyl,
           and scans C and D are RNA polymerases from untreated hypocotyl.
           Peaks between 195 and 120 kDa in panel a are degradation products
           of the 195-kDa subunit of RNA polymerase I.

modification (i.e., phosphorylation, ADP-ribosylation, and acetylation) of
polypeptide subunits might play some role in enzyme activation or deactiva-
tion.   Rather than qualitative changes in the RNA polymerase molecules
themselves, it is more likely that nuclear RNA polymerase activities are
regulated, at least in part, by ancillary transcription factors, some of
which probably include transcription initiation factors which have been
identified upon fractionation of soluble in vitro transcription extracts.
Another likely means of regulating RNA polymerase activities is by altering
the total amount of enzyme in the cell or nucleus. It is likely that the
amounts of both specific transcription factors and specific classes of RNA
polymerases control the rate of transcription in the nucleus.

     In plants, RNA polymerase I and II activities have been studied in a
number of cases where quiescent or stationary-phase cells are induced to
proliferate by an agent such as auxin (9,10,11). In general, this onset of
cell proliferation is preceded by large increases in rRNA, ribosomal proteins, ribosomes, ratio of polyribosomes to monoribosomes, nucleolar volume, and nuclear-associated or chromatin-bound RNA polymerase I activity.
While chromatin-engaged RNA polymerase I activity may increase greater than
ten-fold on a nuclear DNA basis, chromatin-bound RNA polymerase II generally shows much less dramatic increases during the transition from stationary
phase to growth phase (8,10,23). The changes in nuclear RNA polymerase activities that do occur during proliferation are probably accounted for by
direct changes in amounts of RNA polymerase as well as by changes in nuclear structure and/or transcription factors. During auxin-induced proliferation in the mature soybean hypocotyl, the amounts of RNA polymerases I and
II increase up to 20-fold and six-fold, respectively, on a tissue fresh
weight basis (Fig. 7), but this reduces to three- to six-fold and two-fold,
respectively, on a nuclear DNA basis (8). The increase in amounts of RNA
polymerases I and II probably results from de novo synthesis of RNA polymerase subunits in a relatively coordinate fashion (Fig. 8). During proliferation, the absolute amount of incorporation of labeled amino acids into
RNA polymerase II subunits increases about two- to three-fold and into RNA
polymerase I subunits about ten- to 20-fold; however, the relative incorporation of labeled amino acids into each RNA polymerase subunit (using
the second largest subunit as a baseline) is similar in slowly and rapidly
growing hypocotyls.

RNA POLYMERASE SUBUNIT GENES

Genes for the largest subunits of RNA polymerases I, II, and III (16, 17,25,28), the second largest subunit of RNA polymerases I and II (6,25, 28), and several smaller subunits (25) have recently been isolated from animals and/or yeast and characterized. The largest subunit of RNA polymerase II has been the most extensively studied to date. Probes corresponding to this gene hybridize to an mRNA of about 6.5 to 7.5 kb, which is of sufficient size to code for a polypeptide of 220 to 240 kDa. Several of the genes have been sequenced in part or entirely, and there exist six domains of high sequence homology among nuclear RNA polymerases II and III as well as E. coli RNA polymerase (1,2). A unique sequence domain occurs at the carboxyl terminus of the largest subunit of RNA polymerase II. This domain consists of a heptapeptide, Pro-Thr-Ser-Pro-Ser-Tyr-Ser, which is tandemly repeated 26 times in yeast (1), 42 times in fruit fly (20), and 52 times in mouse (4) and hamster (15). The sequence of this domain indicates that it offers multiple sites for phosphorylation of this subunit.

Recently, we have isolated four independent genomic clones from soybean that share sequence homology with animal and yeast RNA polymerase II largest subunit genes (M. Dietrich and T. Guilfoyle, unpubl. results). Unlike the situation with yeast and animals where this gene is single copy or two copies, the gene in soybean is low multicopy. Each of these genes hybridizes to an mRNA of about 6.5 kb in soybean. The carboxyl termini of two of these genes have been sequenced: one gene contains 26 heptapeptide repeats, while a second gene contains 31 heptapeptide repeats within this domain. These repeats are not perfect, since some deviations from the heptapeptide consensus sequence occur, especially at positions 2 (where Ser may substitute for Thr) and 5 (where Gly, Ala, or other amino acids may substitute for Ser). Physiological studies using these genes as hybridization probes indicate that treatment of soybean hypocotyls with auxin results in a substantial increase in the mRNA for the 220-kDa subunit of RNA polymerase II. This northern blot analysis agrees with our previous studies on enzyme subunit synthesis (see section on "Regulation of RNA Polymerases" above) which suggested that auxin treatment results in de novo synthesis of RNA polymerases in mature hypocotyl. How the accumulation of this mRNA is regulated along with other subunit mRNAs during growth and developmental transitions is a challenging and interesting question.

ACKNOWLEDGEMENTS

The work from the authors' laboratory was supported by Grants GM24096 and GM37950 from the National Institutes of Health.

REFERENCES

1. Allison, L.A., M. Moyle, M. Shales, and C.J. Ingles (1985) Extensive homology among the largest subunits of eukaryotic and prokaryotic RNA polymerases. Cell 42:599-610.
2. Biggs, J., L.L. Searles, and A.L. Greenleaf (1985) Structure of the eukaryotic transcription apparatus: Features of the gene for the largest subunit of Drosophila RNA polymerase II. Cell 42:611-621.
3. Ciliberto, G., L. Castagnoli, and R. Cortese (1983) Transcription by RNA polymerase III. Curr. Top. Develop. Biol. 18:59-88.

4. Corden, J.L., D.L. Cadena, J.M. Ahearn, and M.E. Dahmus (1985) A unique structure at the carboxyl terminus of the largest subunit of eukaryotic RNA polymerase II. Proc. Natl. Acad. Sci., USA 82:7934-7938.

5. Dahmus, M.E., and C. Kedinger (1983) Transcription of adenovirus-2 major late promoter inhibited by monoclonal antibody directed against RNA polymerases II and II$_A$. J. Biol. Chem. 258:2303-2307.

6. Faust, D.M., R. Renkawitz-Pohl, D. Falkenburg, A. Gasch, S. Bialojan, R. Young, and E.K.F. Bautz (1986) Cloning and identification of the gene coding for the 140-kd subunit of Drosophila RNA polymerase II. EMBO J. 5:741-746.

7. Grummt, I. (1982) Nucleotide sequence requirements for specific initiation of transcription by RNA polymerase I. Proc. Natl. Acad. Sci., USA 79:6908-6911.

8. Guilfoyle, T.J. (1980) Auxin-induced deoxyribonucleic acid dependent ribonucleic acid polymerase activities in mature soybean hypocotyl. Biochemistry 19:6112-6118.

9. Guilfoyle, T.J. (1981) DNA and RNA polymerases. In The Biochemistry of Plants, Vol. 6, A. Marcus, ed. Academic Press, Inc., New York, pp. 207-247.

10. Guilfoyle, T.J. (1983) DNA-dependent RNA polymerases of plants and lower eukaryotes. In Enzymes of Nucleic Acid Synthesis and Modification, Vol. II, S.T. Jacob, ed. CRC Press, Inc., Boca Raton, Florida, pp. 1-42.

11. Guilfoyle, T.J. (1986) Auxin-regulated gene expression in higher plants. CRC Crit. Rev. Plant Sci. (in press).

12. Guilfoyle, T.J., G. Hagen, and S. Malcolm (1984) Immunological studies on plant DNA-dependent RNA polymerases with antibodies raised against individual subunits. J. Biol. Chem. 259:640-648.

13. Guilfoyle, T.J., G. Hagen, and S. Malcolm (1984) Size heterogeneity of the largest subunit of nuclear RNA polymerase II: An immunological analysis. J. Biol. Chem. 259:649-653.

14. Guilfoyle, T.J., J. Suzich, and M. Lindberg (1986) Synthesis of 5S rRNA and putative precursor tRNAs in nuclei isolated from wheat embryos. Plant Mol. Biol. 7:95-104.

15. Ingles, C.J., M. Moyle, L.A. Allison, and J.K.-C. Wong (1986) Eukaryotic- and prokaryotic-specific domains in the largest subunits of RNA polymerases. In RNA Polymerase and the Regulation of Transcription, University of Wisconsin 16th Steenbock Symposium Abstracts, P-I-62.

16. Ingles, C.J., J. Biggs, J.K.-C. Wong, J.R. Weeks, and A.L. Greenleaf (1983) Identification of a structural gene for an RNA polymerase II polypeptide in Drosophila melanogaster and mammalian species. Proc. Natl. Acad. Sci., USA 80:3396-3400.

17. Ingles, C.J., H.J. Himmelfarb, M. Shales, A.L. Greenleaf, and J.D. Friesen (1985) Identification, molecular cloning, and mutagenesis of Saccharomyces cerevisiae RNA polymerase genes. Proc. Natl. Acad. Sci., USA 81:2157-2161.

18. Jendrisak, J.J., and R.R. Burgess (1977) Studies on the subunit structure of wheat germ ribonucleic acid polymerase II. Biochemistry 16:1959-1964.

19. Jendrisak, J.J., and T.J. Guilfoyle (1978) Eukaryotic RNA polymerases: Comparative subunit structures, immunological properties, and α-amanitin sensitivities of the class II enzymes from higher plants. Biochemistry 17:1322-1327.

20. Jokerst, R.S., W.A. Zehring, J.R. Weeks, and A.L. Greenleaf (1986) Genetic and molecular characterization of RpII215, the gene encoding the large subunit of RNA polymerase II in D. melanogaster. In RNA

Polymerase and the Regulation of Transcription, University of Wisconsin 16th Steenbock Symposium Abstracts, P-II-72.

21. Lewis, M.K., and R.R. Burgess (1982) Eukaryotic RNA polymerases. In The Enzymes, Vol. 15B, P.D. Boyer, ed. Academic Press, Inc., New York, pp. 109-153.

22. Manley, J.L. (1983) Analysis of the expression of genes encoding animal mRNA by in vitro techniques. Prog. Nucl. Acid Res. Mol. Biol. 30:195-244.

23. Miassod, R., C. Got, and J.-P. Torreton (1984) Immunological estimation of changes in the absolute amounts of nuclear RNA polymerases in strictly auxin-requiring, cultured soybean cells upon addition of 2,4-dichlorophenoxyacetic acid. Planta 162:434-440.

24. Paule, M.R. (1981) Comparative subunit composition of eukaryotic nuclear RNA polymerases. Trends Biochem. Sci. 6:128-131.

25. Riva, M., S. Memet, J.-Y. Micouin, J. Huet, I. Treich, J. Dassa, R. Young, J.-M. Buhler, A. Sentenac, and P. Fromageot (1986) Isolation of structural genes for yeast RNA polymerases by immunological screening. Proc. Natl. Acad. Sci., USA 83:1554-1558.

26. Roeder, R.G. (1975) Eukaryotic nuclear RNA polymerases. In RNA Polymerase, R. Losick and M. Chamberlin, eds. Cold Spring Harbor Laboratory, Cold Spring Harbor, New York, pp. 285-329.

27. Sharp, S.J., J. Schaack, L. Cooley, D.J. Burke, and D. Soll (1985) Structure and transcription of eukaryotic tRNA genes. CRC Crit. Rev. Biochem. 19:107-204.

28. Young, R.A., and R.W. Davis (1983) Yeast RNA polymerase II genes: Isolation with antibody probes. Science 222:778-782.

AN ANALYSIS OF PHYSIOLOGICAL AND MOLECULAR ASPECTS

OF HEAT SHOCK GENE EXPRESSION

J.L. Key,[1] E. Czarnecka,[2]
W.B. Gurley,[2] and R.T. Nagao[1]

[1]Botany Department
University of Georgia
Athens, Georgia 30602

[2]Department of Microbiology and Cell Science
University of Florida
Gainesville, Florida 32611

INTRODUCTION

The following discussion represents a brief summary of some aspects of the heat shock (HS) response, emphasizing observations made using soybean seedlings as the primary experimental system.

GENERAL FEATURES OF THE HEAT SHOCK RESPONSE

There are several features of the HS response that make it an attractive system for study. The rapidity of the induction of HS gene expression, the magnitude of the response in terms of the levels of HS mRNAs and HS proteins that accumulate over a short period of time, the ease of manipulation of the stimulus, and the great reproducibility of results make it an excellent model system for studies on the mechanisms operative in the regulation of gene expression. Additionally, the HS response is one of the most highly conserved genetic systems known in the biological world; it is also universal, having been observed in organisms ranging from eubacteria to archebacteria, from lower eukaryotes to plants and man. It occurs in most every cell and tissue type and in cultured cells of plants and animals. The response has great physiological importance, since it appears to be critical in protecting cells from thermal damage to excessively high temperatures and possibly to other stress agents. The system has significant implications for genetic manipulation. [See reviews by Lindquist (12), Nagao et al. (14), Key et al. (9), Bienz (2), Craig (4), Pelham (18), Kimpel and Key (10), Neidhardt et al. (16), and Nover et al. (17) for background and details of the HS response.]

Several levels of regulation are clearly involved in the HS response. Reference here will be made primarily to work with plants, but as noted above most systems respond similarly. Upon elevation of the growth temperature of an organism from its norm to one near the limits of its survival (usually an increase of 10° ± 4°C), protein synthesis is redirected from the spectrum characteristic of normal growth for that tissue/stage of development primarily to the production of HS proteins. This results from the action of a number of controls operative both at the level of transcription and at the level of translation. There is rapid slowing of normal mRNA translation (e.g., Ref. 8), a rapid induction (or in some cases only enhancement) of transcription of HS genes, and accumulation of high levels of HS mRNAs (21), followed by extensive translation of HS mRNAs. With continuous HS (for example, at 40°C with soybean seedlings), transcription of the HS genes slows or ceases after 1 to 2 hr, and HS protein accumulation slows after several hours. The slowing or shut-down of synthesis of HS mRNAs and proteins occurs as a result of mechanisms which may be referred to as autoregulation, apparently as a result of the accumulation of functional HS proteins. Results of this level of regulation are much more well-defined for Drosophila, for example (see Ref. 12), than for plants, but the basic response in plants seems to be similar. A brief HS of soybean seedlings at a supraoptimum temperature (e.g., 3 to 10 min at 45°C) results in a HS response essentially identical to a continuous HS at 40°C. A similar HS of 3 to 10 min at 40°C results only in a very low level and brief transient HS response. A gradual increase in temperature from 30°C to 45°C (e.g., 3°C per hr) results in a typical HS response similar to that caused by a rapid shift from 30°C to 40°C. Such a response essentially mimics what would be expected to occur under normal environmental conditions where HS occurs (e.g., Ref. 11); the HS response varies under field conditions at a given temperature depending upon the water status of the soil and level of evapotranspiration by plants. An understanding of the regulatory events that lead to these responses are poorly understood, but much progress is being made (see Ref. 12 and other reviews referred to above).

As noted above, the HS genetic system is highly conserved. Yet, there are significant differences in the complexity and relative abundance of HS proteins in different organisms. In Drosophila, for example, there are seven major HS proteins, with the 70-kDa HS proteins representing by far the major accumulating protein during HS (e.g., Ref. 12). The complexity of the pattern of HS proteins is much greater in plants, probably ranging from about 20 to 30 or more depending upon the plant species. Moreover, the low molecular weight HS proteins generally accumulate to much higher levels than the more conserved high molecular weight HS proteins during HS in plants. The pattern of low molecular weight HS proteins assayed on two-dimensional gels varies greatly with plant species, while the pattern of the high molecular weight HS proteins is much more similar. This latter observation is consistent with the fact that the high molecular weight HS proteins (e.g., HS proteins of 70 and 83 kDa) are much more conserved than other HS proteins across the wide range of organisms studied to date (see Ref. 4 and 12).

The physiological significance of HS proteins is not fully understood. Strong correlative evidence exists that the accumulation of HS proteins relates to the acquisition of thermotolerance to otherwise lethal temperatures (see Ref. 4, 9, 12, and 16); there is also limited genetic evidence which supports these correlative data. There is accumulating evidence for the regulated expression of some HS proteins at specific stages of development under non-HS conditions (see Ref. 2 and 12). These observations may imply specific enzymatic or other regulatory functions for some HS proteins under non-HS conditions. The high abundance of some of these proteins is also suggestive of structural roles for cellular stabilization during HS. There is only limited evidence for specific functions for any HS proteins (see Ref. 12, 16, and 20).

THERMOTOLERANCE

Thermotolerance is used here to define the ability of an organism to withstand an otherwise lethal heat treatment if it has been pretreated with some appropriate nonlethal HS or some agent which induces a HS response (e.g., arsenite). Several kinds of HS treatments lead to the acquisition of thermotolerance in plants: (a) a HS at or near the optimum HS temperature (e.g., 40°C for soybean seedlings) for 1 to 2 hr prior to the shift to an otherwise lethal treatment (e.g., 2 hr at 45°C); (b) a HS at 40°C for 1 to 2 hr followed by several hours at 28°C to 30°C prior to the 45°C exposure; (c) a gradual increase in temperature (e.g., 3°C per hr) from the normal growth temperature up to as high as 47.5°C for soybean seedlings; (d) a 5 to 10 min treatment at 45°C followed by about 2 hr at 30°C prior to an otherwise lethal treatment at 45°C for 2 hr; and (e) treatment with 50 to 100 µM arsenite for 2 to 4 hr, which is itself a somewhat toxic or growth inhibitory treatment, prior to HS at 45°C for 2 hr. All of these treatments share in common the induction and accumulation to high levels of HS proteins. If, however, cycloheximide is included to inhibit protein synthesis during any of these inductive treatments which lead to the acquisition of thermotolerance, the subsequent 45°C, 2-hr HS treatment is lethal (C.-Y. Lin and J.L. Key, unpubl. data). In animal systems, the inclusion of amino acid analogs and their incorporation into protein during the tolerant HS prevent the acquisition of thermotolerance to lethal HS (see Ref. 12). These correlative data suggest that it is the accumulation, stability, and selective localization of normal HS proteins (i.e., no amino acid analog substitutions) during permissive HS which allows organisms to survive otherwise lethal HS treatments (see Ref. 9 and 12), although other mechanisms may also contribute to the development of thermotolerance.

Thermotolerance may be assessed by measuring growth and survival of seedlings, viability and/or growth of cells in culture, and at the cell structural/ultrastructural level. Heat shock treatments which lead to the acquisition of thermotolerance cause the stabilization of the basic architectural features of cells, including membrane and organellar integrity. There are, however, some changes (based on electron microscopy analyses) in the ultrastructural features of the cell and its organelles in response to a permissive HS and to 45°C treatments that would otherwise be lethal. Membrane integrity and cell architecture are completely disrupted by a 45°C treatment without a pretreatment that permits the acquisition of thermotolerance in soybean seedlings (e.g., Ref. 13; C.-Y. Lin and J.L. Key, unpubl. data). These structures survive a 45°C HS treatment if a tolerant HS treatment preceded the otherwise lethal HS.

While some fundamental parameters of thermotolerance have been established, much remains to be learned about the development of thermotolerance and the role(s) of HS proteins in the process(es). There seems to be little question, however, that at least some HS proteins play critical roles in the maintenance of cell structure and the acquisition of thermotolerance during HS and in the ability of cells to resume normal functions following HS, upon return to normal growth conditions. The stage of development

and metabolic state of cells and tissues seem also to have "modulating" influences on the HS response and the acquisition of thermotolerance. These
remain fruitful areas for experimentation and significant discovery along
with investigations into the heat sensitivity of reproductive tissues (see
Ref. 1, 3, and 12).

HEAT SHOCK GENE STRUCTURE AND EXPRESSION

As noted above, plants produce a very complex set of HS proteins compared to many organisms; these proteins are the products of several sets of
"multigene" families (e.g., Ref. 21), recognizing possible contributions of
ploidy levels and allelic variation to this general complexity in plants.

A number of soybean genes have been characterized at the DNA sequence
level, and deductions have been made about the proteins they encode (e.g.,
Ref. 6, 14, 15, and 22). These genes primarily represent a large related
family of 15- to 18-kDa HS proteins. Members of several other families
(e.g., those related to the 21- to 24-kDa, and to the 70-kDa HS proteins)
are in various stages of characterization. The HS genes characterized in
these studies do not have introns, a property shared by most HS genes in
those systems that have been analyzed. The most notable exceptions are the
HS genes that encode the 83-kDa HS proteins and the 70-kDa HS cognate protein genes of Drosophila. The 70-kDa HS cognate genes contain introns and
are developmentally regulated but not induced by HS. The 83-kDa HS protein
is synthesized at normal temperatures but its synthesis is enhanced by
high temperatures. Recently, Rochester et al. (19) reported on the presence of an intron in a HS gene which codes for a heat-induced 70-kDa HS
protein from maize. Introns also occur in some other families of HS genes
(R. Nagao et al., unpubl. data), such as the family of pCE54 HS proteins of
soybean (see Ref. 5) and in the gene for a nuclear-encoded, chloroplast-
localized HS protein (see Ref. 24). The presence of introns in some HS
genes poses some interesting questions relating to the expression of these
genes during HS based on the possible impairment of intron-processing of
some transcripts during high temperature HS treatments (see Ref. 12; E.
Czarnecka et al., unpubl. data).

While the phenomenon has not yet been studied in detail in the soybean
system, there is at least some clustering of HS genes based on restriction
digestion mapping and DNA sequence analysis showing multiple HS genes on
several genomic clones isolated from a soybean λ genomic library. The
genes for the four major low molecular weight HS proteins of Drosophila
were reported several years ago to be clustered on a 12-kb fragment of
cloned DNA (see Ref. 4).

An analysis of the transcription regulatory regions of HS genes is important from a number of points of view. In addition to the intrinsic value of defining the structure of the cis-acting elements responsible for the
heat-inducibility of these genes, the responsiveness of some of these genes
to multiple stress agents, to developmental regulation at normal temperatures, to hormonal influences on expression, etc., raises the possibility
of the presence of multiple elements which are responsive to different in-
ducer signals and trans-acting transcription factors. An understanding
of these regulatory regions should prove valuable for potentially useful
manipulation of these genes as well as for gaining greater insights into
the mechanisms operative in the regulation of gene expression.

The cis-acting element responsible for high temperature inducibility of HS genes has been partially characterized for Drosophila HS genes (see Ref. 2 and 18). The consensus element (CT-GAA--TTC-AG) from Drosophila HS genes has been summarized as a minimally hyphenated dyad of C--GAA--TTC--G (18). Small variations on this sequence have been noted, but seven of these eight (or eight of 14 overall) bases generally seem to be both necessary and sufficient for HS activation of transcription of these genes.

The sequence homologies of some potential proximal HS promoter or regulatory elements positioned a few bases (usually about 30) 5' to the TATA motif, which positions RNA polymerase II for the start site of transcription, have been noted for HS genes from plants (Tab. 1). The very high conservation of this HS consensus element (HSE) undoubtedly accounts for the transcription of HS genes in heterologous systems (see Ref. 2, 18, and 23). In the case of the soybean gene Gmhsp 17.5E (6), probably the most highly expressed of the HS genes in this plant, detailed analysis of the promoter element is underway (Ref. 7; E. Czarnecka et al., unpubl. data).

The Gmhsp 17.5E gene, with over 3 kb of untranscribed 5' flanking sequence and several hundred bases of untranscribed 3' flanking sequence, has been incorporated into the T-DNA region of the Ti plasmid of Agrobacterium tumefaciens, and the bacteria harboring these chimeric plasmids have been used to infect and transform sunflower seedlings (7). This gene is highly expressed in the tumors from the transformed sunflower plants in response to a HS; it is weakly expressed in the tumor tissue at non-HS temperatures, while it is not expressed at detectable levels in non-HS, two-day-old soybean seedlings. Figure 1 displays certain features of the 5' flanking regions of this gene and emphasizes potentially interesting sequences. A construct which deletes the 5' flanking region to position -95 is expressed in the tumors during HS, but at only 2% to 5% the level of the full

Tab. 1. Comparison of soybean and Drosophila sequences: Potential proximal heat shock promoter or regulatory elements (HSEs).

Sequence	Source	Reference
CT-GAA--TTC-AG or C--GAA--TTC--G	Drosophila consensus	(18)
CT-GAA--TAC-AT	Soybean hs 6871	(22)
CT-GAA--TAC-AG	Soybean Gmhsp 17.5E	(6)
CT-GAA--TTC-AG	Soybean Gmhsp 17BR	R.T. Nagao et al., unpubl. data
CT-GAA--TAC-CG	Soybean Gmhsp 17.5M	(15)
CT-GAA--TAC-AG	Soybean Gmhsp 17.6L	(15)
AT-GGA--TTC-AG	Soybean Gmhsp 22K	R.T. Nagao et al., unpubl. data
CC-GAA--TTC-GG	Corn HSP 70	(19)

Proximal HSE represents the sequence having the greatest homology to the Drosophila consensus positioned just upstream of the TATA box; most soybean genes sequenced to date have multiple HSEs positioned 5' to this proximal element and often overlapping HSEs.

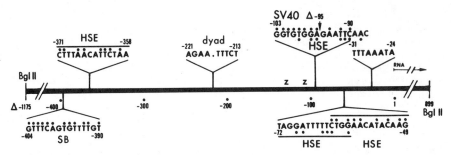

Fig. 1.   Schematic representation of the Gmhsp 17.5E gene, showing the
          position of the −1,175 and −95 bp 5' deletions (Δ). Numeric des-
          ignations denote base pairs from the start of transcription.
          Regions of consensus homology with sequences present in other eu-
          karyotic genes are shown. Dots indicate positions of nucleotide
          homology.   Abbreviations: HSE, heat shock consensus element;
          dyad, pentameric palindrome; SB, steroid-binding site in a Dro-
          sophila HS gene; Z, potential Z-DNA (eight uninterrupted alter-
          nating purine-pyrimidine pairs); SV40, simian virus 40 enhancer
          core (from Ref. 7).

construct (i.e., out to −3250 or to −1175). While site-directed mutational
and deletion analyses are not complete, it appears that the two overlapping
HSEs proximal to the TATA motif are sufficient for high temperature-induced
expression of this gene; the 5' sequences which up-modulate the expression
of this gene in the tumors by 20- to 50-fold appear to be positioned between the two overlapping proximal HSEs (−49 to −72) and the upstream HSE
(at −358) noted in Fig. 1. This region contains a simian virus 40 (SV40)-
like enhancer sequence, regions of potential Z-DNA conformation as noted,
and an additional region of dyad symmetry. Additional HSEs are present upstream 5' to the presumed major regulatory regions for maximum HS expression; their role, if any, is not known. Sequences similar to metal responsive elements (MREs) are present around the cap site of this gene, which is
also responsive to cadmium-induced expression.

     While it is not known if any of the many plant steroids alter the ex-
pression of the Gmhsp 17.5E gene in plants, the region −404 to −390 bp 5'
to the cap site shows very high homology to a steroid-response element
which is present in some Drosophila HS genes that are ecdysone-induced in
some tissues and at selected stages of development (2). While the transcriptionally functional elements of this gene are not fully defined, gel
retardation/competition analyses and DNase footprint analyses have demonstrated the presence of a "factor(s)" in plant extracts which binds to and
protects much of the region between positions −40 and −300, including the
proximal HSE (E. Czarnecka et al., unpubl. data).

PERSPECTIVES AND CONCLUSIONS

     Plants respond to HS to produce a relatively complex group of HS
proteins. These proteins appear to be functionally important in providing
thermotolerance to otherwise lethal temperatures, to permit transcription
of HS genes and translation of the HS mRNAs at otherwise nonpermissive temperatures, and to permit recovery to normal function upon return to normal

growth temperatures. The HS genes show homology to those from other systems; more homology exists between HS genes for HS proteins 70 and 83 of Drosophila and plants than between the genes for the low molecular weight HS proteins. However, there is striking conservation in some structural features of the corresponding low molecular weight HS proteins. There appears to be very high conservation of at least one or more transcriptional regulatory regions of these genes (e.g., HSE) between organisms. Essentially no information is available about trans-acting transcription factors involved in the HS-induction of these genes in plants; some information is accumulating on such factors in bacteria and animal systems. Cis-elements involved in the up-modulation of the expression of the soybean genes have been localized but remain undefined. These could be enhancer elements or regions which otherwise relate to increased rates of transcription (i.e., importance of location and orientation has not been determined).

Based on the current understanding of the HS response, considerable research effort is needed to (a) define the mechanism (cis- and trans-acting factors) operative in regulating the expression of the HS genes in response to elevated temperatures and other regulatory stimuli, (b) define the mechanism(s) of transduction of the signal (e.g., elevated temperature) into the regulatory events of transcriptional and translational control operative during HS, (c) define the role(s) (and mechanism) of HS proteins in the acquisition of thermotolerance, (d) define the role of HS proteins in development, and (e) ascertain various enzymatic functions which HS proteins may impart. These problems are under vigorous experimentation, and most, if not all, of the answers will come from technologies currently in use.

In the meantime, HS promoter elements can be used in a wide range of analyses on the expression of foreign genes in transgenic plants, since the level of expression is precisely manipulatable by the temperature and duration of a HS treatment. These very strong promoters may also be used in the regulated expression of antisense RNAs in studies directed to the analysis of phenotype resulting from the expression of a given mRNA. The promoters and mRNA leader sequences may also be useful in expressing some key genes (e.g., resistance genes) during HS which would otherwise not be expressed during heat stress. Undoubtedly, many other uses of HS gene regulatory elements will be forthcoming.

ACKNOWLEDGEMENTS

The research on which this summary report is based was supported by U.S. Department of Energy Contract DE AS09-80ER1078 to J.L.K. and by contracts from Agrigenetics Research Associate to J.L.K. and to W.B.G.

REFERENCES

1. Altschuler, M., and J.P. Mascarenhas (1982) The synthesis of heat-shock and normal proteins at high temperatures in plants and their possible roles in survival under heat stress. In Heat Shock from Bacteria to Man, M.J. Schlesinger, M. Ashburner, and A. Tissieres, eds. Cold Spring Harbor Laboratory, Cold Spring Harbor, New York, pp. 321-327.
2. Bienz, M. (1985) Transient and developmental activation of heat-shock genes. Trends Biochem. Sci. 10:157-161.

3. Cooper, P., T.-H.D. Ho, and R.M. Hauptman (1984) Tissue specificity of the heat shock response in maize. Plant Physiol. 75:431-441.
4. Craig, E.A. (1985) The heat shock response. CRC Crit. Rev. Biochem. 18:239-280.
5. Czarnecka, E., L. Edelman, F. Schöffl, and J.L. Key (1984) Comparative analysis of physical stress responses in soybean seedlings using cloned heat shock cDNAs. Plant Mol. Biol. 3:45-58.
6. Czarnecka, E., W.B. Gurley, R.T. Nagao, L. Mosquera, and J.L. Key (1985) DNA sequence and transcript mapping of a soybean gene encoding a small heat shock protein. Proc. Natl. Acad. Sci., USA 82:3726-3730.
7. Gurley, W.B., E. Czarnecka, R.T. Nagao, and J.L. Key (1986) Upstream sequences required for efficient expression of a soybean heat shock gene. Mol. Cell. Biol. 6:559-565.
8. Key, J.L., C.-Y. Lin, and Y.-M. Chen (1981) Heat shock proteins of soybean. Proc. Natl. Acad. Sci., USA 78:3526-3530.
9. Key, J.L., J. Kimpel, E. Vierling, C.-Y. Lin, R.T. Nagao, E. Czarnecka, and F. Schöffl (1985) Physiological and molecular analyses of the heat shock response in plants. In Changes in Eukaryotic Gene Expression in Response to Environmental Stress, B.G. Atkinson and D.B. Walden, eds. Academic Press, Inc., New York, pp. 327-348.
10. Kimpel, J.A., and J.L. Key (1985) Heat shock in plants. Trends Biochem. Sci. 10:353-357.
11. Kimpel, J.A., and J.L. Key (1985) Presence of heat shock mRNAs in field grown soybeans. Plant Physiol. 79:672-678.
12. Lindquist, S. (1986) The heat-shock response. Ann. Rev. Biochem. 55:1151-1191.
13. Mansfield, M.A. (1986) The heat shock response of soybean: Synthesis, accumulation, and distribution of the low molecular weight heat shock proteins. Ph.D. dissertation, University of Georgia, Athens, Georgia.
14. Nagao, R.T., J.A. Kimpel, E. Vierling, and J.L. Key (1986) The heat shock response: A comparative analysis. In Oxford Surveys of Plant Molecular and Cell Biology, B.J. Miflin, ed. Oxford University Press, Oxford, England (in press).
15. Nagao, R.T., E. Czarnecka, W.B. Gurley, F. Schöffl, and J.L. Key (1985) Genes for low-molecular-weight heat shock proteins of soybeans: Sequence analysis of a multigene family. Mol. Cell. Biol. 5:3417-3428.
16. Neidhardt, F.C., R.A. Van Bogelen, and V. Vaughn (1984) The genetics and regulation of heat-shock proteins. Ann. Rev. Genet. 18:295-329.
17. Nover, L., D. Hellmund, D. Neumann, K.-D. Scharf, and E. Serfling (1984) The heat shock response of eukaryotic cells. Biol. Zbl. 103:357-435.
18. Pelham, H. (1985) Activation of heat-shock genes in eukaryotes. Trends Gen. Sci. 1:31-35.
19. Rochester, D.E., J.A. Winter, and D.M. Shah (1986) The structure and expression of maize genes encoding the major heat shock protein, hsp70. EMBO J. 5:451-458.
20. Schlesinger, M.J. (1986) Heat shock proteins: The search for functions. J. Cell Biol. 103:321-325.
21. Schöffl, F., and J.L. Key (1982) An analysis of mRNAs for a group of heat shock proteins of soybean using cloned cDNAs. J. Mol. Appl. Genet. 1:301-314.
22. Schöffl, F., E. Raschke, and R.T. Nagao (1984) The DNA sequence analysis of soybean heat shock genes and identification of possible regulatory promoter elements. EMBO J. 3:2491-2497.

23. Spena, A., R. Hain, U. Ziervogel, H. Saedler, and J. Schell (1985) Construction of a heat-inducible gene for plants. Demonstration of heat-inducible activity of the Drosophila hsp70 promoter in plants. EMBO J. 4:2739-2743.
24. Vierling, E., M.L. Mishkind, G.W. Schmidt, and J.L. Key (1986) Specific heat shock proteins are transported into chloroplasts. Proc. Natl. Acad. Sci., USA 83:361-365.

MOLECULAR BIOLOGY OF SALINITY STRESS:

PRELIMINARY STUDIES AND PERSPECTIVES

Subbanaidu Ramagopal

U.S. Department of Agriculture
Agricultural Research Service
Pacific Basin Area, P.O. Box 1057
Aiea, Hawaii 96701

INTRODUCTION

Compared to anaerobiosis and heat shock, the molecular biology of salinity stress in higher plants is not well understood. Salinity tolerance
is a complex trait controlled by a polygenic system (14). Genetic variability of this trait has now been recognized in a wide range of crops (1)
but the genes regulating salt tolerance are yet to be identified. Consequently, plant breeders currently lack a selective marker for salinity tolerance.

An analysis of this complex trait requires a suitable experimental
system. A crucial factor contributing to the difficulty in finding a suitable system is that expression of salinity tolerance is apparently linked
to plant growth and development (12) whose molecular biology is also not as
well understood. I shall discuss below two higher plant systems used in
our laboratory to study gene expression during salinity stress. The future
prospects of these two systems will then be commented upon.

CELL CULTURE SYSTEM

The ease of establishing, growing, and manipulating in vitro tissue
cultures in a few plant species stimulated several workers to study salt
tolerance in cell culture systems. Growth in the presence of salt was the
only selection criterion. Salt-tolerant cell lines have been isolated in a
number of plant species (4), and the tolerant trait was apparently maintained in regenerated plants of tobacco (5) and Datura (16). These studies, although pioneering and interesting, have not led to an understanding
of either the genetic or the molecular bases of salt tolerance.

In recent years, salinity effects on protein synthesis have been investigated in established cultures of tobacco (2,13) and maize (9). In
maize, the amounts of seven newly made proteins were altered by salinity
stress. Three of these (74 kDa, 28.5 kDa, and 26.2 kDa) were apparently

induced de novo and the remainder displayed a reduced or enhanced level of expression. Similar changes were reported in the tobacco system (13), and one polypeptide in particular, a 26-kDa protein, is apparently induced in both tobacco and maize. This protein was induced at a NaCl level as low as 0.5% in maize and 1% in tobacco. Our current studies are focused on long-term salt-adapted cultures of maize; these cells appear to tolerate up to 1.5% NaCl and show unique protein patterns (Fig. 1). The role of these proteins is yet to be established.

BARLEY PLANT AS A MODEL SYSTEM

Barley (Hordeum vulgare) is a cereal grain crop well known for its resistance to salinity (1). Some of the pertinent attributes of the barley salinity-stress system are its well-studied genetics comparable to those of wheat and maize, an appreciable germplasm diversity for the salt-tolerance trait, and the economic importance of the trait. Barley is a self-fertile diploid with 14 chromosomes and has a haploid genome size (5.4×10^9 bp) equivalent to that of wheat (15).

Background of a Pair of Barley Genotypes

Initial studies were focused on two barley genotypes, California Mariout 72 (CM72) and Prato (10,11). These two were among the few barley cultivars identified by the extensive screening efforts of Epstein's group as having differing responses to salinity (3). Studies were conducted during seed germination and seedling growth. These stages in the plant life cycle are particularly attractive because most plants, and in particular barley, respond to salinity stress at these stages. In addition, these stages are also amenable to different approaches in molecular biology. Table 1 documents the responses of CM72 and Prato to salinity stress during germination. Results show that CM72 is a salt-tolerant genotype, whereas Prato is a salt-sensitive genotype. Germination in CM72 was unaffected at up to 2% NaCl, but in Prato it was reduced by 30% at 1% NaCl and by 75% at 2% NaCl.

Three different analyses suggest there may not be major constitutive differences between the two barley genotypes. First, two-dimensional gel patterns of total proteins from the various plant parts, viz., roots, shoots (etiolated), and embryos, showed identical protein patterns except that there was an extra protein in embryonic tissue of Prato which was absent in CM72 (Fig. 2). A protein pair which was present in all three tissues (Fig. 2; shown in squares) showed a pI difference in CM72 and Prato; a similar pI difference was detected in another shoot protein. Later experiments (see below) showed that these proteins are not regulated during salinity stress. Second, poly(A)$^+$ mRNAs isolated from these two genotypes and analyzed by two-dimensional gels after in vitro translation also displayed similar patterns. Although two extra in vitro products were detectable in the mRNA population of CM72 roots, again, these were not regulated by salinity stress (8). Third, mapping of nuclear DNA and total DNA from leaves by digesting with various restriction endonucleases, followed by agarose gel electrophoresis and ethidium bromide staining, showed no discernible band differences between the two genotypes.

To the extent revealed by the above techniques, the data further indicate that CM72 and Prato have an almost identical genetic background. This is a reasonable expectation since both cultivars apparently had common progenitors in their pedigree (10,11). The minor morphological differences

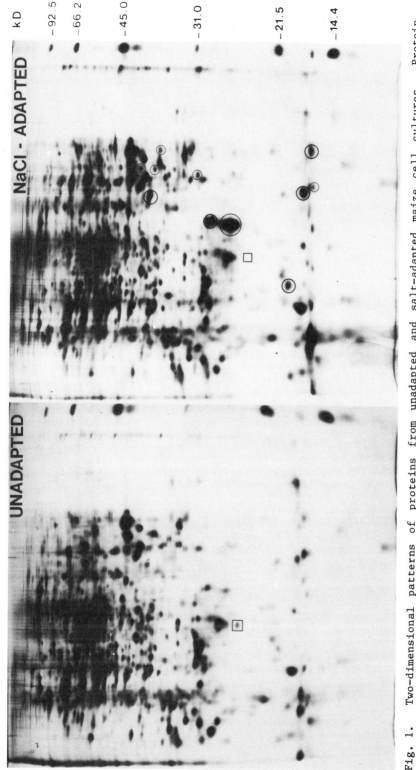

Fig. 1. Two-dimensional patterns of proteins from unadapted and salt-adapted maize cell cultures. Protein changes induced by salinity are marked. The procedures of O'Farrell (6,7) were used with slight modifications (8). Proteins were stained by the silver method.

Tab. 1.   Effects of NaCl on germination and growth of barley genotypes
           CM72 and Prato.

NaCl (%)	Germination* (%)		Root growth** (mg)		Shoot growth** (mg)	
	CM72	Prato	CM72	Prato	CM72	Prato
0	77.0 ± 19.1	68.6 ± 10.8	39.5	22.0	51.5	20.5
1	79.5 ± 13.4	49.0 ± 7.5	33.0	17.0	45.0	13.5
2	80.0 ± 12.2	17.2 ± 7.2	26.0	12.5	35.5	9.5
3	33.0 ± 29.0	3.7 ± 1.2	26.0	--	23.5	--

*Seeds showing the emergence of radicle or plumule after 72 hr of incubation were
 considered as germinated. Means ± standard deviation of four (CM72) or five
 (Prato) experiments.
**Dry weights of roots or shoots from ten seedlings. Means of two independent ex-
 periments.

noted between them (10,11), together with the minor biochemical differences
presented here, suggest that these two genotypes are not exactly isogenic.

It was somewhat disappointing when the above molecular analyses were
unable to bring out differences between the two genotypes which could be
attributable to their salinity tolerance trait. As discussed in the following section, salinity treatment is a necessary trigger for differential
gene induction in the two barley cultivars which then leads to distinct
genotypic differences.

Gene Expression During Salinity Stress

The synthesis and expression of total gene products (e.g., proteins
and mRNAs) in CM72 and Prato were analyzed before and after salt treatment
during seed germination and early seedling growth. Changes were examined
in roots, shoots, and embryos. The major conclusions emerging from these
studies (Ref. 8; S. Ramagopal, unpubl. data) are summarized below:

(a)   Salt treatment did not alter the pattern of steady-state
       protein population (as revealed by staining the gels with
       Coomassie blue or by silver stain) in either genotype.

(b)   Salt treatment did alter the pattern of newly synthesized
       proteins (as analyzed by in vivo labeling with [^{35}S]methio-
       nine and fluorography), and the responses of the two geno-
       types were different.

(c)   The minimal external NaCl level triggering the changes in
       protein expression during germination and seedling growth in
       both genotypes was about 2%.

(d)   Proteins that were altered in abundance during salinity
       stress can be grouped into three classes: (i) proteins
       whose accumulation was repressed; (ii) proteins whose accu-
       mulation was enhanced; and (iii) proteins that were newly
       induced.

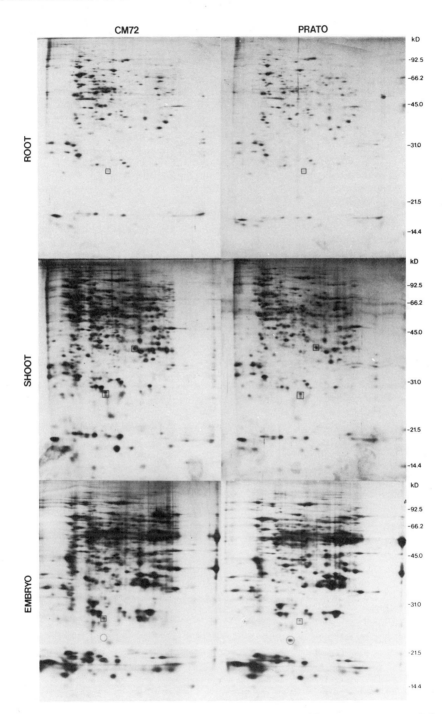

Fig. 2.   Comparison of protein patterns from different tissues of barley
           genotypes CM72 and Prato. Proteins were separated and visualized
           as in Fig. 1. Circle indicates a protein found only in embryos
           of Prato. Proteins found in both genotypes but differing in pI
           are shown within a square.

(e) During germination, new proteins were induced in roots but not in shoots.

(f) During seedling growth, new proteins were induced in both roots and shoots (Tab. 2). Newly induced root proteins were identical in both genotypes, but three of the shoot proteins were unique to Prato.

(g) A "26-kDa" protein pair was one of the salinity-induced new proteins in barley that may be analogous to a similar protein found in tobacco and maize culture cells. In addition, preliminary results suggest that a similar protein might be induced in tissue cultures derived from one of the barley genotypes.

(h) Although some of the salinity stress-induced new proteins are of low apparent molecular weight, they are different from those induced by heat shock (Fig. 3). Salt treatment did not prevent the expression of heat shock proteins and vice versa.

(i) Salt treatment induced distinct sets of new mRNAs in roots and shoots which showed genotypic specificity (Tab. 2; Ref. 8).

(j) Taken together, the data suggest that both transcriptional and post-transcriptional mechanisms would account for the regulation of gene expression during salinity stress in the salt-tolerant and salt-sensitive genotypes.

Tab. 2.   Properties of newly induced proteins and mRNAs during salinity stress in barley.

Tissue	Apparent molecular weight range	pI Range	Number induced	
			CM72	Prato
Proteins (in vivo)				
Root	24.5-27.2	6.1-7.6	6	6
Shoot	20.0-24.0	6.3-7.2	2	5
Translational products (in vitro)				
Root	21.0-34.0	6.1-7.7	9	5
Shoot	18.0-50.5	5.4-7.8	4	6

Barley tissues treated with 2% NaCl were incubated with [^{35}S]methionine. A nuclease-treated reticulocyte cell-free system was used to translate barley mRNAs. Proteins from each sample were resolved by two-dimensional isoelectric focusing (IEF/2D) and two-dimensional nonequilibrium pH gel electrophoresis (NEPHGE/2D), and a summary of the results are presented.

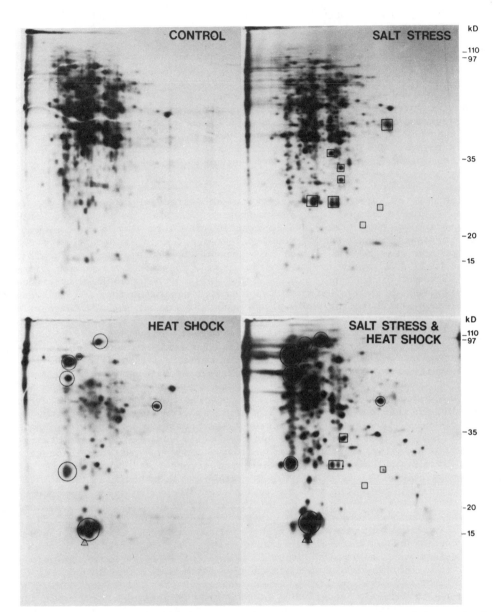

Fig. 3.   Fluorographs of barley proteins induced by salt and heat shock.
Control and treated barley roots were incubated with [^{35}S]methio-
nine and the proteins resolved by two-dimensional nonequilibrium
pH gel electrophoresis. Heat shock was given for 3 hr at 37°C.
For the panel labeled "Salt Stress and Heat Shock," NaCl treatment was given prior to heat shock and continued during heat
shock. Squares denote salt-induced protein changes, and circles
and triangle indicate protein changes induced by heat shock.
Similar results were obtained in CM72 and Prato. The data shown
are for CM72.

PERSPECTIVES AND CHALLENGES

From the above, it should be evident that modest progress has been made toward understanding the molecular details of salinity stress in plants. The knowledge gathered is certainly not as advanced as that for heat shock or anaerobiosis. Our understanding of salinity stress at this time is as good as it was for heat shock and anaerobiosis four or five years ago. Even these limited studies suggest that the response to salinity stress is much more difficult to understand than the responses of the other two environmental stimuli. Our primary emphasis should be on identifying the genes and biochemical mechanisms for salt tolerance. What are the prospects of the two experimental systems described in this chapter for leading to that goal?

The cell culture system is certainly an attractive choice at least to analyze salinity-induced molecular responses at the cellular level. Further studies on the stress-induced proteins may lead to the isolation of genes corresponding to these proteins. However, changes detected at the cellular level may have no direct relevance at the whole plant level, since expression of salt tolerance is apparently associated with tissue organization. The use of the cell culture approach to understand salt tolerance mechanisms would involve defining the "mutant" nature of the salt-tolerant cell lines by regenerating whole plants and carrying out a detailed genetic analysis. Both the maize and the tobacco cells used in molecular biology studies so far are established culture systems. These salt-adapted cell cultures have not been regenerated. This is a serious limitation in discriminating and studying the genetic and epigenetic factors that give rise to salt-tolerant variants in the cell culture system.

The barley system, with emphasis on studies at the whole plant level, is a more natural one and has generated more information than has the in vitro tissue culture system. Our strategy to undertake a comparative analysis of two genotypes of similar genetic background and identifiable responses to salinity is worth reemphasizing. This approach would not have been possible without the prior relentless efforts of plant breeders and plant physiologists. It should prove worthwhile to extend similar strategies to other crops. Our ability to now identify salinity stress-induced proteins and mRNAs opens new avenues for further characterizing the system, applying techniques of molecular genetics and isolating the corresponding genes. Extension of these preliminary studies should determine whether such genes indeed confer salt tolerance in plants. Two potential problems are foreseen which may present formidable challenges to the molecular biologist. One is the lack of understanding of the intricate involvement of plant growth and development in the expression of salt tolerance, i.e., the need to elucidate the underlying factors in the interaction between two multigenic systems. The second is our need to distinguish the contributions of ionic and osmotic components of salinity stress and to identify their molecular determinants.

A final note: suppose we have isolated most of the salt tolerance genes in the next few years. What are our prospects of tailoring these genes into salt-sensitive economic crops? Will we have the transformation technology that can instill a multigenic trait and yet not interfere with other desirable traits? In this context, another facet of the same two barley cultivars studied here is worth mentioning. Genotype CM72 was introduced in 1974 and Prato, in 1978. Although the intention of the plant breeders obviously was to successively improve the crop, the latter variety turned out to be more salt-sensitive but retained a higher yield potential than did the salt-tolerant CM72 genotype (10). This illustrates yet another dimension of challenge of which we should be aware.

ACKNOWLEDGEMENTS

I thank Paul Moore and Thomas Tew for reading the manuscript. Roger Thom and Harumi Wong provided technical assistance during various phases of this research. My special thanks to Stella Uehara for typing the manuscript on short notice.

REFERENCES

1. Downton, W.J.S. (1984) Salt tolerance of food crops: Perspectives for improvements. CRC Crit. Rev. Plant Sci. 1:183-201.
2. Ericson, M.C., and S.H. Alfinito (1984) Proteins produced during salt stress in tobacco cell cultures. Plant Physiol. 74:506-509.
3. Epstein, E., J.D. Norlyn, D.W. Rush, R.W. Kingsbury, D.B. Kelley, G.A. Cunningham, and A.F. Wrona (1980) Saline culture of crops: A genetic approach. Science 210:399-404.
4. Mailga, P. (1984) Isolation and characterization of mutants in plant cell culture. Ann. Rev. Plant Physiol. 35:519-542.
5. Nabors, M.W., S.E. Gibbs, C.S. Bernstein, and M.E. Meis (1980) NaCl-tolerant tobacco plants from cultured cells. Z. Pflanzenphysiol. 97: 13-17.
6. O'Farrell, P.H. (1975) High resolution two-dimensional electrophoresis of proteins. J. Biol. Chem. 250:4007-4021.
7. O'Farrell, P.Z., H.M. Goodman, and P.H. O'Farrell (1977) High resolution two-dimensional electrophoresis of basic as well as acidic proteins. Cell 12:1133-1142.
8. Ramagopal, S. (1986) Differential mRNA transcription during salinity stress in barley. Proc. Natl. Acad. Sci., USA (in press).
9. Ramagopal, S. (1986) Protein synthesis in a maize callus exposed to NaCl and mannitol. Plant Cell Reports (in press).
10. Schaller, C.W., J.D. Prato, and M.J. Smith (1977) Registration of CM72 barley. Crop Sci. 19:741.
11. Schaller, C.W., J.D. Prato, M.J. Smith, and C.I. Chim (1977) Registration of CM72 barley. Crop Sci. 17:485.
12. Shannon, M.C. (1984) Breeding, selection and the genetics of salt-tolerance. In Salinity Tolerance in Plants, R.C. Staples and G.A. Toeniessen, eds. John Wiley and Sons, New York, pp. 232-253.
13. Singh, N.K., A.K. Handa, P.M. Hasegawa, and R.A. Bressan (1985) Proteins associated with adaptation of cultured cells to NaCl. Plant Physiol. 79:126-137.
14. Tal, M. (1985) Genetics of salt-tolerance in higher plants: Theoretical and practical considerations. Plant and Soil 89:199-226.
15. Thompson, W.F., and M.G. Murray (1981) The nuclear genome: Structure and function. In The Biochemistry of Plants: A Comprehensive Treatise. Vol. 6. Proteins and Nucleic Acids, P.K. Stumpf and E.E. Conn, eds. Academic Press, Inc., New York, pp. 1-81.
16. Tyagi, A.K., A. Rashid, and S.C. Maheshwari (1981) Sodium chloride resistant cell line from haploid Datura innoxia Mill: A resistance trait carried from cell to plantlet and vice versa in vitro. Protoplasma 105:327-332.

CHARACTERIZATION AND EXPRESSION OF A WOUND-INDUCIBLE

PROTEINASE INHIBITOR II GENE FROM POTATO

Robert W. Thornburg,* Gyn An, Thomas A. Cleveland,**
and Clarence A. Ryan

Institute of Biological Chemistry
Washington State University
Pullman, Washington 99164

SUMMARY

An 8-kb fragment of potato DNA containing the potato Inhibitor II gene (called Inhibitor IIK gene) was isolated from a library of EcoRI-restricted potato DNA in λ bacteriophage. A 2.6-kb TaqI fragment containing the gene was subcloned into the plasmid pUC13 and sequenced. This gene is one of 10 to 12 Inhibitor II genes identified by analysis of fragments from restriction enzyme digests of total Russet Burbank genomic DNA by hybridization with nick-translated tomato Inhibitor II complementary DNA (cDNA). A 1.0-kb fragment from the 3' region of the gene, containing only 11 bp of the open reading frame, hybridized strongly with mRNA species from wounded leaves, but only weakly with mRNA from unwounded leaves or tubers. This indicated that the gene is a wound-inducible gene. Approximately 900 bases from the 5' region of the gene and 1,000 bases from the 3' region were fused with the open reading frame of the reporter gene encoding the enzyme chloramphenicol acetyl transferase (CAT) gene. The chimeric gene was cloned into a binary transformation vector derived from the Ti plasmid and successfully used to transform tobacco plants with a wound-inducible CAT gene. Thus, nucleotide sequences in the 5' and 3' regions of the Inhibitor IIK gene are sufficient for wound-inducible expression of CAT activity. These experiments also demonstrate that biochemical components present in cells of wounded tobacco can recognize the potato Inhibitor IIK regulation sequences and can activate the expression of the CAT gene.

---

*Present address: Department of Biochemistry and Biophysics, Iowa State University, Ames, Iowa 50011.
**Present address: U.S. Department of Agriculture, Agricultural Research Service, Southern Regional Research Laboratory, New Orleans, Louisiana 70448.

INTRODUCTION

Proteinase Inhibitor II (molecular weight 12,300) (4) is one of several proteinase isoinhibitors whose synthesis and accumulation in potato and tomato leaves are induced by insect attacks or other mechanical wounding (8,12,19). The inhibitors are also expressed in potato tubers (22), where they cumulatively can represent over 10% of the soluble proteins (21). Thus, inhibitors are regulated in specific tissues under different environmental or developmental conditions. The serine proteinases inhibited by Inhibitor II isoinhibitors are the major digestive endopeptidases of animals and microorganisms, but not of plants (20). Therefore, the inhibitors are considered to be antinutrients that are synthesized in leaves and tubers as part of an array of defensive chemicals of plants (6).

As part of our ongoing research to understand the structure, function, and regulation of proteinase inhibitors in plants, genes coding for proteinase Inhibitors II have been isolated from potato plants. The regulatory regions of one of these genes, called Inhibitor IIK (23), have been fused with the open reading region of the CAT gene (1) and used to transform tobacco plants with wound-inducible CAT activity.

MATERIALS AND METHODS

Potatoes, Solanum tuberosum cv. Russet Burbank, were propagated vegetatively from tubers.*

Estimation of Gene Copy Number

Total DNA was isolated (18) from Russet BurbanK potato plants three weeks after sprouting. Foliage from the entire plant was used for the extraction. The DNA (3 to 10 µg) was digested with restriction endonucleases, and the fragments were separated by electrophoresis on agarose gels (14). Hybridization was conducted in the dried agarose gels following denaturation and neutralization (24). Fragments containing the Inhibitor IIK gene were identified in the gels by hybridization with a nick-translated (17) tomato Inhibitor II cDNA (10).

Screening of a Library of Potato Genes for Inhibitor II Genes

A Russet Burbank genomic library was a gift of Dr. David Anderson, Phytogen Corporation, Pasadena, California. Escherichia coli strain K802 was used as the host. About 3.5×10^5 plaques were screened using nick-translated tomato Inhibitor II cDNA as a probe (15). The DNA was isolated from the amplified clones for restriction nuclease digestion, Southern analysis, and subcloning of restriction fragments.

DNA Sequence Determination

Selected restriction fragments obtained from a 2.6-kb TaqI-TaqI insert were cloned into various sites within M13 bacteriophage. Conditions for cloning, transformation, propagation of M13, isolation of both replicative-

---

*Potatoes were kindly provided by Dr. Thomas Moore, Department of Plant Pathology, Washington State University, Pullman, Washington.

form and single-stranded DNA, and dideoxy sequencing were by published procedures (10,25).

Preparation of Specific 3' Probe

A 1.15-kb TaqI-MspI fragment containing the entire 3' region and a portion of the Inhibitor IIK coding region was isolated and closed into pUC13. This fragment was further cut at a unique RsaI site, which removed all but 11 bp of the open reading frame of the Inhibitor IIK gene. The resulting 1.0-kb fragment was used to probe the poly(A)$^+$ mRNAs from tubers and leaves.

Poly(A)$^+$ Messenger RNA Isolation

Isolation of poly(A)$^+$ mRNA from potato leaves and tubers was performed by the method of Nelson and Ryan (16).

Dot-Hybridization Analysis of Messenger RNA

Hybridization of specific Inhibitor II mRNA sequences within the total poly(A)$^+$ mRNA pools from leaves and tubers was performed according to the procedure of White and Bancroft (26).

Vector Constructions for Transformation

The potato Inhibitor IIK gene provided the opportunity to construct a chimeric gene containing the potential regulatory regions of this apparently wound-inducible gene and the open reading frame of the CAT gene, in order to transform plants with a capacity to express CAT under wound-inducible control. A ScaI site in the inhibitor IIK gene, 18 bases upstream from the translation initiation codon and 30 bases downstream from the transcription start site, provided a 900-bp fragment of the 5' flanking regions of the gene; a RsaI site, 11 bp upstream from the termination codon of the Inhibitor IIK gene, provided a 3' fragment of about 1,000 bp. The resulting construct, pRT45 (Fig. 1a), contained none of the open reading frame of Inhibitor IIK. In Fig. 1b, the essential components of the Inhibitor II-CAT fused gene in the transformation vector pRT45 are shown.

The fused gene was analyzed by restriction mapping and Southern blotting (Fig. 2), and the region of sequence of the chimeric gene at the site of ligation between the Inhibitor IIK promoter and the CAT gene was determined and compared to the sequence of the Inhibitor IIK gene (Fig. 3). The sequence shows that the Inhibitor IIK open reading frame plus 18 bp of the 5' untranslated region are replaced with the CAT coding region and 42 bp of its own 5' untranslated region. The translation initiation codon of the CAT gene is at a position 80 bp downstream from the transcription initiation site, as compared to the 47 bp present in the intact Inhibitor IIK gene.

RESULTS AND DISCUSSION

Estimation of Inhibitor II Gene Copy Number in Restriction Fragments of Genomic DNA

That several Inhibitor II genes are present as a multigene family in the potato genome was demonstrated by hybridization analysis of the

(a)

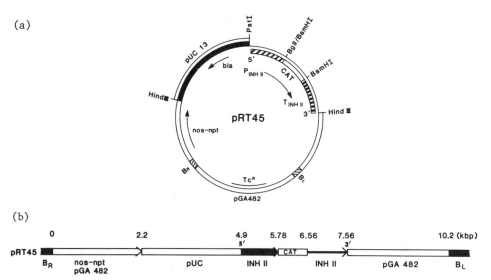

(b)

Fig. 1.   (a) Inhibitor IIK gene–CAT fused gene in pUC13 containing approx-
           imately 1,000 bp of the Inhibitor IIK 5' region, beginning 18 bp
           upstream from the translation initiation codon, and 900 bp of the
           Inhibitor IIK 3' untranslated region, beginning 11 bp upstream
           from the translation termination codon, fused with the open read-
           ing frame of the CAT gene (construct #45).   (b) Construct #45 is
           cloned into the transformation vector pGA482 to produce pRT45.

restriction fragments of potato genomic DNA after electrophoresis on agarose gels.   Figure 4 shows patterns of restriction endonuclease fragments
of potato DNA hybridized with nick-translated tomato Inhibitor II cDNA and
identified by autoradiography.   Multiple, distinct fragments are present in
the potato genome that contain the Inhibitor II gene sequences.   The fragments range in size from 2 kb to 20 kb.   It is not possible to determine an
exact gene copy number, but it is estimated to be about 10.   Proteinase Inhibitor II proteins had previously been shown to exist in potato tubers as
a mixture of four major groups of protomers (23) which are apparently products of some of these genes.

    Individual potato Inhibitor II genes were identified within a library
of potato genes in Charon 4 λ phage, using nick-translated tomato Inhibitor II cDNA (10) as a hybridization probe.   Approximately 3.5 x 10^5
plaques were screened at a density of 50,000 plaques per 150-mm petri
plate.   Twenty-nine positive plaques that hybridized with the cDNA probe
were subsequently rescreened at a lower density.

    A clone called Inhibitor IIK, containing an 8-kb EcoRI insert, hybrid-
ized most strongly with the wound-induced cDNA probe and was isolated and
characterized with restriction enzymes.   A 2.6-kb TaqI fragment was subjected to further restriction analysis and sequencing (25).

    In the 5' region of the gene, the putative regulatory sequence TATAA
is located 72 bp upstream from the initiation codon and 24 bp upstream from
the transcription start, as deduced by primer extension experiments with
wound-induced tomato Inhibitor II mRNA (13).

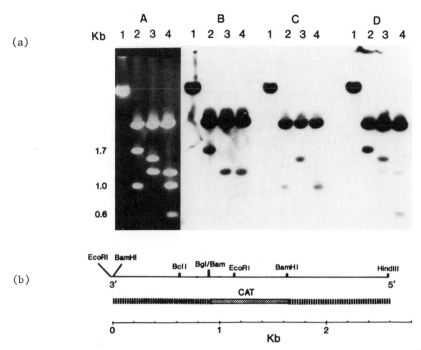

Fig. 2. Analysis of an Inhibitor IIK-CAT construction. (a) Southern mapping of the Inhibitor IIK-CAT chimeric gene. Plasmid pRT45 was digested with restriction endonucleases (lane 1, HindIII; lane 2, HindIII/BamHI; lane 3, HindIII/EcoRI; and lane 4, HindIII/BamHI/EcoRI). These digests were then electrophoretically separated on 2% agarose gels, and the gels were either stained in situ with ethidium bromide (panel A), or denatured, neutralized, and transferred to nitrocellulose (panels B, C, and D). These transfers were prehybridized overnight and then hybridized with nick-translated pRT24 (plasmid containing an approximately 1,000-bp fragment from the 5' end of the Inhibitor IIK gene) (panel B), pRT38 (plasmid containing a 1.0-kb fragment from the 3' end of the Inhibitor IIK gene) (panel C), and pGA425 (plasmid containing a 780-bp fragment including the coding region of the chloramphenicol acetyl transferase gene) (panel D). (b) The Inhibitor IIK-CAT chimeric gene.

```
▸ACCCCAAAATTAAAAGAAAAAGAGGCAGTACTAATTAATTATCCATC ATG GAT GTT CAC AAG GAA GTT AAT TTC GTT GCT▸
                              Sca I              Met Asp Val His Lys Glu Val Asn Phe Val Ala—
                                                         preINHIBITOR II
```

```
▸ACCCCAAAATTAAAAGAAAAAGAGGCAGgactctagagGATCTGAGCTTGGCGAGATTTTCAGGAGCTAAGGAAGCTAAA ATG GAG AAA▸
                            Xba I Bgl/Bam                                          Met Glu Lys—
                                                                                       CAT
```

Fig. 3. Comparison of the nucleotide sequence of the Inhibitor IIK gene-CAT gene 5' fusion region with that of the intact Inhibitor IIK 5' region.

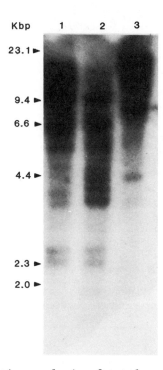

Fig. 4.   Blot hybridization analysis of total genomic DNA from Russet Bur-
           bank potato plants. The DNA isolated from the leaves of un-
           wounded potato plants was digested with EcoRI (lane 1), BamHI
           (lane 3), or both (lane 2), and 10 µg of each digest was separat-
           ed electrophoretically on a 0.7% agarose gel. The gel was dena-
           tured, neutralized, and dehydrated, and then probed with a full-
           length, nick-translated insert from the wound-induced tomato
           Inhibitor II cDNA clone. A HindIII digest of λ DNA was used as a
           calibration standard.

Potato Inhibitor IIK Gene Codes for a Wound-Inducible Messenger RNA

        Because of the complexity of the Inhibitor II gene family, which is
expressed in potato tubers in a developmental manner and in potato leaves
in response to wounding, we attempted to use the 3' region of the gene as a
hybridization probe with the mRNAs from tuber and from unwounded and wounded leaves to determine if specific 3' sequences would identify tissue-
specific Inhibitor II mRNAs. Messenger RNA was isolated from the leaves of
control plants and from their tubers, as well as from the leaves of wounded
plants, and hybridized with the 3' end of the Inhibitor IIK gene. Only the
wound-induced mRNA from wounded potato leaves hybridized strongly with the
3' end of the inhibitor IIK gene (Fig. 5).

Transformation of Tobacco with an Inhibitor IIK-CAT Fused Gene
and Wound-Induction of CAT Expression

        Tobacco (Nicotiana tabacum cv. Xanthi) tissue was transformed with the
plasmid vector by the method described by An (2). Transformed callus
tissue, which was selected using kanamycin resistance, did not exhibit any

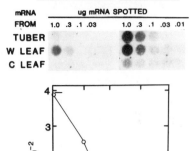

Fig. 5.   Hybridization of Inhibitor IIK 3' untranslated regions to mRNA
           populations from leaves and tubers. Messenger RNA was isolated
           from the leaves (□) and tubers (●) of control plants, and from
           the leaves of wounded plants (o), as described in the "Materials
           and Methods" section (see text). Aliquots of each mRNA pool were
           applied to gene screen membranes at 1.0 µg, 300 ng, 100 ng, and
           30 ng mRNA per spot. Identical membranes were denatured, neu-
           tralized, and hybridized with either the wound-induced tomato
           cDNA, or the Inhibitor IIK 3' region that lacked Inhibitor II
           coding sequences. Following washing (see the "Materials and
           Methods" section in text), the membranes were exposed to X-ray
           film. To quantitate the amount of hybridization, the exposed
           films were aligned with the hybridized membranes, and regions
           containing radioactivity were cut out and counted on a Packard
           Model 3265 liquid scintillation counter.

detectable expression of the CAT gene. Nearly all 80 plantlets that were
regenerated and tested exhibited a very low CAT expression. After the regenerated plants had grown in a greenhouse to a height of 20 to 30 cm, they
were tested for wound-inducibility of the CAT gene. In Fig. 6 is shown a
typical wound-induction of CAT expression in transformed tobacco plants.
In this experiment the leaf at position 1 was removed prior to wounding,
and the leaf was wounded by crushing the tissue between a flat file and a
rubber stopper. The wounded leaf was assayed after 24 hr, as well as unwounded leaves just above and below the wounded leaf. It is clear that the
CAT gene is expressed in response to injury. In this severely wounded
plant, the CAT gene was expressed in the adjacent upper unwounded leaf, indicating that a systemic wound signal was activating CAT expression, similar to the natural response found with proteinase inhibitors in tomato,
potato, and alfalfa plants (8,9,12,19). Little or no CAT expression was
found in leaves below the wounded leaf. This is consistent with previous
data that showed that the wound signal, PIIF, is transported primarily up-
ward (4).

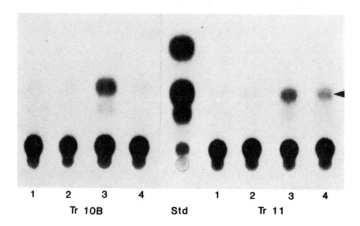

Fig. 6.   Typical wound-inducibility of CAT activity in transgenic tobacco
           plants transformed with the Inhibitor IIK-CAT gene fusion shown
           in Fig. 1.   Two plants regenerated from independently transformed
           tobacco callus tissues were wounded on a lower leaf at 0 time
           and the leaf juice assayed for CAT activity at 24 hr.   The arrow
           shows the migration on thin layer chromatography of 3-acetyl-
           [^{14}C]chloramphenicol, the major product of the CAT enzyme.   Shown
           is the CAT activity in a lower unwounded leaf from the plant re-
           moved at 0 time (lane 1), the lower unwounded leaf adjacent to
           the wounded leaf (lane 2), the wounded leaf (lane 3), and the up-
           per leaf adjacent to the wounded leaf (lane 4).

CONCLUSIONS

     Important conclusions can be drawn from the experiments reported here.
The nucleotide sequences required for wound induction are present in the
pRT45 constructs made from the potato Inhibitor IIK gene, and cellular components are present in tobacco leaves that can regulate wound induction of
CAT expression, both locally and systemically.   These data now provide the
groundwork that will allow us to help determine the sequences in the Inhibitors IIK gene that regulate wound-induction.   Other constructs are being
prepared with deletions in both the 5' and 3' regions of this gene, as well
as in a wound-inducible Inhibitor I gene from tomato, in order to seek
these regulatory sequences.   These experiments, along with other methodolo-
gies such as footprinting (11), genomic sequencing (5), and transient expression (7), should help further identify and define these sequences.
This information will be of significant importance to future research in
determining the nature of the proteins or other cellular components that
regulate the expression of the genes in response to wounding.

ACKNOWLEDGEMENTS

     The support of grants from the National Science Foundation and the
U.S. Department of Agriculture Competitive Grants Program is gratefully acknowledged.

REFERENCES

1. An, G. (1986) High efficiency transformation of cultured tobacco
    cells. Plant Physiol. 81:86-91.
2. An, G., B.D. Watson, and B.H. Howard (1982) Development of plant pro-
    moter expression vectors and their use for analysis of differential
    activity of nopaline synthase promoter in transformed tobacco cells.
    Mol. Cell. Biol. 2:1044-1051.
3. Brown, W.E., and C.A. Ryan (1984) Isolation and characterization of a
    wound-induced trypsin inhibitor from alfalfa leaves. Biochemistry
    23:3418-3422.
4. Bryant, J., T.R. Green, T. Gurusaddaiah, and C.A. Ryan (1976) Protein-
    ase inhibitor II from potatoes: Isolation and characterization of the
    isoinhibitor subunits. Biochemistry 15:3418-3424.
5. Church, G.M., and W. Gilbert (1984) Genomic sequencing. Proc. Natl.
    Acad. Sci., USA 81:1991-1995.
6. Feeny, P. (1976) Plant apparency and chemical defense. In Recent Ad-
    vances in Phytochemistry, Vol. 10, J.W. Wallace and R.L. Mansell, eds.
    Plenum Press, New York, pp. 1-40.
7. Fromm, M., L.P. Taylor, and V. Walbot (1985) Expression of genes
    transferred into monocot and dicot plant cells by electroporation.
    Proc. Natl. Acad. Sci., USA 82:5824-5828.
8. Graham, J.S., and C.A. Ryan (1981) Accumulation of a metallo-carboxy-
    peptidase inhibitor in leaves of wounded potato plants. Biochem. Bio-
    phys. Res. Commun. 101:1164-1170.
9. Graham, J.S., G. Hall, G. Pearce, and C.A. Ryan (1986) Regulation of
    synthesis of proteinase inhibitors I and II mRNAs in leaves of wounded
    tomato plants. Planta (in press).
10. Graham, J.S., G. Pearce, J. Merryweather, K. Titani, L.H. Ericsson,
    and C.A. Ryan (1985) Wound-induced proteinase inhibitor mRNA from
    tomato leaves II. The cDNA-deduced primary sequence of pre-inhibitor
    II. J. Biol. Chem. 260:6561-6564.
11. Gralla, J.D. (1985) Rapid "footprinting" on supercoiled DNA. Proc.
    Natl. Acad. Sci., USA 82:3078-3081.
12. Green, T., and C.A. Ryan (1972) Wound-induced proteinase inhibitors in
    plant leaves a possible defense mechanism against insects. Science
    175:776-779.
13. Lee, J.S., W.E. Brown, J.S. Graham, G. Pearce, E. Fox, T. Dreher, K.
    Ahern, G.D. Pearson, and C.A. Ryan (1986) Molecular characterization
    and phylogenetic studies with a wound-inducible proteinase inhibitor
    gene in Lycopersicon species. Proc. Natl. Acad. Sci., USA (in press).
14. Maniatis, T., I. Fritsch, and J. Sambrook, eds. (1982) Molecular Clon-
    ing: A Laboratory Manual, Cold Spring Harbor Laboratory, Cold Spring
    Harbor, New York.
15. Maniatis, T., R.C. Hardison, E. Lacy, J. Lauer, C. O'Connell, D. Quon,
    D.K. Sim, and A. Efstradiadis (1978) The isolation of structural genes
    from libraries of eucaryotic DNA. Cell 15:687-692.
16. Nelson, C.E., and C.A. Ryan (1980) In vitro synthesis of pre-proteins
    of two vacuolar compartmented proteinase inhibitors that accumulate in
    leaves of tomato plants. Proc. Natl. Acad. Sci., USA 77:1975-1979.
17. Rigby, P.W.J., M. Dickman, C. Rhodes, and P. Berg (1977) Labelling DNA
    to high specific activity in vitro by nick-translation with DNA polym-
    erase I. J. Mol. Biol. 113:237-251.
18. Riven, C.J., E.A. Zimmer, and V. Walbot (1982) Isolation of DNA and
    DNA recombinants from maize. In Maize for Biological Research, W.F.
    Sheridan, ed. Plant Molecular Biology Association, Charlottesville,
    Virginia, pp. 161-164.

19. Ryan, C.A. (1978) Proteinase inhibitors in plant leaves: A biochemi-
     cal model for pest-induced natural plant protection. Trends Biochem.
     Sci. 5:148-151.
20. Ryan, C.A. (1981) Proteinase inhibitors. In The Biochemistry of
     Plants, Vol. 6, P.K. Stumpf and E.E. Conn, eds. Academic Press, Inc.,
     New York, pp. 351-370.
21. Ryan, C.A., T. Kuo, G. Pearce, and R. Kunkel (1976) Variability in the
     concentration of three heat stable proteinase inhibitor proteins in
     potato tubers. Am. Potato J. 53:443-455.
22. Ryan, C.A., G. Pearce, G. An, and R.W. Thornburg (1986) The regulation
     of expression of proteinase inhibitor genes in food crops. Acta Hor-
     ticulturae (in press).
23. Thornburg, R.W., G. An, T.E. Cleveland, R. Johnson, and C.A. Ryan
     (1986) Wound-inducible expression of potato Inhibitor II gene in
     transgenic tobacco plants. Proc. Natl. Acad. Sci., USA (in press).
24. Tsao, S.G.S., C.F. Brunk, and R.E. Pearlman (1983) Hybridization of
     nucleic acids directly in agarose gels. Analyt. Biochem. 131:365-372.
25. Vieira, J., and J. Messing (1982) The pUC plasmids, an M13mp7-derived
     system for insertion mutagenesis and sequencing with synthetic univer-
     sal primers. Gene (Amst.) 19:259-268.
26. White, B.A., and F.C. Bancroft (1982) Cytoplasmic dot hybridization.
     J. Biol. Chem. 257:8569-8572.

POST-TRANSLATIONAL REGULATION

REGULATION OF STARCH SYNTHESIS: ENZYMOLOGICAL AND GENETIC STUDIES

Jack Preiss,[1] Mark Bloom,[1] Matthew Morell,[1]
Vicki L. Knowles,[1] William C. Plaxton,[1]
Thomas W. Okita,[2] Ray Larsen,[2] Alice C. Harmon,[3]
and Cindy Putnam-Evans[3]

[1]Department of Biochemistry
Michigan State University
East Lansing, Michigan 48824

[2]Institute of Biological Chemistry
Washington State University
Pullman, Washington 99164

[3]Department of Biochemistry
University of Georgia
Athens, Georgia 30602

INTRODUCTION

The biosynthesis of the α-1,4-glucosidic linkages found in the two polyglucans present in the starch granule, amylose and amylopectin, occurs via two reactions (for reviews, see Ref. 22 and 23). First, ADP-glucose (ADPG) is synthesized from ATP and α-glucose-1-P (reaction 1). Second, the glucosyl portion of ADPG is transferred to the nonreducing end of the maltodextrin or starch primer to form a new α-1,4 glucosyl linkage (reaction 2). These reactions are summarized as follows:

(1)   ATP + α-glucose-1-P $\rightleftharpoons$ ADP-glucose + PP$_i$

(2) ADP-glucose + α-glucan $\longrightarrow$ α-1,4-glucosyl-glucan + ADP

The synthesis of the α-1,6 linkages found in the branched polyglucan, amylopectin, is catalyzed by a branching enzyme.

Genetic evidence from maize endosperm mutants strongly indicates that incorporation of glucose residues into starch is via the ADPG pathway (6,29,36). Moreover, there is much causal evidence in leaves that suggests that the ADPG pathway is the main route towards starch synthesis (see Ref. 22 and 23 for review of data).

Regulation of starch synthesis occurs at the first reaction, which is catalyzed by ADPG synthetase (also named ADPG pyrophosphorylase). It has been fully documented that 3-phosphoglycerate (3-PGA) is an allosteric positive effector of ADPG synthesis and that inorganic phosphate (P_i) is an inhibitor (4,10,22,25,28,30,32), and evidence suggesting that variations in the concentrations of 3-PGA and P_i modulate the levels of starch in leaves has been reviewed (22,23).

In the leaf, fixation of carbon during photosynthesis may be utilized to form either sucrose or starch. In the past three years, it has been shown that fructose-2,6-bisphosphate (fructose-2,6-P_2) may indirectly affect starch synthesis via its inhibition of the cytosolic fructose-1,6-bisphosphatase, thus preventing carbon flow towards sucrose (14,34,35). The triose-phosphates would therefore remain in the chloroplast and be utilized for starch synthesis.

If the structural gene coding for ADPG synthetase is isolated, then it may be possible via various in vitro mutagenesis techniques to alter the regulatory properties and activity of the enzyme and thus alter starch synthesis. This, in turn, may alter the carbon partitioning in the plant and, in a number of situations and environments, may contribute towards improvement of plant growth. The following reports the current status of information on the structure of the plant ADPG synthetase, the nature of the allosteric effector sites, and the attempts to clone the gene from rice endosperm.

METHODS*

Purification of ADP-Glucose Synthetases

The purification of maize endosperm enzyme has recently been described (21). The purification of the spinach leaf ADPG synthetase has also been described (4,26).

Assay of ADP-Glucose Synthetase

Synthesis of ADP-glucose. Synthesis of ADPG was measured as previously described (10). The reaction mixtures assaying the spinach enzyme contained 20 µmol of Bicine-NaOH buffer, pH 8.0, 1 µmol of $MgCl_2$, 0.1 µmol of [^{14}C]glucose-1-P (1,105 cpm per nmol), 0.2 µmol of ATP, 50 µg of bovine serum albumin, 0.1 unit of inorganic pyrophosphatase, varying concentrations of activator (3-PGA or pyridoxal phosphate) as indicated in the figures and tables, and enzyme in a volume of 0.2 ml. Reaction mixtures were incubated for 10 min at 37°C. The reaction mixture for assay of the maize endosperm enzyme (21) was the same except it contained 2 µmol of $MgCl_2$ and the buffer was Hepes-NaOH, pH 7.4 (16 µmol).

Production of Antibody Towards Spinach Leaf ADP-Glucose Synthetase

The rabbit antibody preparation has been described (21).

---

*All procedures other than those given below are described or referred to in the figures and tables in this chapter.

Gel Electrophoresis

The polyacrylamide gel electrophoresis system utilized was the discontinuous system based on the procedure of Laemmli (17), which includes sodium dodecyl sulfate (SDS).

Protein Determination

Protein concentration was measured by the method of Smith et al. (31).

RESULTS

Characterization of Plant ADP-Glucose Synthetase

Molecular weight. ADP-Glucose synthetase has been purified to homogeneity from spinach leaf (4,26), potato tuber (32), and reportedly from maize endosperm (9). Table 1 lists the molecular weights found for various bacterial and plant ADPG synthetases (see Ref. 24). The native molecular weights were estimated in most cases by sucrose density gradient ultracentrifugation of partially purified or purified enzymes. In the case of the Escherichia coli and Rhodospirillum rubrum enzymes, sedimentation equilibrium ultracentrifugation analysis was done. The range of molecular weights is 185,000 to 237,000. The subunit molecular weights are in the range of 45,000 to 54,000, suggesting that both the bacterial and the plant enzymes are tetrameric.

Our findings with the maize endosperm enzyme are contrary to the previous results reported by another laboratory. Fuchs and Smith (9) reported a subunit molecular mass of about 96,000 Da. However, our finding of a

Tab. 1. Native and subunit molecular weights of various ADPG synthetases.

Source	Native (MW x 10^{-3})	Subunit (MW x 10^{-3})
Spinach leaf	206	54, 51
Potato tuber	200	50
Maize endosperm	230	54
Escherichia coli B	185	50
Salmonella typhimurium	190	48
Rhodopseudomonas gelatinosa	197	
Rhodopseudomonas sphaeroides	204	51
Rhodopseudomonas viridis	200	
Rhodospirillum fulvum	205	
Rhodospirillum molischianum	205	
Rhodospirillum rubrum	200	50
Rhodospirillum tenue	186	45
Rhodopseudomonas globiformis	200	
Serratia marcescens	96, 186	
Rhodopseudomonas acidophila	206	

54,000-Da subunit molecular mass is consistent with the subunit masses we
have obtained with all other ADPG synthetases, and is based on immunoblotting experiments (3) utilizing antibody prepared against spinach leaf ADPG
synthetase (21). It has been shown that the spinach leaf anti-ADPG synthetase is reactive with ADPG pyrophosphorylases from many plant tissues (16).
It should also be pointed out that the maize enzyme preparation of Fuchs
and Smith, although reportedly homogeneous, had an eight-fold lower specific activity than did the maize endosperm ADPG synthetase purified by us in
the presence of protease inhibitors (21). It is very possible that the
maize protein in the preparation of Fuchs and Smith was a major contami-
nant, having a subunit molecular weight of 96,000 (9).

Structural studies of the spinach leaf ADPG synthetase. The spinach
leaf ADPG synthetase appears to have two subunits of molecular weights
54,000 and 51,000, respectively (4,26). These two subunits are also seen
in leaf extracts of rice, wheat, and maize in western blotting experiments
(3,16) using the antibody prepared against the spinach leaf enzyme (21).
It is quite possible that the two subunits of the ADPG synthetase present
in the leaf extracts are due to proteolytic degradation of the higher
molecular weight form to the lower molecular weight form. These two different subunits may also be the products of two different genes. Therefore, studies were initiated towards determining if there was a relationship between the subunits.

The spinach leaf enzyme was purified using a modified procedure from
the one previously reported (4), which also incorporated an FPLC step with
the Pharmacia Mono Q HR column (26). About a 1,200-fold purification was
obtained with a 31% recovery. The specific activity of the purified enzyme
was 105 μmol of ADPG pyrophosphorylyzed per min per mg of protein. The enzyme was estimated to be about 95% pure, with a slight contamination of
peptides of 62- and 64-kDa subunit weight (Fig. 1).

Isoelectric focusing studies under denaturing conditions indicated
that the pI value for the 54-kDa subunit is higher than that for the 51-kDa
subunit (26). The peptides were also observed in crude extracts prepared
in the presence of 9.5 M urea and SDS. Electrophoresis on a two-dimensional gel system according to O'Farrell (18) was done, and the gel was elec-
troblotted to nitrocellulose paper and reacted with affinity-purified antibody to the spinach leaf ADPG synthetase. Two bands were observed strongly
indicating that the lower molecular weight subunit was not generated by
proteolysis during preparation of the crude extract. If post-translational
modification or proteolysis had occurred to generate the smaller subunit,
it would have occurred in vivo, presumably before the tissue was disrupted.

The N-terminal sequences of the two subunits were determined after
separation of the subunits via FPLC fractionation in 8 M urea on a Mono Q
anion exchange column (26). As seen in Fig. 2, the N-terminal sequences of
the two subunits were found to be different.

Kinetic studies. Table 2 shows that the ADPG synthetases are quite
sensitive to activation by 3-PGA and inhibition by P_i. The kinetic constants for the enzyme can vary depending on the source of plant and tissue.
Only 7 μM 3-PGA is required to give half-maximal activation of the barley
leaf enzyme activity. The most insensitive enzymes to 3-PGA activation are
those from maize leaf mesophyll and bundle sheath cells, with $A_{0.5}$ values
of 950 and 490 μM, respectively (33).

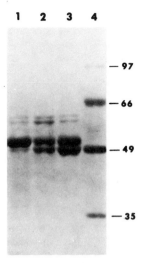

Fig. 1. Electrophoresis of spinach ADPG synthetase. Aliquots from various stages of the purification were electrophoresed on a 10% SDS
polyacrylamide gel and stained with Coomassie blue. Lane 1,
DEAE-cellulose fraction (20 μg) prepared as previously reported
(4); lane 2, Mono Q fraction (13 μg); lane 3, ethyl agarose fraction (20 μg); lane 4, standards: 5 μg each of rabbit muscle phos-
phorylase B (97,000 Da), bovine serum albumin (66,000 Da), E.
coli ADPG synthetase (49,000 Da), and rabbit muscle lactate dehydrogenase (35,000 Da).

High sensitivity to P_i inhibition is also observed. The highest is
observed for the barley and tobacco leaf enzymes, where the $I_{0.5}$ value is
in the range of 20 to 30 μM. Table 2 also shows that the presence of activator causes the respective ADPG synthetases to be less sensitive to inhibition. For example, in the absence of activator the spinach leaf enzyme
requires 42 μM P_i for 50% of inhibition, while in the presence of 1 mM
3-PGA, P_i at 1.2 mM is required for 50% inhibition. Relative to this, it
has been [1] shown that in the presence of P_i, the apparent affinity of the enzyme for 3-PGA is reduced; i.e., the activator concentration necessary for

54-kDa Fraction	[1]Ser – Val – Thr – Ala – Asp – Asn – Ala – Ser – Glu – Thr[10] Lys – Val – Arg – Glu – Ile – Gly – Gln – Glu – Lys –( )[20] (Ser)-(Ser)
51-kDa Fraction	[1]Val – Ser – Asp – Ser – Gln – Asn – Ser – Gln –(Asp)-(Gly)[10] (Leu)-(Asp)-(Pro)-(Glu)

Fig. 2. Amino-terminal sequences of the spinach leaf ADPG synthetase subunits. The placing of amino acids in parentheses indicates that
identification is only tentative. Residue 20 of the 54-kDa subunit was not identified. Sequence analysis was done by automated
Edman degradation as previously described (1), but using a Beck-
man model 890M sequencer. Phenylthiohydantoin amino acids were
identified by HPLC as described (2).

Tab. 2.   Kinetic parameters for activators and inhibitors of higher plant ADPG synthetases.

Enzyme source	$A_{0.5}$* 3-PGA (μM)	$P_i I_{0.5}$* -3-PGA (μM)	$P_i I_{0.5}$* +3-PGA (μM)	Concentration of 3-PGA (mM)
Spinach leaf	20	42	1,200	1.0
Barley leaf	7	20	2,300	1.4
Tobacco leaf	45	30	1,010	1.0
Sorghum leaf	370	190	410	2.2
Tomato leaf	90	80	880	2.5
Sugar beet leaf	190	50	430	0.9
Rice leaf	180	60	270	1.0
Maize leaf				
Mesophyll	950	--	(50) 610	(0.10) 10.0
Bundle sheath	490	--	(38) 900	(0.10) 10.0
Xerosicyos danguyii	100	500	(40) 460	(0.15) 2.0
Hoya carnosa	250	220	(80) 350	(0.25) 2.0
Potato tuber	400	--	(120) 330	(0.25) 3.0
Maize endosperm	120	--	(440) 9,800	(1.00) 10.0

*$A_{0.5}$ is the concentration of activator required for 50% of maximal activation and $I_{0.5}$ is the concentration giving 50% inhibition. The concentration of 3-PGA present in the reaction mixtures, in which $I_{0.5}$ was measured in the presence of activator is shown in the last column on the right. The numbers in parentheses in the fourth column correspond to the $I_{0.5}$ value obtained at a 3-PGA concentration listed in the last (fifth) column in parentheses. Abbreviation: 3-PGA, 3-phosphoglycerate.

half-maximal activity is increased. This 3-PGA-P_i interaction, reported for all of the plant ADPG synthetases, is probably the prime aspect in the regulation of ADPG synthesis and, therefore, of starch synthesis. A high 3-PGA/P_i ratio stimulates ADPG and starch synthesis, while a low ratio has the reverse effect.

There are a few ADPG synthetases [from maize leaf (33) and potato tuber (32)] for which P_i inhibition studies presumably were done in the presence of activator, since the activity under those conditions was quite low. However, with the maize endosperm enzyme (21) and the enzymes from the Crassulacean acid metabolism (CAM) plants, Xerosicyos danguyii and Hoya carnosa (30), sensitivity to P_i inhibition in the absence of the activator 3-PGA was low. Indeed, in the absence of activator only 20% inhibition of the maize endosperm activity occurs with 10 mM P_i. If a relatively small amount of activator was present in the reaction mixture, then the enzymes from the CAM plants and maize endosperm were more sensitive to inhibition. However, even with these last-mentioned ADPG synthetases, a further increase in the 3-PGA concentration caused these enzymes to be less sensitive or more resistant to P_i inhibition. Thus, these enzymes, although requiring a small concentration of activator for optimal P_i inhibition, still have their activity modulated in the same way at physiological concentrations of 3-PGA and P_i. Namely, a high 3-PGA/P_i ratio promotes synthesis, while a low ratio leads to inhibition.

Purification of maize endosperm enzyme. Purification of maize endosperm enzyme in the presence of protease inhibitors yields enzyme that has
greater sensitivity to allosteric activation and inhibition.

Purification of the maize enzyme by a previously reported procedure
(5) resulted in an enzyme that was poorly stimulated by 3-PGA (only two-
to three-fold). In contrast, if the protease inhibitors chymostatin
(10 µg/ml) and phenylmethylsulfonyl fluoride (PMSF; 1.5 mM) were added to
the buffer used in preparation of the crude extract and the enzyme subsequently purified from the extract, a purified fraction was obtained that
was stimulated 28-fold by 3-PGA (Tab. 3; Ref. 21). Moreover, the $A_{0.5}$ value for the activator 3-PGA was 18-fold lower with the enzyme purified in
the presence of protease inhibitors than with the enzyme isolated in the
absence of these inhibitors (Tab. 3).

In the presence of saturating concentrations of 3-PGA, both enzyme
preparations had very similar K_m values for ATP and glucose-1-P (Tab. 3).
However, in the absence of activator, the enzyme prepared in the presence
of protease inhibitors had K_m values for ATP and glucose-1-P that were
approximately seven-fold and 20-fold higher than that of the activated enzyme, respectively. The proteolyzed enzyme's K_m values for ATP and glu-
cose-1-P in the presence or absence of 3-PGA differed only by a factor of
two (Tab. 3).

Tab. 3.   Kinetic constants of maize endosperm ADPG synthetase purified in
          the presence and absence of the protease inhibitors phenylmethyl-
          sulfonyl fluoride (PMSF) and chymostatin.

Substrate/Effector	+ Protease inhibitors*				− Protease inhibitors*			
	$S_{0.5}$	$A_{0.5}$	$I_{0.5}$	V_{max}	$S_{0.5}$	$A_{0.5}$	$I_{0.5}$	V_{max}
ATP	0.84			0.4	0.17			1.9
ATP (+10 mM 3-PGA)	0.11			10.9	0.10			3.7
α-Glucose-1-P	0.67				0.10			
α-Glucose-1-P (+10 mM 3-PGA)	0.04				0.05			
3-PGA		0.12				2.2		
3-PGA (+1 mM P_i)		1.20				--		
3-PGA (+6 mM P_i)		--				12.8		
3-PGA (+8 mM P_i)		3.60				--		
P_i			--				3.0	
P_i (+1 mM 3-PGA)			0.44				--	
P_i (+8 mM 3-PGA)			9.80				10.0	

*Values given in mM.
Note: V_{max} values are µmol of ADPG formed per min per mg of protein. The assay procedure is described in Ref. 21. $S_{0.5}$ is defined as the concentration of substrate
giving 50% of the maximal activity. Values reported for the enzyme purified in the
absence of protease inhibitors are from Dickinson and Preiss (5). The pH values of
the reaction mixtures were 7.4 for the enzyme preparation purified in the absence of
protease inhibitors and 6.8 for the preparation purified in the presence of the inhibitors. Abbreviation: 3-PGA, 3-phosphoglycerate.

In the absence of P_i, the activation curve with 3-PGA is hyperbolic in shape. Inorganic phosphate at 1 mM and 8 mM increased the $A_{0.5}$ value of 3-PGA ten- and 30-fold, respectively (Tab. 3), and changed the shape of the saturation curve from a hyperbolic to a sigmoidal form with respective Hill slope coefficients of 1.5 and 2.6. The affinity for 3-PGA of the enzyme prepared in absence of protease inhibitors was less sensitive to increasing concentrations of P_i, since 6 mM P_i increased the $A_{0.5}$ value of 3-PGA only six-fold (Tab. 3). The two enzyme preparations differed in their responses to inhibition by P_i. In the absence of added activator, the enzyme purified in the presence of protease inhibitors (21) showed little inhibition by P_i concentrations of up to 10 mM, whereas the enzyme prepared in the absence of the inhibitor(s) had an $I_{0.5}$ value of 3 mM P_i (Tab. 3) and was inhibited by over 75%. The presence of 1 mM 3-PGA greatly increased the sensitivity of the enzyme prepared in the presence of the protease inhibitors to inhibition by P_i, with half-maximal inhibition occurring at 0.44 mM P_i (Tab. 3; Ref. 21). However, higher concentrations of 3-PGA greatly reduced the inhibition by P_i. With 10 mM 3-PGA, both enzyme preparations had an $I_{0.5}$ value of approximately 10 mM P_i (Tab. 3).

Thus, enzyme prepared in the presence of the protease inhibitors has a higher affinity for the activator and inhibitor and is much more dependent on the presence of 3-PGA for activity. In the absence of 3-PGA, the enzyme also has much lower apparent affinity for the substrates ATP and glucose-1-P than does the enzyme purified in the absence of protease inhibitors. These findings suggest that the crude extracts of maize endosperm contain a protease(s) that hydrolyzes the ADPG synthetase during the purification procedure, yielding an enzyme modified both in its catalytic efficiency and in its allosteric properties. That the enzyme is indeed degraded when purified in the absence of the protease inhibitors PMSF and chymostatin in the initial extract has been demonstrated (21). Using antibody prepared against the spinach leaf ADPG synthetase, it was shown in western blotting experiments that on incubation of the crude extract, an immunoreactive 53-kDa peptide was formed. If the protease inhibitors were present in the buffer solution used in the endosperm extraction procedure, the 53-kDa peptide was not formed and the only antigenic peptide observed was the 54-kDa peptide. Moreover, following purification of the ADPG synthetase in the absence of the protease inhibitors, both the 53-kDa and the 54-kDa proteins were observed in immunoblotting experiments. If the protease inhibitors were present in the initial extract, the purified ADPG synthetase contained the 54-kDa protein subunit as the only immunoreactive component (21).

Thus, the nonphotosynthetic maize endosperm ADPG synthetase is just as sensitive to allosteric inhibition and activation as has been observed for the leaf ADPG synthetases (Tab. 2). It was earlier postulated from previous results with the maize endosperm enzyme that the nonphotosynthetic ADPG synthetases evolved to a form having insensitive allosteric function (22, 23,37). However, the finding that the maize endosperm (21) and potato tuber enzymes (32) are quite dependent on 3-PGA for activity and are sensitive to P_i inhibition strongly suggests that allosteric regulation of starch synthesis is very important even in the nonphotosynthetic tissues.

Studies on the ADP-Glucose Synthetase Allosteric Sites

The activator and inhibitor sites of the ADPG synthetase are critical for regulation of starch synthesis. If the site is to be manipulated, then more insight is required for the understanding of the structure-function relationship of these effector sites.

Pyridoxal-P (PLP) has been previously used as a site-specific probe for the P_i/triose-P/3-PGA translocator (7,8), as well as for the bacterial ADPG synthetase (19,20). It was therefore of interest to see if it would be a useful site-specific probe for the plant ADPG synthetase.

Activation of ADP-glucose synthetase by pyridoxal-P. Figure 3 shows the activation of the spinach leaf ADPG synthetase by PLP and by 3-PGA. Whereas 15 µM 3-PGA gives 50% of maximal activity ($A_{0.5}$), the $A_{0.5}$ value for PLP is about 6 to 8 µM. However, 3-PGA gives about a 25-fold stimulation, whereas PLP only gives about a six-fold activation. Moreover, the maximal velocity observed with optimal concentrations of PLP is only 20% that observed with 3-PGA as the activator. Similar results have been obtained with ADPG pyrophosphorylase from maize endosperm and Arabidopsis thaliana (T.P. Lin and J. Preiss, unpubl. results). Pyridoxal-P does not appreciably affect the K_m of the substrates. However, 3-PGA does significantly reduce the K_m for ATP. Pyridoxal-P can also reverse P_i inhibition as does 3-PGA. In the absence of activator, the enzyme is inhibited 50% by 45 µM P_i. In the presence of 100 µM PLP, however, 50% inhibition requires 230 µM P_i. Pyridoxal-P, because of its lower stimulation, can inhibit the activation seen with 3-PGA (Fig. 4). In the presence of 1 mM 3-PGA, 0.39 mM PLP gives 50% inhibition, while in the presence of 0.5 mM 3-PGA, one observes 50% inhibition with 0.25 mM PLP.

All these results suggest that PLP does bind at or near the 3-PGA activator site. Since PLP can be irreversibly covalently bound to the protein by reduction with $NaBH_4$, it was of interest to determine the properties of the reduced phosphopyridoxylated enzyme. If it indeed bound to the activator site and placed the enzyme in the active conformation, one would expect the modified enzyme to be more active in the absence of activator.

As shown in Tab. 4, reductive phosphopyridoxylation causes the enzyme to be more active in the absence of activator. The activity ratio of ADPG synthesized in the presence and in the absence of 3-PGA is lowered. There is no change in the ratio when either $NaBH_4$ or PLP is omitted. Presence of the substrate ADPG plus $MgCl_2$ seems to protect the activity slightly but does not affect reduction of the +3-PGA/-3-PGA activity ratio. However, the presence of 3-PGA and P_i inhibits the increase in unactivated activity and decreases the extent of the +3-PGA/-3-PGA activity ratio reduction.

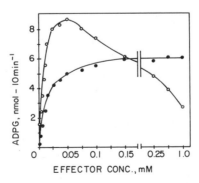

Fig. 3.   Activation of ADPG synthesis by PLP (o—o) and 3-PGA (•—•). The assay procedure is described in the "Methods" section (see text). Eight times more enzyme was used to determine the PLP activation curve, relative to the amount for the 3-PGA curve.

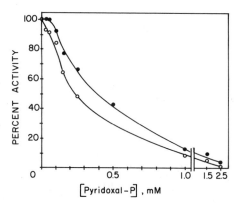

Fig. 4.   Inhibition of 3-PGA-activated spinach leaf ADPG synthetase by
PLP. The reaction mixtures are described in the "Methods" section (see text). Reaction mixtures contained either 0.5 mM 3-PGA
(o—o) or 1.0 mM 3-PGA (•—•).

        Figure 5 shows the same experiment using [^{3}H]-PLP and varying the PLP
concentration.   Even when reductive phosphopyridoxylation is carried out
with 10 µM PLP, there is a dramatic decrease in the +3-PGA/-3-PGA activity
ratio from 20 to 5.6.   About 0.6 to 0.9 mole of [^{3}H]-PLP per mole of tetrameric enzyme is incorporated.   Further incorporation is seen at higher concentrations of [^{3}H]-PLP.   When the activity ratio of +3-PGA/-3-PGA is decreased to about 2.8 to 3.9 with reductive phosphopyridoxylation at 200 µM
PLP, about 2.3 to 2.8 mole of PLP has been incorporated per mole of native
enzyme.   There is further incorporation of PLP at 1 mM [^{3}H]-PLP with very
little additional decrease in the activity ratio.

Tab. 4.   The effect of reductive phosphopyridoxylation on the activity of
spinach leaf ADPG synthetase.

Additions / Omissions to assay	ADPG formed		+3-PGA/-3-PGA
	-3-PGA	+3-PGA	
	(μmol$\cdot$10 min$^{-1}\cdot$ml^{-1})		
No PLP	16.7	522	31.3
None	83	417	5.0
ADPG, 1 mM + MgCl$_2$, 6 mM	104	601	5.8
3-PGA	58	570	9.9
P$_i$	33	576	17.4

Modification mixtures contained 0.25 mg enzyme, 0.1 M bicine (pH
8.0), PLP, and ligand protector in a final volume of 1.0 ml. The
concentration of PLP used was 50 µM. Reaction mixtures were
incubated for 30 min at room temperature in the dark. NaBH$_4$ was
added to a six-fold molar excess relative to PLP and the reaction
mixtures incubated for an additional 60 min. The reaction mixtures were dialyzed against 0.1 M Hepes buffer, pH 7.0, containing 20% sucrose. Abbreviations: 3-PGA, 3-phosphoglycerate; PLP,
pyridoxal-P; ADPG, ADP-glucose.

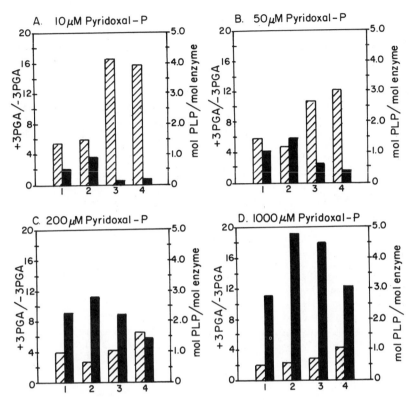

Fig. 5.   Effect of PLP concentration on incorporation of [³H]-PLP into
           spinach leaf ADPG synthetase and on activation of the enzyme by
           3-PGA. The reductive phosphopyridoxylation reaction mixtures are
           similar to those described in Tab. 4, except that 31 μg of enzyme
           were used and the reaction volume was 0.25 ml. Varying [³H]-PLP
           concentrations as indicated were used, and the specific activity
           was 2.53×10^5 cpm/nmol. Following the reduction reaction, 60-μl
           aliquots were electrophoresed on a 10% SDS polyacrylamide gel.
           Coomassie blue-stained gel slices containing the enzyme were sol-
           ubilized in 0.3 ml 30% hydrogen peroxide prior to scintillation
           counting. Aliquots of the modification reactions were dialyzed
           against 0.1 M Hepes (pH 7) containing 20% sucrose. The synthesis
           of ADPG was measured as described in the "Methods" section (see
           text) in the presence or absence of 1 mM 3-PGA. Lane 1 rep-
           resents the reaction mixture that had no ligands. Lane 2 repre-
           sents the reaction mixtures that had ADPG (1 mM) and $MgCl_2$
           (6 mM). Reaction mixtures for lane 3 had 3-PGA (1 mM), and for
           lane 4, P_i (1 mM). The activated/unactivated activity ratio for
           the unmodified enzyme is about 20. The solid bars refer to the
           incorporation of PLP into enzyme, and the cross-hatch bars are
           the +3-PGA/-3-PGA activity ratios.

The incorporation of [3H]-PLP is inhibited by the allosteric effectors 3-PGA and P_i (Fig. 5). Concomitant with this is the retainment of the high activity ratio of +3-PGA/-3-PGA. However, if the reductive phospho-pyridoxylation is carried out at the higher concentrations of PLP, incor-poration of [3H]-PLP occurs along with the decrease in the +3-PGA/-3-PGA activity, despite the presence of 3-PGA and P_i. These results are also consistent with the notion that [3H]-PLP is binding at or near the acti-vator site.

The 3H-labeled PLP binds to both of the subunits of the spinach leaf ADPG synthetase (Tab. 5). There is about two times more incorporation of [3H]-PLP into the higher molecular weight peptide. The significance of this is not known at present, since the relative amounts of each subunit peptide present in the enzyme have not been conclusively established. At any rate, the incorporation of the labeled PLP into the two subunits of ADPG synthetase will enable us to determine the sequences of the activator binding sites of both subunits and whether they are the same. It will also allow us to compare the activator binding site sequences with other ADPG synthetases having different activator specificities (12,19,20,24).

The phosphopyridoxylated modified enzyme is quite insensitive to P_i inhibition (Fig. 6). Whereas the untreated enzyme is 50% inhibited by about 60 μM P_i, only 16% inhibition at 1.0 mM P_i is noted for the en-zyme chemically modified with 1 mM PLP. When chemically modified with 50 μM PLP, the enzyme shows 42% inhibition at 1 mM P_i. Both P_i and 3-PGA, when present during the reductive phosphopyridoxylation, prevent to a great extent the desensitization of the enzyme to P_i inhibition (26). These re-sults are also in keeping with the view that PLP binds to the activator site and places the enzyme in a conformation more resistant to P_i inhibi-tion.

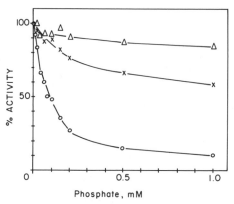

Phosphate, mM

Fig. 6.   Inhibition of PLP-modified ADPG synthetase by P_i. The enzyme was reductively phosphopyridoxylated as described in Tab. 4. (o—o) The curve obtained with the unmodified enzyme. (x—x) The curve obtained with enzyme modified with 50 μM PLP in the presence of ADPG and $MgCl_2$ (1.51 mol PLP incorporated per mol of enzyme). (Δ—Δ) The curve obtained with enzyme modified with 1.0 mM PLP in the presence of ADPG and $MgCl_2$ (4.82 mol PLP/mol enzyme).

Tab. 5. Incorporation of [³H]pyridoxal-P onto ADPG synthetase.

Treatment:	Unprotected				+ADPG, Mg^+				+3-PGA				+P_i			
μM PLP:	10	50	200	1,000	10	50	200	1,000	10	50	200	1,000	10	50	200	1,000
pmoles PLP/ upper band	12	25	51	59	21	35	61	98	2.7	15	51	98	4.3	10	33	61
pmoles PLP/ lower band	5.5	9.3	23	31	9	13	30	57	1.5	6.3	22	46	2.1	4.0	14	38
upper/lower	2.18	2.69	2.22	1.90	2.33	2.69	2.03	1.72	1.80	2.38	2.32	2.13	2.05	2.50	2.36	1.61

*The procedure for reductive phosphopyridoxylation is described in Tab. 4 and in the legend to Fig. 5. The concentrations of ligand added are ADPG, 1 mM; $MgCl_2$, 6 mM; 3-PGA, 1 mM; and P_i, 1 mM. Abbreviations: 3-PGA, 3-phosphoglycerate; PLP, pyridoxal-P; ADPG, ADP-glucose.

Phosphorylation of Spinach Leaf and Maize Endosperm
ADP-Glucose Synthetases by Protein Kinase from Soybean

    Recent studies utilizing a calcium-dependent protein kinase purified
from soybean cells (11) suggest that it can phosphorylate both the maize
endosperm and the spinach leaf ADPG synthetases. Figure 7 shows incorporation of phosphate from $[\gamma-^{32}P]$-ATP into the subunit corresponding to the

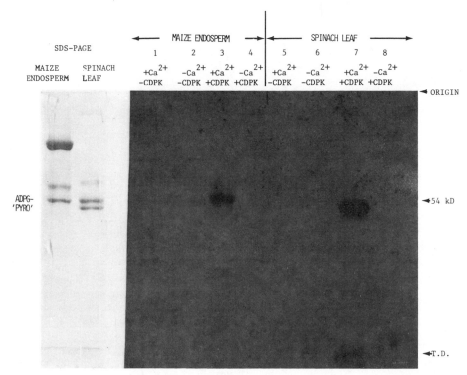

Fig. 7.   Phosphorylation of maize endosperm and spinach leaf ADPG synthetase by soya bean calcium-dependent protein kinase (CDPK). Phosphorylation was performed in the presence and absence of Ca^{2+} or
CDPK. The reaction mixture for examining pyrophosphorylase phosphorylation (final volume 25 µl) contained 16 µg of partially
purified maize endosperm or 10 µg of spinach leaf synthetase,
50 mM Hepes-NaOH (pH 7.0), 10 mM $MgCl_2$, 30 µM $[\gamma-^{32}P]$-ATP (10^6
cpm/nmol), 0.2 mM EGTA, 0.21 mM $CaCl_2$ (final Ca^{2+} concentration =
13 µM), and 35 ng CDPK. Reactions were run at 25°C for 15 min,
terminated by the addition of 25 µl of a solution of 250 mM Tris-
HCl (pH 6.8), 0.2% SDS, 5% 2-mercaptoethanol, 20% glycerol, and
0.1% bromophenol blue, and boiled for 4 min. An aliquot (20 µl)
was then subjected to SDS-gel electrophoresis by the method of
Laemmli (17), and the gel was stained for protein with Coomassie
blue R-250. Following protein staining, the gel was autoradio-
graphed for 4 hr at -80°C using an intensifying screen and Kodak
XAR-5 X-ray film. Shown at the left of the autoradiogram is the
corresponding SDS-gel electrophoresis of partially purified maize
endosperm pyrophosphorylase (6 µg) and spinach leaf pyrophosphorylase (4 µg) following protein staining with Coomassie blue
R-250. "ADPG-'pyro'" refers to ADPG synthetase.

maize endosperm 54-kDa peptide and spinach leaf 54-kDa and 51-kDa peptides that correspond to ADPG synthetase. With respect to the spinach enzyme, about 80% to 90% of the incorporated radioactivity was associated with the 51-kDa peptide. Less than 3% of the radioactivity was associated with any of the other peptide bands in the maize endosperm preparation or in the spinach leaf fraction. The phosphorylation required both the simultaneous presence of Ca^{2+} and the protein kinase (Fig. 7; Tab. 6).

In recent experiments, approximately up to 0.5 to 1.0 mole of ^{32}P has been incorporated per mole of subunit of either the maize or spinach ADPG synthetase. The effect of the phosphorylation of the ADPG synthetases on their kinetic properties is currently being studied. The finding of the phosphorylation of the ADPG synthetase may bring another dimension to the regulation of ADPG and starch synthesis. Studies are currently underway to investigate this phenomenon in more detail with respect to the nature of the phosphate–amino acid linkage, to the presence of homologous protein kinases in the spinach chloroplast (or maize amyloplast) that are capable of phosphorylating the ADPG synthetase, and to the structure and amino acid sequence of the phosphorylated site. Of interest also would be the presence of phosphatases to allow the potential regulation to be reversible and the physiological conditions inducing this potential phosphorylation-dephosphorylation process.

Preparation of an ADP-Glucose Synthetase Complementary DNA Clone from Rice Endosperm Messenger RNA

Recently, an ADPG synthetase complementary DNA (cDNA) was isolated from rice endosperm tissue using the λgt11 technique as described by Huynh et al. (15) and using the antispinach leaf ADPG synthetase (16). Recent sequencing of the cDNA fragment, which is about 1.5 kbp, was done based on the method of Henikoff (13). The deduced amino acid sequence derived from the nucleotide sequence obtained is seen in Fig. 8. If one compares it

Tab. 6.   Incorporation of ^{32}P from $[\gamma-^{32}P]$-ATP into maize endosperm and spinach leaf ADPG synthetase.

ADPG synthetase	Conditions	cpm	pmol
Maize endosperm	$+Ca^{2+}$, $-$Kinase	113	0.09
	$-Ca^{2+}$, $-$Kinase	87	0.07
	$+Ca^{2+}$, $+$Kinase	2,457	2.05
	$-Ca^{2+}$, $+$Kinase	120	0.10
Spinach leaf	$+Ca^{2+}$, $-$Kinase	213	0.18
	$-Ca^{2+}$, $-$Kinase	205	0.17
	$+Ca^{2+}$, $+$Kinase	7,182	6.00
	$-Ca^{2+}$, $+$Kinase	200	0.17

The reaction mixtures are described in the legend to Fig. 7. After termination of the reaction with 25 μl of the Tris-HCl-SDS solution, a 30-μl aliquot was subjected to SDS-gel electrophoresis. Bands corresponding to the ADPG synthetase subunit(s) were excised, digested with 0.3 ml H_2O_2 at 50°C overnight, and ^{32}P-radioactivity determined by liquid scintillation counting.

```
      1                                                                        20
a.   Val Glu Val Leu Ala Ala Gln Gln Ser Pro Asp Asn Pro Asn Trp Phe Gln Gly Thr Ala
b.   Val Asp Leu Leu Pro Ala Gln Gln Arg Met Lys Gly Glu Asn Trp Tyr Arg Gly Thr Ala

      21                                                                       40
a.   Asp Ala Val Arg Gln Tyr Leu Trp Leu Phe Glu Glu His Asn Val Met Glu Phe Leu Ile
b.   Asp Ala Val Thr Gln Asn Leu Asp Ile Ile Arg Arg Tyr Lys Ala Glu Tyr Val Val Ile

      41                                                                       60
a.   Leu Ala Gly Asp His Leu Tyr Arg Met Asp Tyr Ser Lys Phe Ile Gln Ala His Arg Glu
b.   Leu Ala Gly Asp His Ile Tyr Lys Gln Asp Tyr Ser Arg Met Leu Ile Asp His Val Glu

      61                                                                       80
a.   Thr Asp Ser Asp Ile Thr Val Ala Ala Leu Pro Met Asp Glu Lys Arg Ala Thr Ala Phe
b.   Lys Gly Val Arg Cys Thr Val Val Cys Met Pro Val Pro Ile Glu Glu Ala Ser Ala Phe

      81                                            ◆              100
a.   Gly Leu Met Lys Ile Asp Glu Glu Gly Arg Ile Val Glu Phe Ala Glu Lys Pro Lys Gly
b.   Gly Val Met Ala Val Asp Glu Asn Asp Lys Thr Ile Glu Phe Val Glu Lys Pro Ala Asn

      101                                                                     120
a.   Glu Gln Leu Lys Ala Met Met Val Asp Thr Thr Ile Leu Gly Leu Asp Asp Val Arg Ala
b.   Pro Pro Ser Met Pro Asn Asp Pro Ser Lys Ser Leu Ala Ser Met Gly Ile Tyr Val Phe

      121                                                                     140
a.   Lys Glu Met Pro Tyr Ile Ala Ser Met Gly Ile Tyr Val Ile Ser Lys Asn Val Met Leu
b.   Asp Ala Asp Tyr Leu Tyr Glu Leu Leu Glu Glu Asp Asp Arg Asp Glu Asn Ser Ser His

      141                                                                     160
a.   Gln Leu Leu Arg Glu Gln Phe Pro Gly Ala Asn Asp Phe Gly Ser Glu Val Ile Pro Gly
b.   Asp Phe Gly Lys Asp Leu Ile Pro Lys Ile Thr Glu Ala Gly Leu Ala Tyr Ala His Pro

      161                                                                     180
a.   Ala Thr Asn Ile Gly Met Arg Val Gln Ala Tyr Leu Tyr Asp Gly Tyr Trp Glu Asp Ile
b.   Phe Pro --- Leu Ser Cys Val Gln Ser Asp Pro Asp Ala Glu Pro Tyr Trp Arg Asp Val

      181                                                                     200
a.   Gly Thr Ile Glu Ala Phe Tyr Asn Ala Asn Leu Gly Ile Thr Lys Lys Pro Val Pro Asp
b.   Gly Thr Leu Glu Ala Tyr Trp Lys Ala Asn Leu Asp --- Leu Ala Ser Val Val Pro Lys

      201                                                                     220
a.   Phe Ser Phe Tyr Asp Arg Ser Ala Pro Ile Tyr Thr Gln Pro Arg His Leu Pro Pro Ser
b.   Leu Asp Met Tyr Asp Arg Asn Trp Pro Ile Arg Thr Tyr Asn Glu Ser Leu Pro Pro Ala

      221                                                                     240
a.   Lys --- Val Leu Asp --- --- --- --- --- Ala Asp Val Thr Asp Ser Val Ile Gly Glu
b.   Lys Phe Val Gln Asp Arg Ser Gly Ser His Gly Met Thr Leu Asn Ser Leu Val Ser Gly

      241                                                                     260
a.   Gly Cys Val Ile Lys Asn Cys Lys Ile His His Ser Val Val Gly Leu Arg Ser Cys Ile
b.   Gly Cys Val Ile Ser Gly Ser Val Val Val Gln Ser Val Leu Phe Ser Arg Val Arg Val

      261                                                                     280
a.   Ser Glu Gly Ala Ile Ile Asp Lys Asn Ala Arg Ile Gly Asp Asn Val Lys Ile Ile Asn
b.   Asn Ser Phe Cys Asn Ile Asp Ser Ala Val Leu Leu Pro Glu Val Trp Val Gly Arg Ser

      281                                                                     300
a.   Val Asp Asn Val Gln Glu Ala Ala Arg Glu Thr Asp Gly Tyr Phe Ile Lys Ser Gly Ile
b.   Cys Arg Leu Arg Arg Cys Val Ile Asp Arg Ala Cys Val Ile Pro Glu Gly Met Val Ile

      301                                                                     319
a.   Val Thr Val Ile Lys Asp Ala Leu Leu Leu Ala GLu Gln Leu Tyr Glu Val Ala Ala STOP
b.   Gly Glu Asn Ala Glu Glu Asp Ala Arg Arg Phe Tyr Arg Ser Glu Glu Gly Ile Val Leu

      321                                            335
b.   Val Thr Arg Glu Met Leu Arg Lys Leu Gly His Lys Gln Glu Arg STOP
```

Fig. 8.   Comparison of the primary sequence of the rice endosperm (lane A)
            and E. coli (lane B) ADPG synthetase. Only the last 332 amino
            acids of the E. coli enzyme are shown. The homologies are indi-
            cated by the enclosed boxes. The nucleotide sequencing strategy
            used was based on the method of Henikoff (13). The cDNA fragment
            was subcloned into the EcoRI of the "bluescribe" (Bethesda Re-
            search Laboratories, Gaithersburg, Maryland) M13-plasmid vector
            in both orientations. The cloned vector was then digested with
            SphI and BamHI to give a 3' overhang (resistant to exonuclease
            III) and a 5' overhang (susceptible to exonuclease III), respec-
            tively. The cDNA fragment was digested with exonuclease III, ob-
            taining deletions of about 70 bp per min at 30°C. Samples were
            obtained every 3 min. Samples were repaired by first blunting
            with S1 nuclease and then treatment with the Klenow fragment of
            DNA polymerase and the four deoxynucleotide triphosphates. The
            deleted cDNA fragments were subcloned and the JM101 cells were
            transformed with the plasmids containing the deletions about 200
            bp apart. Sequencing employed the dideoxynucleotide method (27).

with the known amino acid sequence of the E. coli ADPG synthetase (1),
about a 24% homology is found (Fig. 8). Of great interest is the homology
seen at amino acid residues 93 to 98. It was shown with E. coli enzyme
that lysine residue 97 was chemically modified by PLP and that the residue
is protected from chemical modification by the substrate ADPG plus Mg^{2+}
(19,20). This would suggest that the lysine residue 97 is involved in
binding of the substrate.

The allosteric inhibitor and activator binding sites are present in
the first 110 to 120 amino acid residues in the N-terminal sequence of the
E. coli ADPG synthetase (1). Unfortunately, this part of the sequence of
the rice endosperm enzyme is still incomplete.

SUMMARY

Significant advances have been made with respect to elucidating the
structure, the allosteric site, interactions of effectors, covalent modifications, and the amino acid sequence of the ADPG synthetase. It is hoped
that in the near future, sufficient information will be obtained to enable
facile manipulation of the plant tissue ADPG synthetase gene and its product.

ACKNOWLEDGEMENTS

The research described herein was supported by the U.S. Public Health
Service research grant AI22835, the National Science Foundation research
grant 85-10088, and by the McKnight Foundation. We thank Dr. Y.M. Lee of
the Biochemistry Department at Michigan State University for his determination of the NH_2-terminal amino acid sequences of the spinach leaf ADPG synthetase subunits.

REFERENCES

1. Baecker, P.A., C.E. Furlong, and J. Preiss (1983) Biosynthesis of bac-
    terial glycogen. Primary structure of Escherichia coli ADPglucose
    synthetase as deduced from the nucleotide sequence of the glgC gene.
    J. Biol. Chem. 258:5084-5088.
2. Bhown, A.S., J.E. Mole, A. Weissinger, and J.C. Bennett (1978) Metha-
    nol solvent system for rapid analysis of phenylthiohydrantoin amino
    acids by high-pressure liquid chromatography. J. Chromatography 148:
    532-535.
3. Burnette, W.N. (1981) "Western Blotting": Electrophoretic transfer of
    proteins from sodium dodecyl sulfate-polyacrylamide gels to unmodified
    nitrocellulose and radiographic detection with antibody and radio-
    iodinated protein A. Analyt. Biochem. 112:195-203.
4. Copeland, L., and J. Preiss (1981) Purification of spinach leaf ADPG
    pyrophosphorylase. Plant Physiol. 68:966-1001.
5. Dickinson, D., and J. Preiss (1969) ADPglucose pyrophosphorylase from
    maize endosperm. Arch. Biochem. Biophys. 130:119-128.
6. Dickinson, D., and J. Preiss (1969) Presence of ADPglucose pyrophos-
    phorylase in Shrunken-2 and Brittle-2 mutants of maize endosperm.
    Plant Physiol. 44:1058-1062.
7. Fliegge, R., U.-I. Flügge, K. Werdan, and H.W. Heldt (1978) Specific
    transport of inorganic phosphate, 3-phosphoglycerate and triose phos-
    phates across the inner membrane of the envelope in spinach chloro-
    plasts. Biochim. Biophys. Acta 502:232-247.
8. Flügge, U.-I., and H.W. Heldt (1984) The phosphate-triose phosphate-
    phosphoglycerate translocater of the chloroplast. Trends Biochem.
    Sci. 9:530-533.
9. Fuchs, R.L., and J.D. Smith (1979) The purification and characteriza-
    tion of ADPglucose from developing maize seeds. Biochim. Biophys.
    Acta 566:40-48.
10. Ghosh, H.P., and J. Preiss (1966) Adenosine diphosphate glucose pyro-
    phosphorylase. A regulatory enzyme in the biosynthesis of starch in
    spinach chloroplasts. J. Biol. Chem. 241:4491-4504.
11. Harmon, A.C., C. Putnam-Evans, and M.J. Cormier (1987) Calcium-depend-
    ent but calmodulin-independent protein kinase from soybean. Plant
    Physiol. (submitted for publication).
12. Haugen, T.H., A. Ishaque, and J. Preiss (1976) Biosynthesis of bac-
    terial glycogen. Characterization of the subunit structure of
    Escherichia coli B glucose-1-phosphate adenyl transferase (E.C.
    2.7.7.27). J. Biol. Chem. 251:7880-7885.
13. Henikoff, S. (1984) Unidirectional digestion with exonuclease III cre-
    ates targeted breakpoints for DNA sequencing. Gene 28:351-359.
14. Huber, S.C. (1986) Fructose 2,6-bisphosphate as a regulatory metabo-
    lite in plants. Ann. Rev. Plant Physiol. 37:233-246.
15. Huyhn, T.V., R.A. Young, and R.W. Davis (1984) Constructing and
    screening cDNA libraries in λgt10 and λgt11. In Cloning Techniques:
    A Practical Approach, D. Glover, ed. IRL Press, Oxford, pp. 49-78.
16. Krishnan, H.B., C.D. Reeves, and T.W. Okita (1986) ADPglucose pyro-
    phosphorylase is encoded by different mRNA transcripts in leaf and en-
    dosperm of cereals. Plant Physiol. 81:642-645.
17. Laemmli, U.K. (1970) Cleavage of structural proteins during the assem-
    bly of the head of bacteriophage T₄. Nature 227:680-685.
18. O'Farrell, P.H. (1975) High resolution two-dimensional electrophoresis
    of proteins. J. Biol. Chem. 250:4007-4021.

19. Parsons, T.F., and J. Preiss (1978) Biosynthesis of bacterial glycogen. Incorporation of pyridoxal-phosphate into the allosteric activator site and an ADPglucose-protected pyridoxal-P binding site of Escherichia coli B ADPglucose synthase. J. Biol. Chem. 253:6197-6202.
20. Parsons, T.F., and J. Preiss (1978) Biosynthesis of bacterial glycogen. Isolation and characterization of the pyridoxal-P allosteric activator site and the ADPglucose-protected pyridoxal-P binding site of Escherichia coli B ADPglucose synthase. J. Biol. Chem. 253:7638-7645.
21. Plaxton, W.C., and J. Preiss (1987) Purification and properties on non-proteolytic degraded ADPglucose pyrophosphorylase from maize endosperm. Plant Physiol. (in press).
22. Preiss, J. (1982) Regulation of the biosynthesis and degradation of starch. Ann. Rev. Plant Physiol. 33:431-454.
23. Preiss, J., and C. Levi (1980) Starch biosynthesis and degradation. In The Biochemistry of Plants. Vol. 3. Carbohydrates, Structure and Function, J. Preiss, ed. Academic Press, Inc., New York, pp. 371-423.
24. Preiss, J., and D.A. Walsh (1981) The comparative biochemistry of glycogen and starch. In Biology of Carbohydrates, Vol. 1, V. Ginsburg, ed. John Wiley and Sons, New York, pp. 199-314.
25. Preiss, J., H.P. Ghosh, and J. Wittleop (1967) Regulation of the biosynthesis of starch in spinach leaf chloroplasts. In Biochemistry of Chloroplasts, Vol. 2, T.W. Goodwin, ed. Academic Press, Inc., New York, pp. 131-153.
26. Preiss, J., M. Morell, M. Bloom, V. Knowles, and T.-P. Lin (1987) Starch synthesis and its regulation. In Proceedings of the VII International Congress on Photosynthesis, J. Biggins, ed. Martinus Nijhoff Publishers, Amsterdam (in press).
27. Sanger, F., S. Nicklen, and A.R. Coulson (1977) DNA sequencing with chain terminating inhibitors. Proc. Natl. Acad. Sci., USA 74:5463-5467.
28. Sanwal, G.G., E. Greenberg, J. Hardie, E.C. Cameron, and J. Preiss (1968) Regulation of starch synthesis in plant leaves: Activation and inhibition of ADPglucose pyrophosphorylase. Plant Physiol. 43:417-427.
29. Shannon, J.C., and D.L. Garwood (1984) Genetics and physiology of starch development. In Starch: Chemistry and Industry, R.L. Whistler, E.F. Paschall, and J.N. BeMiller, eds. Academic Press, Inc., New York, pp. 26-86.
30. Singh, B.K., E. Greenberg, and J. Preiss (1984) ADPglucose pyrophosphorylase from the CAM plants Hoya carnosa and Xerosicyos danguyii. Plant Physiol. 74:711-716.
31. Smith, P.K., R.I. Krohn, G.T. Hermanson, A.K. Mallia, F.H. Gartner, M.D. Provenzano, E.K. Fujimoti, N.M. Goeke, B.J. Olson, and D.C. Klenk (1985) Measurement of protein using bicinchoninic acid. Analyt. Biochem. 150:76-85.
32. Sowokinas, J.R., and J. Preiss (1982) Pyrophosphorylases in Solanum tuberosum III. Purification, physical, and catalytic properties of ADPglucose pyrophosphorylase in potatoes. Plant Physiol. 69:1459-1466.
33. Spilatro, S.R., and J. Preiss (1987) Regulation of starch synthesis in the bundle sheath and mesophyll of Zea mays L. Intracellular compartmentalization of enzymes of starch metabolism and properties of ADPglucose pyrophosphorylases. Plant Physiol. (in press).
34. Stitt, M., B. Herzog, and H.W. Heldt (1984) Control of photosynthetic sucrose synthesis by fructose 2,6-bisphosphate. I. Coordination of CO_2 fixation and sucrose synthesis. Plant Physiol. 75:548-553.

35. Stitt, M., B. Kürzel, and H.W. Heldt (1984) Control of photosynthetic
     sucrose synthesis by fructose 2,6-bisphosphate II partitioning between
     sucrose and starch. Plant Physiol. 75:554-560.
36. Tsai, C.-Y., and O.E. Nelson (1966) Starch deficient maize mutant
     lacking adenosine diphosphate glucose pyrophosphorylase activity.
     Science 151:341-343.
37. Tsai, C.Y., F. Salamini, and O.E. Nelson (1970) Enzymes of carbohy-
     drate metabolism in the developing endosperm of maize. Plant Physiol.
     46:299-306.

MODIFICATION OF GENES AND GENE EXPRESSION

A STRATEGY TOWARDS ANTISENSE REGULATION OF PLANT GENE EXPRESSION

D.P.S. Verma, A.J. Delauney, and T. Nguyen

Centre for Plant Molecular Biology
Department of Biology
McGill University
Montreal, Quebec, Canada   H3A 1B1

The advent of recombinant DNA technology has enabled the isolation of virtually any gene; indeed, the construction of complete gene libraries from any given organism is now routine. However, in many instances, it is extremely difficult to ascertain the biological function of a cloned gene sequence. Similarly, it is difficult to isolate a gene with a known phenotype for which there is no biochemical marker, e.g., a gene(s) affecting the shape or size of an organ.

The main obstacle to elucidating the function of individual genes in higher eukaryotes stems from the difficulty in producing specific dominant mutations in these genes. Traditionally, the delineation of complex metabolic and developmental pathways in living organisms has depended upon the availability of mutants that are defective at various stages of the pathway. Whereas such mutants are readily obtainable in bacteria and simple eukaryotes by classical genetic techniques, many higher eukaryotes are not amenable to these approaches.

With respect to the symbiotic nitrogen fixation process in plants, a number of genes that encode nodule-specific proteins, nodulins, have been identified (see Ref. 19 and 20). Several legumes have been shown to produce 20 to 30 nodulins in the course of nodule development, and there are indications that as many as 50 nodulin genes may be involved in the process of symbiosis between a legume plant and Rhizobium. Our laboratory has isolated a number of soybean nodulin complementary DNA (cDNA) clones, six of which have been characterized to the level of complete DNA sequencing (6). Using antibodies against various cellular fractions, the subcellular locations of the encoded nodulins have been determined (see Tab. 1). However, apart from the previously extensively studied leghemoglobin proteins, functions have been ascribed to only two nodulins: nodulin-35 encodes a nodule-specific uricase (1,13), and nodulin-100 encodes a nodule-specific sucrose synthetase (F. Thummler and D.P.S. Verma, unpubl. data). This was accomplished by purifying the nodulin peptide, followed by antibody preparation and assaying for various enzyme activities known to be elevated in

Tab. 1.   Characteristics of soybean nodulins (data obtained from Ref. 6).

Nodulin	Apparent molecular weight[a] (kDa)	Actual molecular weight[b] (kDa)	Subcellular location	Function
23	23.5	24.3	pbm	--
24	24	15.1	pbm	--
26	26.5	22.5	pbm	--
26b	25.5	23.5	cytoplasmic	--
27	27	22.4	cytoplasmic	--
35	33	35.1	peroxisome	uricase II
(44) E-27*	42	39	--	--
100**	90	--	cytoplasmic	sucrose synthetase

[a]Estimated by SDS-PAGE.
[b]Calculated from the deduced protein sequence.
*Data obtained from Ref. 17.
**Partial sequence.

nodule tissues. Since no mutations are known to exist in these genes and most of the nodulin genes are induced at about the same time during symbiosis, it is difficult to ascertain their function.

As a strategy for specifically "mutating" (reducing expression of) a given gene in higher eukaryotes, the use of antisense RNA transcripts to block the expression in vivo of the corresponding sense transcripts holds great promise. Considerable success has already been documented with various animal systems, notably the inhibition of expression of the thymidine kinase gene in mouse L cells (5,7); the repression of β-globin synthesis in Xenopus oocytes (10); the inhibition of a Kruppel gene in Drosophila, resulting in phenocopies of the Kruppel mutations (16); and the inhibition of heat shock protein synthesis in Drosophila tissue culture cells (9).

The antisense RNA approach has also been successfully applied to the regulation of genes in Escherichia coli. For example, virtually complete inhibition of β-galactosidase synthesis using the antisense RNA strategy has been demonstrated (15), and Coleman et al. (3) similarly blocked the expression of lipoprotein mRNAs. The work of Coleman et al. (3) followed their earlier finding that the expression of two genes coding for outer membrane proteins are reciprocally regulated by a natural mechanism involving the antisense RNA concept (11). There are, in fact, an increasing number of reports in bacteria where the regulation of gene expression and replication are normally mediated by an antisense mechanism (see Ref. 5 and references therein).

In eukaryotes, the natural occurrence of antisense-mediated gene regulation has not yet been demonstrated. However, there is some evidence implicating such mechanisms in eukaryotic gene regulation. Earlier work in our laboratory revealed the presence of a putative promoter located downstream from the soybean nodulin-23 promoter, but oriented in the opposite direction to the main promoter (23). The so-called "anti-nodulin" promoter was identified by promoter analysis of the nodulin-23 gene in a heterologous in vitro transcription assay. In vitro transcription analysis revealed two α-amanitin-sensitive transcripts: one corresponding to the major start site observed in vivo, and a second whose origin was not immediately apparent. Additional transcription assays using templates of varying lengths indicated that the second transcript originated from the postulated "anti-nodulin" promoter. Thus, there is an 80-base overlap between the putative antisense transcript and the nodulin-23 transcript (see Fig. 1). However, while this finding is suggestive of a possible antisense regulatory mechanism, attempts to isolate the antisense transcript from root or nodule tissue have so far been unsuccessful.

Recently, Williams and Fried (22) identified a region of mouse DNA encoding two convergent RNA transcription units which overlap by 133 bases at their 3' ends. They speculated that the overlapping transcripts may have a role in the control of gene expression. Similarly, Spencer et al. (18) reported finding an 88-base overlap between the 3' termini of a pair of convergent transcription units in the Drosophila genome and discussed the regulatory implications of a possible sense/antisense hybridization in vivo.

Whereas it is not yet conclusively established that antisense transcription is a natural regulatory mechanism for control of eukaryotic

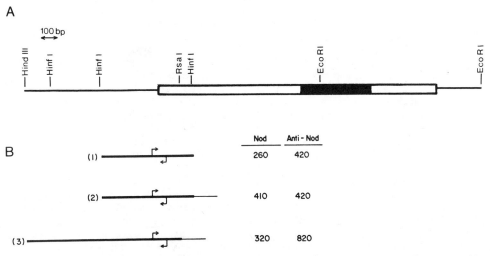

Fig. 1. (A) Structure of the soybean nodulin-23 gene. Open boxes indicate exons, and the shaded area is an intron. (B) DNA templates used for in vitro transcription of nodulin-23 gene. Fragment 1 is a 600-bp HinfI fragment. Fragment 2 consists of fragment 1 plus 150 bp of the pUC9 plasmid (thin line). Fragment 3 is a 950-bp HindIII-RsaI fragment with the same 150-bp pUC9 DNA as in fragment 2. Arrows above and below the templates show the direction and location of transcription of nodulin (→) and antinodulin (←) promoters. The table to the right lists the sizes of the α-amanitin-sensitive transcripts obtained from each template (see Ref. 23 for details).

genes, the antisense RNA concept still provides a powerful tool for experimentally manipulating gene expression in vivo, and potential applications
of this strategy have been widely discussed (see Ref. 8 and 21).

We are interested in using the antisense gene repression strategy to
elucidate the function of cloned nodulin genes. Our approach is to make
several constructs containing nodulin cDNA inserts cloned in an antisense
orientation downstream from a strong nodule-specific promoter. The antisense constructs will then be transferred to the host plant using the Ti-
or Ri-plasmid transformation techniques. If sufficiently high expression
of the antisense transcripts can be achieved, repression of the corresponding nodulin RNAs may result in detectable phenotypic changes in nodule
structure or physiology, and we hope to be able to correlate these changes
with the function of the nodulins identified to date. In addition, one can
develop a nodule-specific cDNA "shotgun" library in the antisense orientation, and transform legume plants for identification and isolation of genes
for which no biochemical markers are available.

Since techniques for transformation and regeneration of soybean are
not yet routine, we envisage it may be necessary to work with a legume system such as Lotus which is more amenable to tissue culture manipulation.
Both Lotus and alfalfa can be easily regenerated from transformed tissues.
Identification of Lotus nodulin clones will be simplified by probing a
Lotus nodule cDNA library with our currently available soybean nodulin
clones.

Before embarking on this project, we have chosen to establish the feasibility of the approach by using a tobacco model system. This may avoid
potential complications associated with legume transformation and regeneration, and circumvent difficulties in achieving high levels of gene expression in the nodules of transgenic plants. We have initiated a program to
transform tobacco explants with tobacco cDNA clones oriented in an antisense direction downstream from the strong 35S promoter of cauliflower
mosaic virus (CaMV). A cDNA library is constructed using a vector-template
strategy which orients the cDNA inserts in a particular chosen orientation.
The plasmid template used for priming cDNA synthesis, pV130, is a deriva-
tive of the binary Ti-plasmid vector pBin19 (2) and allows cDNA clones to
be used directly for tobacco transformation without intermediate subcloning
steps. The essential features of this plasmid are shown in Fig. 2.

The plasmid pV130 contains within the T-DNA border repeats the CaMV
35S promoter and the nos 3' region which provides polyadenylation signals.
The 35S promoter is a relatively strong promoter which has been shown to be
10 to 15 times stronger than the commonly used nos promoter in petunia
cells (12). Between the 35S and the nos regions are a range of unique restriction sites which allow dT-tailing of the vector and subsequent cDNA
synthesis. Other features of the plasmid which confer kanamycin resistance
in bacteria and transformed plant tissue are as previously described (2).

The steps followed for construction of the cDNA clones, based on the
procedure of Okayama and Berg (14), are outlined in Fig. 3. First, pV130
is cleaved at a unique site between the 35S promoter and the nos 3' region.
The DNA termini are then tailed with dT residues, and the dT tail adjacent
to the nos region is subsequently removed by digestion with an appropriate
restriction enzyme. The dT tail downstream from the 35S promoter serves
as a primer for cDNA synthesis after the annealing of poly(A)$^+$ mRNA. As
illustrated in Fig. 3, the position of the oligo(dT) tail ensures that all

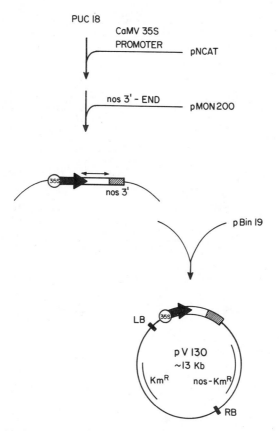

Fig. 2.   Construction of a binary Ti-plasmid vector for the cloning of
          antisense cDNAs. The CaMV 35S promoter (solid arrow) was ob-
          tained from pNCAT (supplied by Dr. N.-H. Chua). The nos 3'
          region (hatched box) was obtained from pMON200 (4). The multi-
          linker of pUC18 is indicated by a double-headed arrow. The 35S
          promoter, multilinker, and nos 3' region were transferred to
          pBin19 (2) to give the vector pV130. LB and RB indicate the left
          and right T-DNA border repeats, respectively.

cDNA molecules are synthesized in an antisense orientation relative to the
promoter. Following cyclization of the vector-cDNA molecules, an E. coli
strain is transformed to kanamycin resistance.

    This library will be mobilized into Agrobacterium tumefaciens for the
transformation of tobacco leaf discs, and whole plants transformed with the
antisense constructs will be regenerated. Using this strategy, it should
be possible to detect phenotypic variations in transformed plants and to
correlate each mutant phenotype with a particular gene whose expression is
repressed.

    While this is meant to serve primarily as a model for testing the
applicability of antisense-mediated gene regulation in plants, we have
not overlooked its potential for isolating key developmental genes for
which there are currently no available probes. This approach can then be

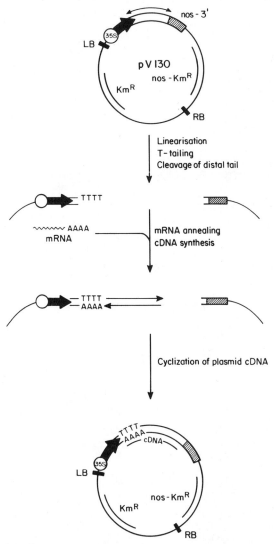

Fig. 3.   Steps in the construction of an antisense cDNA library. Symbols
          are as designated in Fig. 2. The pV130 plasmid is linearized by
          KpnI and dT-tailed. The distal tail of dT residues is removed
          with XbaI. Poly(A)$^+$ mRNA from tobacco flowers is annealed to the
          dT-tailed vector and cDNA synthesized. Following cyclization of
          the vector-cDNA molecules, E. coli strain DH5 is transformed and
          a library generated.

extended to legume systems for studying the role of nodulin genes in symbiosis and obtaining desired phenotypes of agricultural importance. A general application of this approach may open up new avenues towards controlling genes whose function is undesirable, such as those involved in the
production of plant secondary metabolites that are harmful to animal and
human health. Moreover, this may aid in identifying genes which control
plant development, shape, and form at large.

REFERENCES

1. Bergmann, H., E. Preddie, and D.P.S. Verma (1983) Nodulin-35: A sub-
    unit of nodule-specific uricase (uricase II) induced and localized in
    uninfected cells. EMBO J. 2:2333-2339.
2. Bevan, M. (1984) Binary Agrobacterium vectors for plant transforma-
    tion. Nucl. Acids Res. 12:8711-8721.
3. Coleman, J., P.J. Green, and M. Inouye (1984) The use of RNAs comple-
    mentary to specific mRNAs to regulate the expression of individual
    bacterial genes. Cell 37:429-436.
4. Fraley, R.T., S.G. Rogers, R.B. Horsch, D.A. Eichholtz, J.S. Flick,
    C.L. Flick, N.L. Hoffmann, and P.R. Sanders (1985) The SEV system:
    A new disarmed Ti plasmid vector system for plant transformation.
    Bio/Technology 3:629-635.
5. Izant, J.G., and H. Weintraub (1984) Inhibition of thymidine kinase
    gene expression by anti-sense RNA: A molecular approach to genetic
    analysis. Cell 36:1007-1015.
6. Jacobs, F.A., M. Zhang, M.G. Fortin, and D.P.S. Verma (1986) Several
    nodulins of soybean share structural domains but differ in their sub-
    cellular locations. Nucl. Acids Res. (in press).
7. Kim, S.K., and B.J. Wold (1985) Stable reduction of thymidine kinase
    activity in cells expressing high levels of anti-sense RNA. Cell
    42:129-138.
8. Klausner, A. (1985) Turning off unwanted genes with anti-RNA. Bio/-
    Technology 3:763-764.
9. McGarry, T.J., and S. Lindquist (1986) Inhibition of heat shock pro-
    tein synthesis by heat-inducible anti-sense RNA. Proc. Natl. Acad.
    Sci., USA 83:399-403.
10. Melton, D.A. (1985) Injected anti-sense RNAs specifically block mes-
    senger RNA translation in vivo. Proc. Natl. Acad. Sci., USA 82:144-
    148.
11. Mizuno, T., M.-Y. Chou, and M. Inouye (1984) A unique mechanism regu-
    lating gene expression: Translational inhibition by a complementary
    RNA transcript (micRNA). Proc. Natl. Acad. Sci., USA 81:1966-1970.
12. Morelli, G., F. Nagy, R.T. Fraley, S.G. Rogers, and N.-H. Chua (1985)
    A short conserved sequence is involved in the light-inducibility of a
    gene encoding ribulose 1,5-biphosphate carboxylase small subunit of
    pea. Nature 315:200-204.
13. Nguyen, T., M.G. Zelechowska, V. Foster, H. Bergmann, and D.P.S. Verma
    (1985) Primary structure of the soybean nodulin-35 gene encoding nod-
    ule-specific uricase localized in peroxisomes of uninfected cells of
    soybean. Proc. Natl. Acad. Sci., USA 80:5040-5044.
14. Okayama, H., and P. Berg (1982) High-efficiency cloning of full-length
    cDNA. Mol. Cell. Biol. 2:161-170.
15. Pestka, S., B.L. Dougherty, V. Jung, K. Hotta, and R.K. Pestka (1984)
    Anti-mRNA: Specific inhibition of translation of single mRNA mole-
    cules. Proc. Natl. Acad. Sci., USA 81:7525-7528.
16. Rosenberg, U.B., A. Preiss, E. Seifert, H. Hackle, and D.C. Knipple
    (1985) Production of phenocopies by Kruppel anti-sense RNA injection
    into Drosophila embryos. Nature 313:703-706.
17. Sengupta-Gopalan, C., J.W. Pitas, D.V. Thompson, and L.M. Hoffman
    (1986) Expression of host genes during root nodule development in soy-
    beans. Mol. Gen. Genet. 203:410-420.
18. Spencer, C.A., R.D. Gietz, and R.B. Hodgetts (1986) Overlapping tran-
    scription units in the dopa decarboxylase region of Drosophila. Na-
    ture 322:279-281.

19. Verma,   D.P.S.,   and   K.   Nadler   (1984)   Legume–Rhizobium–symbiosis:
     Host's point of view.   In Genes Involved in Microbe–Plant Interac-
     tions, D.P.S. Verma and T. Hohn, eds.   Springer–Verlag, Wien and New
     York, pp. 57–93.
20. Verma, D.P.S., M.G. Fortin, J. Stanley, V.P. Mauro, S. Purohit, and N.
     Morrison (1986) Nodulins and nodulin genes of Glycine max.   Plant Mol.
     Biol. 7:51–61.
21. Weintraub, H., J.G. Izant, and R.M. Harland (1985) Anti–sense RNA as a
     molecular tool for genetic analysis.   Trends in Genetics 1:22–25.
22. Williams, T., and M. Fried (1986) A mouse locus at which transcription
     from both DNA strands produces mRNAs complementary at their 3' ends.
     Nature 322:275–279.
23. Wong, S.L., and D.P.S. Verma (1985) Promoter analysis of a soybean
     nuclear gene coding for nodulin–23, a nodule–specific polypeptide in-
     volved in symbiosis with Rhizobium.   EMBO J. 4:2431–2438.

MODIFICATION OF PROTEINS ENCODED BY SEED STORAGE PROTEIN GENES

Brian A. Larkins

Department of Botany and Plant Pathology
Purdue University
West Lafayette, Indiana   47907

It has been recognized for many years that seed proteins are deficient in amino acids that are "essential" for human and livestock nutrition (15). In general, cereals are most limiting in lysine while legumes are most limiting in the sulfur amino acids, methionine and cysteine. There has been only limited progress by plant breeders to increase the content of these amino acids in crops, primarily because genes encoding storage proteins with higher levels of essential amino acids do not normally exist. Therefore, genetic engineering of genes encoding seed storage proteins would provide a rather straightforward solution to the problem. But regardless of how straightforward the genetic engineering approach might be, it remains to be seen whether it will be practical.

Genetic engineering of any gene requires a thorough understanding of its structure and regulation as well as the biochemistry of the protein that it encodes. In these areas probably more is known about seed storage proteins than any other plant protein. As a result of biochemical and molecular biological studies during the past ten years, we have a general understanding of the mechanisms by which storage proteins are synthesized and deposited in developing seeds. We also have a general idea of the number and structure of genes encoding these proteins, we know the primary amino acid sequences of some of these proteins, and, in a few cases, we know something about the structure of the proteins. While most of the detailed information comes from studies of a few legume and cereal species, seed proteins from a number of angiosperm families have been examined, and it is possible to make some general conclusions about these proteins.

Two groups of storage proteins can be distinguished: the globulin type that occurs in legumes and most other dicot species, and the prolamin type that appears to be unique to some cereals. While it is possible that the storage globulin and prolamin proteins arose from a common ancestral gene, they have distinctive structures and slightly different mechanisms of synthesis and deposition in the seed. Although other proteins, including lectins, protease inhibitors, and some enzymes such as urease, may constitute a significant portion of the seed protein, I will consider only the common types of storage proteins.

163

Globulin storage proteins occur in most dicot species and in a few monocots. The storage globulins are deposited in protein bodies which usually are found in the cotyledons of the developing embryo. These proteins can be isolated from the developing protein bodies or from saline extracts of the mature seed. The two principal types of storage globulins have sedimentation coefficients of 7S and 11S. These are large proteins with apparent molecular weights of approximately 130,000 and 330,000, respectively, and are composed of multiple subunits (8). Subunits of the 7S and 11S globulins are synthesized as precursors on rough endoplasmic reticulum membranes. Signal peptides direct their transport into the lumen of the endoplasmic reticulum, where they associate into trimers (7). The subunits of the 7S polypeptides undergo glycosylation concomitant with their transport through the rough endoplasmic reticulum, although the subunits of the 11S protein are not glycosylated. Both 7S and 11S globulins are transported through dictyosomes, where the 7S subunits undergo further modification of their carbohydrate chains. Eventually the proteins are deposited in vacuoles which become the protein bodies.

Genes encoding 7S and 11S globulins have been best described in legume species. In pea and soybean, the genes encoding subunits of the 7S protein generally contain five introns and six exons (9). These genes are present in small multigene families of 10 to 20 members. The genes encoding the subunits of the 11S protein contain two or three introns and three or four exons (3). These proteins appear to be encoded by four or five genes. There is striking homology in the 5' flanking sequences that precede 7S genes among different legume species, and this is also true of the flanking sequences that precede the genes encoding subunits of the 11S protein. There is less homology between the 5' flanking sequences of genes encoding 7S and 11S subunits, although they are similarly regulated.

The major storage proteins of most cereal species are alcohol-soluble proteins called prolamins, which were so named because of their high contents of proline and glutamine (14). However, two cereal species, oats and rice, have very little prolamin and instead contain storage proteins that are structurally like the 11S globulins that occur in dicots.

In cereal seeds the endosperm becomes the principal site for storage protein and starch deposition. Cereal storage proteins are deposited in protein bodies, although the mechanisms involved in their transport and deposition are less well-characterized than those of the dicots. Protein bodies in wheat and barley are surrounded by smooth membranes, and there is some evidence to suggest dictyosome involvement in their formation (5,6). However, in maize and sorghum the protein bodies form directly within the lumen of the rough endoplasmic reticulum (14).

The prolamin proteins of wheat, barley, and rye are structurally more closely related to each other than they are to those of maize and sorghum. There are two types of storage protein in wheat, the gliadins and the glutenins. The gliadins are a complex set of proteins that can be separated by charge into groups designated alpha, beta, gamma, and omega. The alpha, beta, and gamma gliadins are proteins of around 300 amino acids that appear to be structurally similar (16). The amino-terminal portion is made up of repeated peptides that are rich in proline. The remainder of the protein consists of four segments, the first and third of which are stretches of 25 to 30 glutamine residues. The second and fourth regions are distinct from the remainder of the molecule and are lower in proline than the region of repeated polypeptides.

The glutenins are large proteins of 600 to 800 amino acids. The first 100 and the last 40 amino acids are nonrepetitive, but the interior of the protein is composed of interspersed segments of six and nine amino acid repeats (18). The NH_2-terminal and COOH-terminal regions of these proteins are thought to be alpha helices, and the formation of disulfide linkages between these regions causes the proteins to aggregate into linear polymers that are responsible for the elasticity of bread dough (19).

Maize storage proteins can be divided into three structurally distinct types (10). Generally, proteins of 22,000 and 19,000 Da are the most abundant and are referred to as alpha zeins. These proteins have an NH_2-terminal region of 40 amino acids which precedes a series of repeated peptides of 20 amino acids. These repeats appear to be alpha helices that fold the protein into a rod-shaped molecule (2). The beta zeins are proteins of 15,000, 14,000, and 10,000 Da that are very rich in methionine and cysteine. These proteins contain no repeated peptides and have no apparent alpha helical structure. The gamma zein is a protein of 27,000 Da that is rich in cysteine. This protein has a NH_2-terminus of 11 amino acids that precedes a hexapeptide repeat of the sequence Pro-Pro-Pro-Val-His-Leu. This protein contains about 25% proline and is presumably a rod-shaped molecule. From immunocytochemical studies, we have found that the alpha zeins make up the core of the protein bodies and the beta and gamma zeins form an outer layer of protein.

Genes encoding cereal prolamins have been found to have a simple structure. In all species thus far examined, prolamin genes have not been found to contain introns. The genes encoding the alpha-type zeins and the gliadins of wheat exist in large multigene families with 75 to 100 members (1,13). However, the beta and gamma zeins and the wheat glutenins are encoded by only a few gene copies (11,20). Sequences preceding some of the maize and wheat storage protein genes have conserved sequences that precede the transcribed region by several hundred nucleotides. We have found this region to be important for transcription of zein genes, but it remains to be demonstrated whether it is important for developmental regulation.

With the development of Ti-plasmid vectors, it is now possible to genetically engineer storage protein genes into plants. The first successful report of this came from Dr. Tim Hall's group at Agrigenetics Corp., where a gene encoding one subunit of the Phaseolus vulgaris 7S protein was transformed into tobacco plants (17). These studies showed that this gene was properly regulated in tobacco and that the bean protein was synthesized and sequestered into protein bodies in cotyledons of the tobacco embryo. Similar results have recently been reported by Dr. Roger Beachy and his colleagues at Washington University in St. Louis, where they observed normal regulation of a gene encoding a subunit of the soybean 7S protein in transformed petunia plants (4). Thus, it appears that the DNA sequences responsible for seed storage protein gene regulation are conserved among dicot species. My laboratory has recently examined petunia plants that were transformed with maize zein genes. Although we found low levels of zein gene expression in seeds of these plants, we also found the gene to be expressed in leaf and stem tissue. So it remains to be seen whether the DNA sequences that regulate the expression of monocot storage protein genes will be recognized in dicots. It will of course be more interesting to study the expression of these genes when a protoplast regeneration system becomes available for maize.

There have not been many reports of expression of modified storage protein genes in plants, although such studies are underway in a number of laboratories. One of the reasons these experiments have been slow to develop is the length of time required for regenerated plants to set seed. Several laboratories are using heterologous systems to analyze more rapidly the consequences of making amino acid substitutions and insertions in storage proteins. In my laboratory we have been using the SP6 in vitro transcription system to synthesize mRNAs corresponding to cloned zein sequences (12). We have found that the native or synthetic mRNAs are efficiently translated in Xenopus oocytes and that the zein proteins which are synthesized aggregate inside membranes to form structures with the physical characteristics of zein protein bodies. Experiments are in progress to determine if lysine insertions in the alpha-type zeins alter their ability to aggregate into protein bodies. Our preliminary results indicate that single lysine additions do not affect aggregation of these proteins; whether this will be true with multiple lysine insertions remains to be determined.

Dr. Niels Nielsen's laboratory at Purdue University is using a somewhat similar approach to study the consequences of adding methionine residues to subunits of soybean 11S globulins. For their studies they translate SP6 glycinin transcripts in a rabbit reticulocyte cell-free translation system. Incubation of the translation products under appropriate conditions leads to the aggregation of glycinin subunits into 8S particles. Aggregation will only occur if the signal peptide sequence is removed from the protein. It has been found that substitution of different acid or basic polypeptides among 11S subunits does not affect their aggregation; however, removal of a 23 amino acid sequence from the most conserved part of the basic polypeptide disrupts aggregation of the subunits. Preliminary experiments indicate that the addition of multiple methionine residues to regions of the protein that are variable among 11S subunits does not affect the aggregation of these polypeptides. Hopefully, these in vitro tests will be good predictors of modifications that will be functional in vivo.

In summary, seed storage proteins have been found to have highly ordered structures, and the extent to which they can be modified by the insertion of essential amino acids remains to be determined. There are, of course, alternative approaches to this problem, such as the substitution from one species to another of seed proteins with higher levels of essential amino acids. In addition to increasing the nutritional value of the seed protein in the recipient species, this could also result in modified rheological properties in flours made from these seeds.

REFERENCES

1. Anderson, O.D., J.C. Little, M.-F. Gautier, and F.C. Green (1984) Nucleic acid sequence and chromosome assignment of a wheat storage protein gene. Nucl. Acids Res. 12:8129-8144.
2. Argos, P., K. Pedersen, M.D. Marks, and B.A. Larkins (1982) A structural model for maize zein proteins. J. Biol. Chem. 257:9984-9990.
3. Baumlein, H., U. Wobus, J. Pustell, and F.C. Kafatos (1986) The legumin gene family: Structure of a B type gene of Vicia faba and a possible legumin gene specific regulatory element. Nucl. Acids Res. 14:2707-2720.

4. Beachy, R.N., Z.-L. Chen, R.B. Horsch, S.B. Rogers, N.J. Hoffmann, and R.T. Fraley (1985) Accumulation and assembly of soybean β-conglycinin in seeds of transformed petunia plants. EMBO J. 4:3047-3053.

5. Bechtel, D.B., R.L. Gaines, and Y. Pomeranz (1982) Early stages in wheat endosperm formation and protein body initiation. Ann. Bot. 50:507-518.

6. Cameron-Mills, V., and D. von Wettstein (1980) Protein body formation in the developing barley endosperm. Carlsberg Res. Commun. 45:577-594.

7. Chrispeels, M.J., T.J.V. Higgins, and D. Spencer (1982) Assembly of storage protein oligomers in the endoplasmic reticulum and processing of the polypeptides in protein bodies of developing pea cotyledons. J. Cell Biol. 93:306-313.

8. Derbyshire, E., D.J. Wright, and D. Boulter (1976) Legumin and vicilin storage proteins of legume seeds. Phytochemistry 15:3-24.

9. Doyle, J.J., M.A. Schuler, W.D. Godethe, V. Zenger, R.N. Beachy, and J.L. Slightom (1986) The glycosylated seed storage proteins of Glycine max and Phaseolus vulgaris: Structural homologies of genes and proteins. J. Biol. Chem. 261:9228-9238.

10. Esen, A. (1986) Separation of alcohol-soluble proteins (zeins) from maize into three different fractions by differential solubility. Plant Physiol. 80:623-627.

11. Forde, J., J.-H. Malpica, N.G. Halford, P.R. Shewry, O.D. Anderson, F.C. Green, and B.J. Miflin (1985) The nucleotide sequence of a HMW glutenin subunit gene located on chromosome 1A of wheat (Triticum aestinum L.). Nucl. Acids Res. 13:6817-6832.

12. Galili, G., E.E. Kawata, R.E. Cuellar, L.D. Smith, and B.A. Larkins (1986) Synthetic oligonucleotide tails inhibit in vitro and in vivo translation of zein mRNAs from maize endosperm. Nucl. Acids Res. 14:1511-1524.

13. Hagen, G., and I. Rubenstein (1981) Complex organization of zein genes in maize. Gene 13:239-249.

14. Larkins, B.A. (1981) Seed storage proteins: Characterization and biosynthesis. In The Biochemistry of Plants: A Comprehensive Treatise, Vol. VI. Proteins and Nucleic Acids, A. Marcus, ed. Academic Press, Inc., New York, pp. 449-489.

15. Nelson, O.E. (1979) Genetic modification of protein quality in plants. Adv. Agron. 21:171-194.

16. Okita, T.W., V. Cheesbrough, and C.D. Reeves (1985) Evolution and heterogeneity of the α/β-type and γ-type gliadin DNA sequences. J. Biol. Chem. 260:8203-8213.

17. Sengupta-Gopalan, C., N.A. Reichert, R.F. Barker, T.C. Hall, and J.D. Kemp (1985) Developmentally regulated expression of the bean β-phaseolin gene in tobacco seed. Proc. Natl. Acad. Sci., USA 82:3320-3324.

18. Sugiyama, T., A. Rafalski, D. Peterson, and D. Soll (1985) A wheat HMW glutenin subunit gene reveals a highly repeated structure. Nucl. Acids Res. 13:8729-8737.

19. Tatham, A.S., P.R. Shewry, and B.J. Miflin (1984) Wheat gluten elasticity: A similar molecular basis to elastin. FEBS Lett. 177:205-208.

20. Wilson, D.R., and B.A. Larkins (1984) Zein gene organization in maize and related grasses. J. Mol. Evol. 29:330-340.

EXPRESSION OF SEQUENCES OF TOBACCO MOSAIC VIRUS IN TRANSGENIC PLANTS

AND THEIR ROLE IN DISEASE RESISTANCE

Roger N. Beachy, D.M. Stark, C.M. Deom,
M.J. Oliver, and R.T. Fraley

Plant Biology Program
Department of Biology
Washington University
St. Louis, Missouri 63130

SUMMARY

Recently, it was reported that transgenic tobacco plants that express the coat protein gene of tobacco mosaic virus (TMV) exhibit a degree of resistance to infection by TMV (11). To determine whether the expression of other viral sequences would also confer resistance, transgenic plants were produced which expressed TMV nucleotides (nt) 3335 to 6395 (representing approximately 52% of the viral genome), their complement (antisense), or nucleotides that encode the 30-kDa protein. Plants that expressed the coat protein gene or other viral RNA sequences were inoculated with TMV and observed for development of disease symptoms. Symptoms were delayed only if transgenic plants expressed the coat protein gene; i.e., plants that express other sequences of TMV, of either the sense or antisense polarity, developed disease symptoms simultaneous with nontransgenic plants. The results indicate that the resistance to TMV infection is greater in transgenic plants that express the viral coat protein gene than in plants that express other sequences of TMV RNA.

INTRODUCTION

The recent development of technologies for introducing genes into plants by transformation has led to the expression of a number of "foreign" genes in transgenic plants. Examples include expression of light-regulated genes (8,13) and genes that are expressed in developing embryos (1). More recently, this approach has been applied to studies of pathogenesis and the induction of disease resistance. It was demonstrated in our laboratory that introduction and expression of a gene encoding the TMV coat protein in transgenic tobacco plants yielded plants that were partially resistant to infection by TMV (11). Transgenic plants that expressed the TMV coat protein gene and that were subsequently inoculated with TMV either developed disease symptoms more slowly than plants which did not express the coat protein gene, or escaped infection and/or disease development. The results

169

of other experiments (R.S. Nelson, P. Powell Abel, and R.N. Beachy, submitted for publ.) demonstrated that plants which did not develop disease symptoms did not have TMV in their upper leaves, indicating that they were not infected. Ongoing research in our laboratory is directed toward determining if single or multiple mechanisms are involved in the observed delay in, or absence of, disease development. These studies will be reported at a later time. The results of these early experiments lead us to suggest that these transgenic plants are protected against TMV infection, and that this protection was similar to plants that are cross-protected against virus infections (6).

In addition to experiments involving the TMV coat protein gene, we have carried out similar experiments with other sequences of TMV in an effort to determine whether resistance can be induced by sequences other than those of the TMV coat protein. Therefore, we introduced sequences from other regions of the TMV genome into tobacco plants and compared the level of the disease resistance in these plants with the resistance in plants that expressed the TMV coat protein gene. The results of those experiments are described here.

METHODS AND MATERIALS

Cloning and Expression of Sequences of Tobacco
Mosaic Virus RNA in Transgenic Plants

The genome of TMV is encoded in its 6,395-nt virion RNA (5), which is of the messenger polarity. Using the cloning strategy previously described (11), cloned complementary DNAs (cDNAs) representing nt 3335 to 6395 were prepared. Restriction enzyme maps of the cloned cDNAs agreed with those for TMV as determined by Goelet et al. (5). The cDNA clone containing nt 3335 to 6395 resulted from ligating cDNAs containing approximately 1 kb (nt 3335 to 4254) and 2 kb (nt 4254 to 6395) of the TMV sequence. The resultant cDNA clone therefore included sequences that contained the carboxy-terminal region of the 180-kDa polypeptide (proposed to be involved in replication of viral RNA), the 30-kDa protein (proposed to be instrumental in spread of TMV from cell to cell), and the coat protein gene (17.5 kDa). A map of the region as cloned is presented in Fig. 1. A cloned cDNA containing only the 30-kDa gene (nt 4872 to 5868) was prepared as described (9). Cloned cDNAs containing either nt 3335 to 6395 or nt 4872 to 5868 were placed under the control of the 35S promoter of cauliflower mosaic virus (CaMV) and were flanked at the 3' end by the nopaline synthetase 3' polyadenylation signal. This was accomplished by using the intermediate plasmid pMON316 (12). In addition to having the 35S promoter and the nopaline synthetase 3' end, this plasmid contains a segment of DNA that allows homologous integration with an octopine-type Ti plasmid, a chimeric gene encoding neomycin phosphotransferase (providing resistance to kanamycin), and a gene encoding nopaline synthetase. After the intermediate plasmid carrying TMV sequences was co-integrated with the Ti plasmid of a disarmed strain of Agrobacterium tumefaciens, the modified A. tumefaciens was used to transform leaf discs of tobacco (Nicotiana tabacum cv. Xanthi). Plants resistant to kanamycin were regenerated and transferred to the greenhouse. Plants were produced that contain TMV cDNA representing nt 3335 to 6395, inserted in such a way as to give positive-strand RNA (i.e., equivalent to the polarity of TMV RNA), or in an orientation to produce antisense RNA (the polarity opposite to that of TMV RNA). Transformed plants were taken to maturity and seeds collected from self-pollinated flowers.

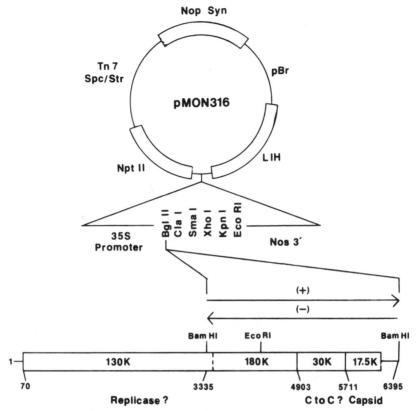

Fig. 1. Construction of intermediate plasmids pMON316:937(+) and pMON316:937(-). Tobacco mosaic virus cDNA is inserted in such an orientation as to give positive-strand RNA, pMON316:937(+), or negative-strand (antisense) RNA, pMON316:937(-).

Analysis of Transgenic Plants Containing Tobacco Mosaic Virus Sequences

Genomic DNA was purified from leaves of transgenic plants and used for Southern blot analyses to examine the organization of the introduced gene and to determine the numbers of copies of TMV DNA in transgenic plants. The methods used for these experiments were similar to those described by Chen et al. (3). The RNA was isolated from leaves of transgenic plants by phenol extraction as previously described (11). Isolation of poly(A)$^{+}$ RNA was carried out by standard procedures (7). The electrophoresis of DNA in agarose gels, the transfer of DNA to nitrocellulose and hybridization with nick-translated ^{32}P-labeled DNA, as well as the separation of RNA in denaturing gels and analysis of those RNAs by blot and hybridization techniques were also as described (7).

Tobacco mosaic virus nt 3335 to 6395 contain sequences of several viral genes, but should not yield TMV coat protein or TMV 30-kDa protein, since RNA molecules produced from such a sequence would not allow for proper initiation of translation. As expected, transgenic plants bearing this construction did not contain TMV coat protein (data not shown).

Testing Transgenic Plants for Resistance to
Virus Infection and Disease Development

Seeds were collected from transgenic plants and seedlings were used in cross-protection experiments for disease resistance. Seedlings were assayed for nopaline production and/or kanamycin resistance to determine the phenotype of the progeny. Seedlings at the three- to four-leaf stage of growth were inoculated with suspensions of TMV U_1 strain and observed for disease development during the following 8 to 14 days. In these experiments seedlings derived from transgenic plants that contained the vector only (i.e., no inserted TMV DNA), and nontransformed plants were also inoculated. As a positive control for disease resistance, seedlings derived from transgenic plants 3404 or 3646 (11), which express the TMV coat protein cDNA and accumulate TMV coat protein, were inoculated with TMV and observed for disease resistance.

RESULTS AND DISCUSSION

As previously reported by Powell Abel et al. (11), transgenic tobacco plants that express the coat protein gene of the common strain of TMV as a chimeric nuclear gene and accumulate TMV coat protein are partially resistant to infection by TMV. This resistance resembles the cross-protection that has been used to confer virus disease resistance in systems in which genetic resistance was not available (6). We have proposed that the resistance caused by such direct gene transfer might be generally applicable to other plant viruses and plant hosts.

To better characterize the nature of the resistance and the specific role of coat protein mRNA versus the coat protein in the reaction, we carried out a number of experiments to address questions related to the efficacy of other viral RNAs or proteins to confer resistance to TMV infection.

Expression of Noncoding Sequences of Tobacco Mosaic Virus
with the Same Polarity as Tobacco Mosaic Virus RNA

In the course of the cDNA cloning of the common strain (U_1) of TMV RNA, a double-stranded cDNA clone representing nt 3335 to 6395 was generated. This cDNA contained a BamHI site at nt 3335, as predicted from the sequence of TMV RNA reported by Goelet et al. (5), and at nt 6395, resulting from the cDNA cloning procedure (11). The BamHI fragment was ligated to the intermediate plasmid pMON316 (12) that was previously restricted by the enzyme BglII (Fig. 1). As described above, this construct should yield in the plant an RNA molecule but not a known viral protein. The modified plasmid was co-integrated with the Ti plasmid BS6S3SE in A. tumefaciens GV3111SE (4). The modified A. tumefaciens was used to transform leaf discs of N. tabacum cv. Xanthi. Transformed cells (selected as kan^r) were regenerated to whole plants and assayed for the presence of TMV DNA sequences and virus-related RNA.

Figure 2 presents the result of a representative experiment to determine the numbers of copies of the cDNA in four different transgenic plants. Each plant contained the equivalent of one copy of the chimeric DNA per haploid tobacco genome. In total, 16 transformants were examined, each of which contained one to two copies of the cDNA per haploid genome. We did not detect rearrangement of the target DNA in any of the plants (data not shown).

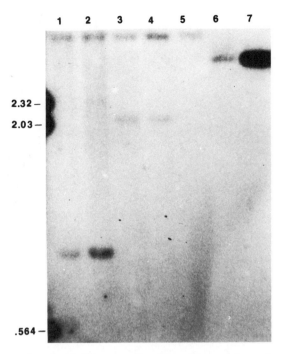

Fig. 2.   Genomic Southern blot analysis to determine the gene copy number
           of transgenic plants expressing positive- or negative-sense TMV
           RNA.   Fifteen μg of genomic DNA from each transgenic plant were
           cut with EcoRI and electrophoresed on a 1% agarose gel.   The
           EcoRI cuts once each in the cDNA and the polylinker region of
           pMON316 (see Fig. 1).   The gel was probed with nick-translated
           cDNA representing sequences 3335 to 6395 of the TMV genome.
           Lambda DNA cut with HindIII was used as a size standard (indicat-
           ed to the left in kilobase pairs).   Lanes 1 and 2 represent DNA
           from transgenic plants, designated 201 and 241, respectively (ex-
           pressing antisense viral RNA).   Lanes 3 and 4 represent DNA from
           transgenic plants, designated 283 and 398, respectively (express-
           ing positive-sense viral RNA).   The DNA from plants transformed
           with only the vector is in lane 5.   Lanes 6 and 7 represent DNA
           corresponding to one and five copies per haploid genome, respec-
           tively.

     Expression of the target gene in different transgenic plants varied
considerably.   In six plants in which TMV sequences 3335 to 6395 were present, TMV-related RNA sequences were found in four, with two plants (transformants 283 and 398) containing relatively larger amounts of RNA than in
the other transformants.   In Fig. 3, the result of a northern blot hybridization reaction using total RNA demonstrated that several sizes of TMV-
related RNAs were found in these tissues.   The expected size of the transcript is about 3,300 nt, including sequences added at the 5' end by
ligation to the CaMV 35S promoter, and sequences added by the NOS 3' end
followed by polyadenylation.   The sizes of RNAs detected were from 3.0 kb
to 1.95 kb.   Chromatography on oligo(dT) cellulose demonstrated that
many or all of these TMV-related sequences were polyadenylated (Fig. 3).

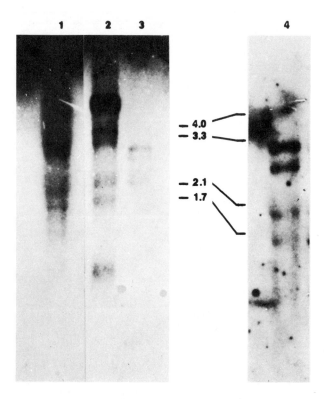

Fig. 3. Northern blot analysis of RNA from transgenic plants expressing
         positive-sense TMV RNA sequences (transformant 283) or negative-
         sense TMV RNA sequences (transformant 241). The RNA was subject-
         ed to electrophoresis on denaturing agarose gels, transferred to
         nitrocellulose, and probed with nick-translated cDNA, represent-
         ing sequences 3335 to 6395 of the TMV genome. The RNA size
         standards are indicated in kilobases. Lane 1 contains 25 µg of
         total RNA from transformant 241. Lanes 2 and 3 contain 8 µg
         of poly(A)$^+$ RNA from transformants 241 and 283, respectively.
         Lane 4 contains 25 µg of total RNA from transformant 283.

Although S_1 mapping was not carried out on these RNAs, we suspect that RNAs
less than the expected size represent molecules that have been spliced or
otherwise processed prior to transport from the nucleus to the cytoplasm.

   To determine the relative amounts of these RNAs in transgenic plants
compared to another mRNA, a northern blot containing 25 µg of RNA from
these transgenic plants, plants containing antisense viral RNA (described
below), and those containing TMV coat protein mRNA were compared (data not
shown). The latter are progeny of plants that were previously shown to be
resistant to infection by TMV (11). These RNAs were hybridized to ^{32}P-
labeled cDNAs containing TMV nt 5704 to 6395 (the coat protein gene sequences). Although the amounts of these RNAs could not be precisely quantitated in these experiments, our experiences strongly suggest that the
amounts of RNA differ by not more than 5X in these plants (data not shown).

To determine whether plants expressing TMV nt 3335 to 6395 were resistant to TMV infection and disease development, transgenic plants were first taken to flowers, self-pollinated, and mature seeds were collected. Three-fourths of the resulting seedlings are expected to inherit the target gene. Leaf disc samples were taken from each seedling and plated on medium containing kanamycin to identify transformed seedlings. Two leaves of a three-leaf seedling were then inoculated with a suspension containing 0.01 or 0.1 µg TMV per ml (sufficient to produce approximately 10 to 100 necrotic local lesions per <u>Xanthi</u> nc leaf). Plants were placed in a growth chamber, and the development of disease symptoms was observed. As a positive control for resistance, seedlings of transformant 3404 (which produce the TMV coat protein) were inoculated with TMV. Nontransformed seedlings of <u>N. tabacum</u> cv. <u>Xanthi</u>, or plants that contain the plasmid pMON316 without TMV sequences, served as nonresistant controls. As shown in Fig. 4, transgenic plants expressing TMV nt 3335 to 6395 (progeny of plant 283) exhibited disease symptoms by four or five days after inoculation, concurrent with disease development in control plants. By contrast, seedlings of transformant 3404 that produce the TMV coat protein either escaped infection, of if

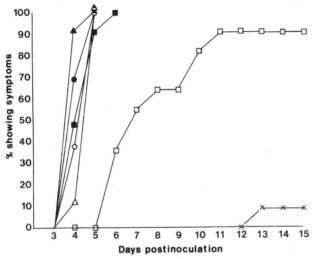

Fig. 4.   The percentage of plants showing systemic symptoms of TMV infection at successive days following inoculation with purified TMV. Seedlings were germinated and assayed for kanamycin expression (transgenic line 283) or nopaline synthetase activity (transgenic lines 306 and 3404). Transgenic line 306 was transformed with vector alone. Transgenic line 3404 expresses TMV coat protein and shows resistance to TMV disease development (11). The two youngest expanding leaves of seedlings at the six- to seven-leaf stage were inoculated with a suspension of TMV; carborundum was used as an abrasive. Seedlings were placed in a greenhouse and observed daily for the presence of systemic symptoms of TMV infection. Seedlings infected with a TMV concentration of 0.01 µg/ml: o, line 283 (16 expressors); Δ, <u>Xanthi</u> (12 seedlings); X, line 3404 (11 expressors). Seedlings infected with a TMV concentration of 0.1 µg/ml: •, line 283 (56 expressors); ■, line 306 (33 expressors); ▲, <u>Xanthi</u> (43 seedlings); □, line 3404 (11 expressors).

infected, developed symptoms of the disease significantly later than the control plants. On the basis of this comparison we concluded that plants expressing TMV nt 3335 to 6395 possess not more than 1% of the level of resistance as do the plants that produce the coat protein. This result suggests that an important feature of the resistance in transgenic plants does not rely on the RNA molecule per se, but rather on the coat protein molecule encoded by the RNA.

Expression of Viral Antisense RNA in Transgenic Plants

We also wished to determine the potential for using antisense viral RNA to control virus infection and disease development. Therefore the double-stranded cDNA representing TMV nt 3335 to 6935 was ligated to the BglII site in pMON316 such that the CaMV 35S promoter would direct the production of RNA complementary to TMV RNA. The expected transcript would be capped near nucleotide (-) 6395 of TMV RNA, and polyadenylation would follow nucleotide (-) 3335. Demonstration that transgenic tobacco plants contained the chimeric DNA is presented in a genomic Southern blot in Fig. 2. As described above, most of the transgenic plants examined contained a single copy of the chimeric DNA fragment. To demonstrate expression of the chimeric gene, RNA was isolated from leaves of transgenic plants and hybridized first to RNA that was the polarity of TMV RNA produced by SP6 polymerase from plasmids (Promega Biotech, Madison, Wisconsin) containing the cloned cDNA. The RNA molecules that accumulated in transgenic plants are presented in Fig. 3. In addition to RNA of the expected size (∿3.3 kb), molecules larger, as well as smaller, than 3.3 kb were detected. The largest RNA (∿5 kb) presumably results from termination of the transcript 3' of the NOS polyadenylation site in pMON316. Similar results were observed for the coat protein mRNA (11). Most or each of the RNAs are polyadenylated as reflected in selection by oligo(dT) cellulose chromatography (Fig. 3). The relative amount of (-) sense TMV RNA sequence in these plants compared to (+) sense TMV RNA sequence is not more than 5X different than the amount of coat protein mRNA present in transgenic plant 3404. This result indicates that the transgenic plants used in these experiments contained approximately equivalent amounts of (-) TMV RNA and (+) TMV RNA sequences 3335 to 6395.

As in the experiments described above, seedlings of the transgenic plants that expressed the (-) TMV RNA sequences were tested for their resistance to infection by TMV. Seedlings were inoculated on two or three leaves with 0.01, 0.05, 0.1, 0.5, or 1.0 µg of TMV per ml, and observed for disease development. Seedlings derived from plants that produce the TMV coat protein were inoculated with 0.5 µg/ml, which was sufficient to produce 100 to 500 necrotic lesions per leaf on the tobacco cultivar Xanthi nc. As shown in Tab. 1, nontransformed seedlings and seedlings derived from transgenic plants containing (-) TMV RNA sequences developed disease symptoms at essentially the same time. This was true at each virus inoculum concentration used.

In contrast, seedlings of transgenic plant 3648, which expresses TMV coat protein, developed disease symptoms significantly later in time. In these plants inoculated with 0.5 µg TMV per ml, symptoms were seen in about 20% of plants by day 6. Disease developed on control seedlings and transgenic plants expressing (-) TMV RNA by day 4 or day 5, regardless of the concentration of TMV in the inoculum (1.0 µg/ml to 0.01 µg/ml).

Tab. 1. Disease development after tobacco mosaic virus (TMV) inoculation of transgenic tobacco plants expressing antisense TMV sequences.

Transformant	Concentration TMV (μg/ml)	Days postinoculation							
		3	4	5	6	7	8	9	10
241	0.05	0	0	90	100	--	--	--	--
241	0.10	0	0	85	95	95	95	95	95
241	0.50	0	0	100	--	--	--	--	--
241	1.00	0	0	100	--	--	--	--	--
3648	0.50	0	0	0	21	64	85	93	100
201	0.01	0	20	95	95	95	100	--	--
Xanthi	0.01	0	33	83	83	83	100	--	--
201	0.05	0	70	100	--	--	--	--	--
Xanthi	0.05	0	83	100	--	--	--	--	--

Transformants 201 and 241 express antisense TMV RNA sequences 3335 to 6395. Transformant 3648 produces the TMV coat protein and serves as a positive control for disease resistance. Nicotiana tabacum var. Xanthi is a nontransformed systemic host of TMV. Two to three leaves of plants at the same stage of development were inoculated with a solution containing increasing concentrations of TMV, and plants were placed in a greenhouse for observation of disease symptom development. Numbers indicate the percentage of plants showing disease symptoms.

Taken together, these results indicate that using relatively high molecular weight RNA molecules complementary to TMV RNA has little or no effect on infection by TMV, or on the development of disease. The limits of our conclusions are based upon several important features of these experiments. First, although expression of the antisense RNA is driven by a strong promoter, other promoters might produce higher levels of expression. Higher levels of (-) RNA than we achieved in these experiments might indeed produce some levels of resistance.

Second, for these experiments we used (-) RNA sequences between nt 3335 and 6395 and observed little or no protection. It is possible that other TMV sequences would be more effective. For example, we previously showed that oligodeoxynucleotides covering a portion of the 5' end of TMV RNA could hybrid-arrest the translation of TMV RNA in vitro (2). It can be predicted that if these sequences were expressed as (-) RNA, a similar effect may be observed in vivo.

Third, the level of resolution of the assay for disease resistance in our experiments is limited to the sensitivity of the experiment. Inoculating the control and transgenic seedlings at a TMV concentration of 0.01 μg/ml caused all of the plants to become infected. If it was possible to achieve 100% infection of the control plants if the inoculum level was 10% or 1% of that level, we might detect a level of resistance in plants that express antisense sequences of TMV RNA. However, under current conditions we can say only that plants expressing (-) TMV RNA do not exhibit more than 1% of the level of resistance of the plants that produce TMV coat protein.

Effect of Expression of Messenger RNA Encoding
the 30-kDa Protein on Disease Resistance

To examine the possibility that a reading frame encoding a viral protein, other than that encoding the coat protein, could cause or induce protection, a cloned cDNA encoding the 30-kDa protein was expressed in transgenic plants, and the plants were evaluated for disease resistance. The
cDNA cloning of the 30-kDa gene is presented elsewhere (9). The expression
and biological activity of this gene in transgenic plants are currently being evaluated (C.M. Deom, M.J. Oliver, and R.N. Beachy, work in progress).

A number of different transgenic plants were examined for accumulation
of the TMV 30-kDa mRNA, and several were shown to produce an amount of mRNA
comparable to the amounts of coat protein mRNA produced in transgenic
plants (data to be presented elsewhere). Seedlings that did not accumulate
nopaline (nop$^-$) were assumed to be negative for the 30-kDa gene, while
those that were nop$^+$ were assumed to express the 30-kDa gene. These seedlings, as well as seedlings that contain the vector alone, were inoculated
with TMV at a concentration of 0.25 µg/ml, placed in the greenhouse, and
observed for symptom development. As shown in Tab. 2, each group of plants
developed symptoms concurrently. Thus there was not an indication that expression of the TMV 30-kDa gene caused a delay of symptoms of infection
equivalent to the resistance when the TMV coat protein gene was expressed.
These results indicate that the resistance in plants that express TMV coat
protein was related to the expression of a subset of the TMV sequences,
rather than all TMV coding sequences.

Tab. 2. Disease development after TMV inoculation of transgenic tobacco
         plants expressing 30-kDa protein sequences.

Transformant	Days postinoculation				
	4	5	6	7	8
285 E	0	0	64	93	93
NE	0	17	67	83	100
274 E	0	0	43	86	93
NE	0	0	50	83	83
306 E	0	0	67	100	--
NE	0	0	38	100	--
Xanthi	0	10	75	90	95

Transgenic lines 285 and 274 express mRNA encoding the TMV
30-kDa protein. Transgenic line 306 is described in the
legend to Fig. 4. Seedlings were assayed for the expression of nopaline synthetase. E, progeny that express
nopaline synthetase; NE, progeny that do not express nopaline synthetase. Seedlings were infected with a TMV suspension (0.25 µg/ml) and maintained as described in the
legend to Fig. 4. Numbers in the table represent the percentage of seedlings showing systemic symptoms of TMV
infection. For each transgenic line, 11 expressors and 11
nonexpressors were tested for disease development.

CONCLUSIONS

During the last five to ten years, a number of articles have been written that suggested a number of approaches that might be taken to produce plants that are resistant to virus infections. In these articles it was proposed that plant cells producing an RNA molecule that is complementary to a viral RNA may arrest translation or replication of viral RNA (10). However, no experimental evidence has been presented that verifies such resistance in whole plants.

As shown by Powell Abel et al. (11) and in Fig. 4, the expression of the TMV coat protein gene and the accumulation of coat protein in transgenic plants conferred resistance to TMV infection. In contrast, the transcription of other TMV sequences in transgenic plants did not provide protection against virus infection. Transgenic plants that produced (+) or (−) polarity sequences of TMV nt 3335 to 6395, but which are not expected to generate a viral protein, failed to provide protection greater than 1% of the protection given by expression of the coat protein gene. Whether similar results will be observed with sequences of TMV other than those used here, or with other plant virus:host combinations, remains to be determined. Our results indicate, however, that expression of (−) TMV RNA sequences had substantially less (if any) efficacy for protection against TMV than predicted or hoped for (10).

Other research in our laboratory is directed toward identifying the mechanism or mechanisms responsible for the resistance in transgenic plants that produce the TMV coat protein (11). Recent results indicate that transgenic plants have a reduced number of sites of infection for TMV as compared to nontransformed plants (R.S. Nelson, P. Powell Abel, and R.N. Beachy, submitted for publ.). This results in some plants that escape infection. Plants that become infected and that develop disease symptoms do so significantly later in time than the control plants (i.e., plants that do not express the TMV coat protein gene). Other results indicate that the spread of virus throughout the plant is slowed; the nature of this reduced spread is also not understood (P. Powell Abel, R.S. Nelson, and R.N. Beachy, work in progress). However, the use of the techniques of gene modification and plant transformation provides the tools to fully understand this disease resistance, and its application to other plant virus:host interactions.

REFERENCES

1. Beachy, R.N. Z.-L. Chen, R.B. Horsch, S.G. Rogers, N.J. Hoffmann, and R.T. Fraley (1985) Accumulation and assembly of soybean β-conglycinin in seeds of transformed petunia plants. EMBO J. 4:3047-3053.
2. Beachy, R.N., P. Abel, M.J. Oliver, B. De, R.T. Fraley, S.G. Rogers, and R.B. Horsch (1985) Potential for applying genetic transformation to studies of viral pathogenesis and cross-protection. In Biotechnology in Plant Science: Relevance to Agriculture in the Nineteen Eighties, M. Zaitlin, P. Day, and A. Hollaender, eds. Academic Press, Inc., New York, pp. 265-275.
3. Chen, Z.-L., M.A. Schuler, and R.N. Beachy (1986) Functional analysis of regulatory elements in a plant embryo-specific gene. Proc. Natl. Acad. Sci., USA Vol. 83 (in press).

4. Fraley, R.T., S.G. Rogers, R.B. Horsch, D.A. Eichholtz, J.S. Flick, C.L. Fink, N.A. Hoffmann, and P.R. Sanders (1985) The SEV system: A new disarmed Ti plasmid vector for plant transformation. Bio/Technology 3:629-635.

5. Goelet, P., G.P. Lomonossoff, P.J.G. Butler, M.E. Aham, M.J. Gait, and J. Karn (1982) Nucleotide sequence of tobacco mosaic virus RNA. Proc. Natl. Acad. Sci., USA 79:5818-5822.

6. Hamilton, R.I. (1980) Defenses triggered by previous invaders: Viruses. In Plant Disease, Vol. V, Academic Press, Inc., New York, pp. 279-303.

7. Maniatis, T., E.F. Fritsch, and J. Sambrook (1982) Molecular Cloning, Cold Spring Harbor Laboratory, Cold Spring Harbor, New York.

8. Morelli, G.M., F. Nagy, R.T. Fraley, S.G. Rogers, and N.H. Chua (1985) A short conserved sequence is involved in the light-inducibility of a gene encoding ribulose 1,5-biphosphate carboxylase small subunit of pea. Nature (London) 31:200-204.

9. Oliver, M.J., C.M. Deom, B.K. De, and R.N. Beachy (1986) In vitro transcription and translation of cloned cDNA encoding the 30-kDa protein gene of TMV. Virology Vol. 155 (in press).

10. Palukaitis, P., and M. Zaitlin (1984) A model to explain the "cross-protection" phenomenon shown by plant viruses and viroids. In Plant-Microbe Interactions. Vol. 1, T. Kosuge and E. Nester, eds. Macmillan Publishing Company, New York, pp. 420-429.

11. Powell Abel, P., R.S. Nelson, B. De, N. Hoffmann, S.G. Rogers, R.T. Fraley, and R.N. Beachy (1986) Delay of disease development in transgenic tobacco plants that express the tobacco mosaic virus coat protein gene. Science 232:738-743.

12. Rogers, S.G., K. O'Connell, R. Horsch, and R.T. Fraley (1986) Investigation of factors involved in foreign protein expression in transformed plants. In Biotechnology in Plant Science: Relevance to Agriculture in the Nineteen Eighties, M. Zaitlin, P. Day, and A. Hollaender, eds. Academic Press, Inc., New York, pp. 219-226.

13. Timko, M.P., A.P. Kausch, C. Castresana, J. Fassler, L. Herrera-Estrella, G. Van den Broeck, M. Van Montagu, J. Schell, and A.R. Cashmore (1985) Light regulation of plant gene expression by an upstream enhancer-like element. Nature (London) 318:579-582.

SCIENTIFIC STRATEGIES FOR THE FUTURE

VISUAL ASSAYS OF TRANSFORMATION IN PLANT CELLS

Virginia Walbot, Jeffrey R. de Wet, and Michael Fromm

Department of Biological Sciences
Stanford University
Stanford, California   94305

SUMMARY

We discuss the utility of visual assays for the expression of genes introduced into plant cells. Such assays are valuable for both transient and stable gene expression studies. We review the properties of three visual assays that are already in use or under development phase for maize and other cereal crops. These assays depend on the expression of β-galactosidase, luciferase, or structural genes required for anthocyanin pigment biosynthesis.

INTRODUCTION

DNA can be readily introduced into cells of many dicot species by exploiting the capacity of <u>Agrobacterium</u> <u>tumefaciens</u> to transfer segments of its plasmid DNA to plant cells (5,14). In addition, DNA enters both monocot and dicot protoplasts after specific treatments, such as, incubation with polyethylene glycol (15,19), DEAE-dextran (13), spheroplasts of <u>Escherichia</u> <u>coli</u> (22), or liposomes (1); electroporation is also effective in stimulating DNA entry into cells (9,10), and a combination of these methods has also been successful (21). Much of the DNA which enters the cells remains extrachromosomal and is not incorporated into the host's chromosomes; such DNA is, however, transiently expressed for several days to several weeks after transfection. Some introduced DNA is stably incorporated into the chromosomes and will then be replicated during mitosis and maintained in the cells.

Detection of gene expression from DNA transiently maintained in cells usually relies on detection of chloramphenicol acetyl transferase (CAT) activity (see Ref. 9 and 13), because a sensitive assay exists for this enzymatic function and most, but not all, plant species contain little endogenous activity. Detection of gene expression in stable transformants is usually achieved by selection for antibiotic resistance [often kanamycin resistance conferred by neomycin phosphotransferase (NPTII) activity

(10,14)] followed by a radioactive assay for the presence of the appropriate enzyme activity and, finally, hybridizational analysis of transformant
DNA to confirm the presence of the introduced gene construct.

An important limitation in both the CAT and NPTII enzymatic assays is
that the cells must be destroyed to obtain data. And, although these methods are very sensitive, some kinds of information are not readily obtained.
For example, in transient expression studies, what fraction of the protoplasts are expressing the introduced gene? Does the level of expression
vary among the protoplast population? Is there a specific morphological
type of protoplast more likely to express introduced DNA than other protoplast types? In studies of stable transformants, it is difficult to determine whether expression of a construct is uniform throughout a tissue mass,
for example, by comparing surface to inner cells, and whether expression is
varying over time.

In situ visual assays of gene expression could, in theory, be used to
provide answers to some of these questions because single cells can be
scored as either expressing or not expressing a particular trait. Ideally,
such assays should be nondestructive, allowing continual or periodic as-
sessment of the same cell or population of cells. Thus, physiological
experiments on a transiently expressing or transformed cell(s) could determine the kinetics of gene activation following experimental treatment; for
example, the properties of a heat shock promoter could be assayed by following the production of a pigment in cells in specific temperature re-
gimes. Visual assays could also be useful in screening for rare events as,
for example, might be encountered in the growth of $\underline{A}$. tumefaciens on monocots (12). Such assays might also be amenable to automation, using a cell
sorter or other scanning device either to count the frequency of transformation or even to select appropriately marked cells.

Limitations of visual assays of gene expression are in most ways similar to the limitations of assays based on extraction and enzymatic reactions. The lower limit of detection will be influenced by whether or not a
background of similar activity exists in some cell types and by the sensitivity of the detection method. An important difference between visual
assays and the currently used CAT and NPTII assays is that signal strength
in the latter is increased by lengthening the enzymatic assay or autoradio-
graphic exposure time while, in visual assays, signal strength depends on
the capacity of individual cells to accumulate pigment or the luciferin
substrate for a light production assay. Thus, the parameters of the assay
are not as readily manipulated in cells as in a cell extract.

In the next section we outline three in situ visual assays and discuss
their individual advantages and disadvantages. Two of these assays are now
established and one is still under development.

PROPERTIES OF THREE IN SITU ASSAYS

Beta-Galactosidase

Beta-galactosidase cleaves the colorless substrate 5-bromo-4-chloro-3-
indolyl β-D-galactopyranoside into an insoluble, bright blue reaction product. This assay is routinely used in bacterial genetics to detect the
presence of plasmids carrying the lacZ gene (β-galactosidase) of E. coli.

Chimeric genes containing the bacterial gene under the control of the cauliflower mosaic virus (CaMV) 35S promoter have been used in transient gene expression assays to estimate the fraction of tobacco protoplasts that are successfully electroporated with the construct (8). The limitations to this assay are: (i) a high level of expression is required to obtain a blue color visible to the human eye, thus, cells expressing a low level of enzyme activity will be missed; (ii) some cell types may have sufficient endogenous β-galactosidase activity to interfere with the assay; (iii) the cells must be permeabilized to allow uptake of the chromogenic substrate.

Despite these limitations, several useful observations have been made with this assay (8,11). For example, electroporation treatment has yielded populations in which about 10% of the protoplasts turned blue. Furthermore, the morphologically normal protoplasts containing a central vacuole and numerous strands of cytoplasm showed the highest expression, suggesting that most of the activity in a transient assay is from the healthiest cells.

Anthocyanin Pigment Deposition

Much is known about the regulation of anthocyanin pigment accumulation in a variety of plant species. A number of genes encoding enzymes of the pigment biosynthetic pathway have already been cloned (4,17). In maize with a genetic background deficient in one step of the pathway, all of the other enzymes are present but pigment biosynthesis is blocked; however, purple pigment develops within 24 hr if the block is overcome by exogenously providing the appropriate substrate (16). Although anthocyanins are nontoxic metabolites and accumulate to high levels in many plant cell types, pigment deposition is rarely this rapid in intact, genetically competent plant tissue. Consequently, a visual assay based on anthocyanin accumulation might require several days of cell metabolism to accumulate sufficient pigment. Once present, anthocyanin pigmentation is readily scored by microscopic inspection in individual maize cells, as carried out in many studies on transposable element activities.

To develop anthocyanin pigmentation as a suitable assay for transient or stable expression of introduced DNA, cells deficient in one step in the biosynthetic pathway will be required. Because anthocyanin deposition in genetically competent plants is tightly regulated as to tissue distribution, cells from an appropriate part of the plant will be required. Provided the genes of the pathway are expressed, even at low levels, there is likely to be sufficient existing substrate in such cells to accomplish a transient assay and to develop a purple color. For assays of stable transformation in cultured cells, it is unknown to what extent the pigment biosynthetic pathway will remain turned on. There are some reports in the literature of maintenance of purple callus in culture for extended periods (20), however, the pigment accumulation occurred in the slowest growing portions of the culture. Thus, a number of parameters must be worked out to test the feasibility of introducing genes required for anthocyanin pigment synthesis into cells derived directly from plants or protoplasts from tissue culture material. The advantage to using anthocyanin pigmentation as a marker gene is that much is already known about the regulation of this pathway, suggesting that manipulation of these genes and the genetic background of the cells into which they are introduced will be a fruitful avenue of future investigation.

Luciferase and Light Production

The previous two assays have relied on deposition of a visibly colored molecule over an extended period of time (i.e., hours or days). An alternative is the expression of firefly luciferase in plant cells followed by provision of substrate to cell lysates or intact cells. The firefly luciferase gene has been cloned recently (2) and sequenced, and its expression has been demonstrated in eukaryotic cells (18), including maize (J.R. de Wet, unpubl. data) under the control of appropriate promoters. Substrate luciferin is transported or diffuses through cellular membranes, allowing an in situ assay of light emission. Light is most conveniently measured in a luminometer, although a scintillation counter can also be used.

The advantages to this assay are the ease of sample preparation and rapid assay; highly sensitive light detectors are available, and there is essentially no background in plant tissues. In addition, the substrate cost is less than 10% that of radioactively labeled chloramphenicol and the sensitivity is probably ten-fold or more greater than typical transient assays.

The major disadvantage of this assay is that a relatively brief flash of light is emitted in cell lysate assays, requiring either control of substrate injection to initiate the reaction or carefully timed reactions to insure that maximal light emission is measured. In a stable transformation or intact cell assay this aspect of the assay is less of a difficulty, but diffusion or transport of the luciferin substrate may not be uniform, resulting in difficulties in evaluating the relative expression of one cell type to another or within tissue heterogeneity. Despite these problems, the luciferase assay seems to be the most sensitive in situ assay available.

CONCLUSIONS

In situ assays for gene expression are useful in identifying individual cells or tissues with a novel trait or level of expression of an introduced gene. Such assays are useful in both transient and stable transformation situations and, if nondestructive, allow continuous monitoring of the same cells over time. At present, conditions have been established for two in situ assays: β-galactosidase and luciferase. The enzymes are useful markers when coupled to regulated plant promoters. Appropriate cloned plant genes exist to develop any additional assays based on various genes of the anthocyanin biosynthetic pathway; such an assay would capitalize on well-defined genetic stocks and normal plant biosynthetic activities to define the molecular basis for the regulation of expression. Another plant gene potentially useful in an in situ assay is alcohol dehydrogenase (ADH) activity, because ADH activity can be detected in individual cells (3). However, because normal plants do express ADH, null mutants would have to be utilized as the tissue source (6,7).

ACKNOWLEDGEMENTS

We thank the Rockefeller Foundation and the National Institutes of Health (GM32422) for support of our research program. M.F. was supported by a gift from Pioneer Hi-Bred International; J.R.D. was supported by a training grant in Cancer Biology at Stanford University (CA09302).

REFERENCES

1. Deshayes, A., L. Herrera-Estrella, and M. Caboche (1985) Liposome-mediated transformation of tobacco mesophyll protoplasts by an Escherichia coli plasmid. EMBO J. 4:2731-2737.
2. de Wet, J., K.V. Wood, D.R. Helinski, and M. De Luca (1985) Cloning of firefly luciferase cDNA and the expression of active luciferase in Escherichia coli. Proc. Natl. Acad. Sci., USA 82:7870-7873.
3. Döring, H.-P., M. Freeling, S. Hake, M.A. Johns, R. Kunze, A. Merckelbach, F. Salamini, and P. Starlinger (1984) A Ds-mutation of the Adhl gene in Zea mays L. Mol. Gen. Genet. 193:199-204.
4. Fedoroff, N.V., D.B. Furtek, and O.E. Nelson, Jr. (1984) Cloning of the bronze locus in maize by a simple and generalizable procedure using the transposable controlling element Activator (Ac). Proc. Natl. Acad. Sci., USA 81:3825-3829.
5. Fraley, R.T., R.B. Horsch, A. Matzke, M.-D. Chilton, and P.R. Sanders (1984) In vitro transformation of petunia cells by an improved method of co-cultivation with A. tumefaciens. Plant Mol. Biol. 3:371-378.
6. Freeling, M., and J.A. Birchler (1981) Mutants and variants of the alcohol dehydrogenase-1 gene in maize. In Genetic Engineering: Principles and Methods, Vol. 5, J.K. Setlow and A. Hollaender, eds. Plenum Press, New York, pp. 45-60.
7. Freeling, M., and D.C. Bennett (1985) Maize Adhl. Ann. Rev. Genet. 19:297-323.
8. Fromm, M., and V. Walbot (1986) Transient expression of DNA in plant cells. In Advances in Plant Gene Research, T. Hohn et al., eds. Springer-Verlag, New York (in press).
9. Fromm, M., L.P. Taylor, and V. Walbot (1985) Expression of genes transferred into monocot and dicot plant cells by electroporation. Proc. Natl. Acad. Sci., USA 82:5824-5828.
10. Fromm, M., L.P. Taylor, and V. Walbot (1986) Stable transformation of maize after gene transfer by electroporation. Nature 319:791-793.
11. Helmer, G., M. Casadaban, M. Bevan, L. Kayes, and M.-D. Chilton (1984) A new chimaeric gene as a marker for plant transformation. Bio/Technology 2:520-527.
12. Hernalsteens, J.-P., L. Thia-Toong, J. Schell, and M. Van Montagu (1984) An Agrobacterium-transformed cell culture from the monocot Asparagus officinalis. EMBO J. 3:3039-3041.
13. Howard, E.A., K.J. Danna, E.S. Dennis, and W.J. Peacock (1985) Transient expression in maize protoplasts. In Plant Genetics, M. Freeling, ed. Alan R. Liss, Inc., New York, pp. 225-234.
14. Krens, F.H., L. Molendijk, G.J. Wullems, and R.A. Schilperoort (1982) In vitro transformation of plant protoplasts with Ti-plasmid DNA. Nature 296:72-74.
15. Lörz, H., B. Baker, and J. Schell (1985) Gene transfer to cereal cells mediated by protoplast transformation. Mol. Gen. Genet. 199:178-182.
16. McCormick, S. (1978) Pigment synthesis in maize aleurone from precursors fed to anthocyanin mutants. Biochem. Genet. 16:777-785.
17. O'Reilly, C., N.S. Shepherd, A. Perieira, A. Schwartz-Sommer, I. Bertram, D.S. Robertson, P.A. Peterson, and H. Saedler (1985) Molecular cloning of the al locus of Zea mays using the transposable elements En and Mul. EMBO J. 4:877-882.
18. Ow, D.W., K.V. Wood, M. DeLuca, J.R. de Wet, D.R. Helinski, and S.H. Howell (1986) Transient and stable expression of the firefly luciferase gene in plant cells and transgenic plants. Science 234:856-859.

19. Potrykus, I., M.W. Saul, J. Petruska, J. Paskowski, and R.D. Shillito (1985) Direct gene transfer to cells of a graminaceous monocot. Mol. Gen. Genet. 199:183-188.
20. Racchi, M.L. (1985) Effect of the genes B and Pl on anthocyanin synthesis in maize endosperm culture. Plant Cell Reports 4:184-187.
21. Shillito, R.D., M.W. Saul, J. Paszkowski, M. Müller, and I. Potrykus (1985) High efficiency direct gene transfer to plants. Bio/Technology 3:1099-1103.
22. Tanaka, N., M. Ikesami, T. Hohn, C. Matsui, and I. Watanabe (1984) Escherichia coli spheroplast-mediated transfer of cloned cauliflower mosaic virus into plant protoplasts. Mol. Gen. Genet. 195:378-380.

FATE AND EXPRESSION OF VECTOR DNA IN PLANT CELLS

Armin P. Czernilofsky, Barbara Baker,
Bruno Gronenborn, Rüdiger Hain, Chris Leaver,*
Volker Matzeit, Ian Moore, Joachim Schalk,
Uwe Wirtz, and Jeff Schell

Max-Planck-Institut für Züchtungsforschung
D-5000 Köln 30, Vogelsang, Federal Republic of Germany

INTRODUCTION

Plant transformation systems based on gene vectors derived from the Ti plasmid of Agrobacterium tumefaciens (16), on direct DNA uptake (6), and on wheat dwarf virus (WDV) DNA (14) were used to introduce a number of chimeric genes into, respectively, tobacco protoplasts, suspension culture cells of Triticum monococcum, and Zea mays. The actual genes involved in these studies were chosen to serve as models for investigating the fate, expression, recombination, and transposition of foreign DNA in plant cells.

Three aspects of plant cell transformation are summarized in this chapter:

(i)   Direct DNA transformation of tobacco protoplasts with selectable marker DNA and recombination of co-transferred, inactivated selectable marker genes to yield intact genes.

(ii) The Ti-plasmid-dependent transformation of tobacco cells with sequences encoding the maize autonomous transposable element Activator (Ac), and subsequent transposition of the element in the heterologous plant.

(iii) Transfection of suspension culture cells of monocotyledonous plants (T. monococcum and Z. mays) with a gemini virus vector.

---

*Department of Botany, University of Edinburgh, Edinburgh, United Kingdom.

STUDIES ON THE STRUCTURE, FUNCTIONAL ORGANIZATION, AND
RECOMBINATION OF FOREIGN DNA IN NICOTIANA TABACUM

Genetic transformation of Nicotiana tabacum protoplasts was achieved
either by incubation of protoplasts with a plasmid DNA-calcium phosphate
co-precipitate, followed by fusion of the protoplasts in the presence of
polyvinyl alcohol and subsequent exposure to high pH (6,8,13), or by a calcium nitrate/polyethylene glycol fusion technique (7,15). Derivatives
(pLGV1103neo or pLGV2103neo) of the plasmid pBR322 containing a chimeric
gene were used for these transformation experiments. These consisted of
the nopaline synthetase promoter, the coding region of the aminoglycoside
phosphotransferase II gene of Tn5 (NPTII), and the polyadenylation signal
region of the octopine synthetase gene. The chimeric gene confers resistance to kanamycin in transformed plant cells. The transformation procedures yielded transformants at frequencies of approximately 0.01% to 0.3%.

To compare the effects of different transformation methods on the integration behavior and structural stability of integrated foreign genes in
plant cells, tobacco protoplasts were also transformed by co-cultivation
with A. tumefaciens harboring the Ti-plasmid derivatives pGV3850::2103neo
or pGV3850::1103neo (6).

The DNA from some of the transformed clones was analyzed by Southern
blot hybridization. The input DNA appears to be integrated into high
molecular weight cellular DNA (3,6). A comparison of the fine structure of
the integrated donor DNA in cells transformed by direct DNA uptake shows
that this DNA undergoes structural changes and concatemerizations, while
the DNA integrated by Agrobacterium-mediated transformation is often un-
altered. The co-transformed nopaline synthetase gene, which is present in
the donor Ti-plasmid DNA, was inactivated in two out of nine cases due to a
deletion in the promoter region. Once integrated, the arrays of selectable
marker DNA appear to be structurally stable under different cell culture
and selection conditions, as well as after genetic transmission (2,3). Genetic analysis of one of the kanamycin-resistant plants shows that the chimeric gene is transmitted to the progeny in a Mendelian fashion as a single
dominant trait (2,6).

Aminoglycoside phosphotransferase II activity was detected in both
transformed calli and regenerated plants. Structural variations observed
in the integrated DNA were correlated with the enzymatic activity of NPTII
detected in the transformed plants. The level of the NPTII activity varies
in independently transformed plants as well as in plants independently regenerated from the same original transformed cells (2). The former observation could be explained by the influence of different integration sites
("position effect"), but the latter observation must be due to either (a)
variation in as yet poorly understood physiological conditions, generating
a heterologous cell population with respect to expression of the foreign
gene, or (b) epigenetic phenomena.

Two different marker genes introduced by direct DNA transfer appear to
be physically linked after integration into the host genome. This linkage
occurred possibly because of recombination events between the different
plasmids which share common sequences (2). In order to evaluate this finding further, pLGV1103neo derivatives were generated by in vitro mutagenesis. The derivatives contained a mutated and inactive Tn5 kanamycin
resistance gene and intact plant regulatory sequences. A second set of
plasmids, designated as "repair plasmids," contained only the Tn5 coding

region, or parts of it, and the bacterial promoter region. These also were generated by in vitro mutagenesis. The pLGV1103neo derivatives and repair plasmids were used for direct DNA uptake co-transformation experiments with protoplasts isolated from N. tabacum. Recombination events that were mediated by homologous sequences produced active NPTII genes, thus rendering the plant cells resistant to kanamycin (15). Analysis of the size of the active enzyme and Southern blot analysis of the integrated donor DNA reveal that precise recombination events (most likely gene conversions) have occurred, producing an NPTII gene that is indistinguishable from the wild-type gene located in the plasmid pLGV1103neo (15).

Presently, we are investigating the recombination mechanisms involved in the reactivation of the deleted NPTII genes described above and in the generation of DNA tandem arrays in tobacco cells. Furthermore, we are exploring the additional possibility of using recombination techniques for target-specific integration into the host genome.

In an extension of this work, the integration of marker genes into organelle genomes is under investigation. Sequences involved in transcription, translation, and recombination, which have been previously isolated from plant mitochondrial genes, will be used to express a selectable marker gene specifically in the mitochondria of transformed tobacco cells.

Expression signals from the cytochrome oxidase subunit I gene of maize mitochondria (9) will be used to induce a selectable chloramphenicol acetyl transferase (CAT) activity in tobacco mitochondria. It has been reported that recombination between repeated sequences is a normal event in the mitochondrial genomes of several species (9,12), and, furthermore, extensive rearrangements in mitochondrial genomes are frequently observed following protoplast fusions (11). Such recombination events and their influence on the integration and stability of foreign DNA in the mitochondrial genome will be investigated using Ti plasmids and direct DNA uptake to transform protoplasts with the selectable marker gene linked in cis to fragments of tobacco mitochondrial DNA or to recombinationally active sequences from other plant mitochondria.

It is hoped that the establishment of such a gene transfer system for plant mitochondria will facilitate further study of their gene expression and genome organization. This will also allow the introduction of foreign sequences that will either provide novel, economically valuable functions or act as cytoplasmic "tags" in somatic hybridization experiments.

WHEAT DWARF VIRUS REPLICATES AND EXPRESSES
FOREIGN GENES IN PLANT TISSUE CULTURE

Wheat dwarf virus is a geminivirus which infects a wide range of species within the Gramineae (10,14). The twinned particles of the WDV contain only one circle of single-stranded DNA as opposed to most geminiviruses of dicotyledonous plants, whose genomes are divided into two circular single-stranded DNA molecules. The size of the WDV genome is 2,749 bases; during replication, it is converted into a double-stranded supercoiled molecule. We have determined the DNA sequence of a cloned copy of the double-stranded replicative form of WDV. From the DNA sequence, five major open reading frames (ORFs) can be deduced. By comparison with the genome of maize streak virus (MSV), the capsid protein gene of WDV has been assigned.

One major viral transcript has been isolated from infected Triticum
and Lolium tissue. It has a length of 1.1 kb and is encoded by the minus-
strand of the virus chromosome. It was mapped by S1 analysis and covers
the coat protein gene and an additional 10.1-kDa ORF preceding the coat
protein gene. Transcripts derived from the plus-strand of the virus are of
low abundance in systemically infected tissue (J. Schalk, J. Schell, and B.
Gronenborn, ms. in prep.).

Wheat dwarf virus is transmitted solely by the leafhopper Psammotettix
alienus; a mechanical transmission has not yet been achieved. Therefore,
the effect of mutations in the genome of WDV on its ability to replicate
was tested in tissue culture. Protoplasts of a T. monococcum suspension
culture cell line were transfected with different WDV recombinants. At
varying intervals after transfection, the total DNA of the cells was isolated and probed for replicating viral sequences in Southern blot experiments. Three to four days post-transfection, replicative forms (ccc- and
oc-form as well as single-stranded DNA) were readily detected. They were
monitored for a period of two weeks.

To test whether the coat protein gene of WDV is essential for replication of the viral genome, the respective gene was replaced by a bacterial
APH 3' II gene which codes for a neomycin phosphotransferase. Protoplasts
of T. monococcum suspension culture cells were transfected, and replication
of the defective transducing viral genome was detected. The expression
of the foreign gene was detected by assaying the activity of the neomycin
phosphotransferase.

In addition, the CAT gene and the β-galactosidase gene of Escherichia
coli were used to replace the coat protein gene. Both genes were replicated and expressed in the same way that the APH 3' II gene was. The insertion of the β-galactosidase gene into the WDV genome doubled its size but
did not interfere with its ability to replicate.

These results indicate that the replication of the WDV genome in suspension culture cells is independent of its coat protein gene (V. Matzeit,
S. Schäfer, J. Schell, and B. Gronenborn, ms. in prep.). Therefore, the
coat protein gene of WDV may be replaced by other genes, whose expression
and replication will be controlled by viral signals.

TRANSPOSITION OF THE MAIZE-CONTROLLING ELEMENT ACTIVATOR IN TOBACCO

The maize transposable controlling Ac element was first identified and
studied genetically by Barbara McClintock. The Ac element is capable of
transposing autonomously, and it can also trans-activate the transposition
of a group of elements, collectively designated Dissociation (Ds) elements.
The Ac and Ds elements comprise a maize transposon family. Many elements
of this family have recently been cloned and subjected to structural analysis. The Ac element is a small, 4.5-kb transposon which has short (11 bp)
terminal inverted repetitions and which generates an 8-bp duplication upon
insertion. Sequence analysis of the element has revealed the presence of
three major ORFs, two of which overlap (4,5).

Some insight into element-encoded functions has been gained from the
study of Ds elements. Genetically, Ds elements are defined by their
ability to transpose only in the presence of an Ac element. The results
of molecular analyses have shown that Ds elements comprise a structurally

heterogeneous group of elements, all of which have similar or identical
11-bp terminal inverted repetitions, but only some of which are closely related to Ac in structure. Several Ds elements that arose directly from an
Ac element by spontaneous mutations have been analyzed and have been found
to have sustained internal deletions, the smallest of which affect only
ORF1 or overlap ORF1 and ORF2 (5). Since a Ds element cannot promote its
own transposition, but since its transposition can be activated by an Ac
element, the deletions must affect the structure or expression of the sequence encoding the transposition function of the element.

To facilitate the further molecular genetic analysis of Ac-encoded
gene products, as well as to explore the possibility of using Ac as a muta-
gen and gene tag in plants other than maize, we introduced cloned Ac elements into tobacco cells.

Tobacco protoplasts were transformed with Ti-plasmid vectors that contained Ac or Ds flanked by short maize wx gene sequences. The structures
of the elements and surrounding wx and T-DNA sequences were investigated in
nine Ac and five Ds tobacco transformants by digestion with restriction enzymes, Southern blotting, and hybridization using specific probes. In four
of the nine Ac-transformed lines, Ac had excised from its original position
within the T-DNA and had inserted at new sites in the tobacco genome. The
Ds element did not excise from its original T-DNA position in any of the
transformants examined. Two Ac fragments and cellular flanking sequences
were cloned from a line of tobacco in which Ac had transposed. Fragments
comprised of sequences flanking the newly integrated Ac elements were used
as hybridization probes to normal tobacco DNA and to the tobacco DNA from
which they were isolated. The Ac copies were integrated into repetitive
tobacco DNA sequences. Two tobacco fragments containing empty wx donor
sites were cloned from the DNA of the same Ac transformant and sequenced.
Both sequences are among the types of excision products previously observed
to result from Ac-catalyzed excision events in maize. All progeny plants
from a selfing of regenerated plants that contained transposed Ac have one,
or usually several, Ac-like elements integrated in their genome. Some
progeny show evidence of novel Ac locations when compared to parental
plants. Our results indicate that the maize-controlling element Ac is capable of self-catalyzed transposition in tobacco (Ref. 1; B. Baker, G.
Coupland, V. Fantes, A.P. Czernilofsky, H. Lörz, N. Fedoroff, P. Starlinger, and J. Schell, ms. in prep.).

CONCLUSIONS

The findings described in this chapter can be summarized as follows:

(a) Stable integration of donor DNA can be observed following
    direct DNA transfer or Agrobacterium-mediated transforma-
    tion. The integrated DNA is structurally stable during veg-
    etative proliferation and sexual transmission, and under
    various selection conditions.

(b) Modifications, deletions, point mutations, duplications, and
    tandemerizations of the donor DNA have been detected.

(c) The expression level of the NPTII gene can vary between in-
    dependent transformants, independent regenerants of the same
    transformed cell, and progeny of plants. The variation can

be due to position effects and the interplay of various regulatory factors. Genetic and epigenetic variations of the
level of expression of donor DNA have been observed. Cell
populations that are heterologous in respect to the NPTII
activity could be generated by transcriptional modulation
due to physiological and environmental conditions, by transcriptional interference, which potentially leads to structural changes as well, and by "leaky" gene regulation during
the early stages of development.

(d)   A Mendelian 3:1 segregation pattern after selfing of trans-
      genic plants indicates that functional tandemerized DNA is
      integrated at one locus in the host genome.

(e)   The copy number of integrated donor DNA does not necessarily
      correspond with the level of expression, possibly due to
      functional divergence of tandemerized DNA.

(f)   Homologous recombination (gene conversion) between co-trans-
      ferred inactivated genes leads to production of active
      genes.

(g)   The successful substitution of the coat protein gene of WDV
      by foreign genes has opened its application to the engineer-
      ing of monocotyledonous plants.

(h)   The ability of Ac to transpose in dicots opens several in-
      teresting possibilities for further experimentation. The Ac
      element functions can be analyzed in substantial detail by
      in vivo mutagenesis, using mutated Ac elements. Another
      possibility is to use the Ac element as a means of mutating
      and marking genes for cloning. Any new mutant allele that
      can be attributed to insertion of the Ac element can readily
      by used to clone the corresponding gene. Finally, the pre-
      cise integration of Ac could be of value in order to promote
      the integration of defined DNA segments in plant genomes.

ACKNOWLEDGEMENTS

     We thank J. Freitag for help with the manuscript. We are grateful to
all our colleagues in our department for stimulating discussions and sug-
gestions.

REFERENCES

1.   Baker, B., J. Schell, H. Lörz, and N. Fedoroff (1986) Transposition of
     the maize controlling element Activator in tobacco. Proc. Natl. Acad.
     Sci., USA 83:4844-4848.
2.   Czernilofsky, A.P., R. Hain, B. Baker, and U. Wirtz (1986) Studies on
     the structure and functional organization of foreign DNA integrated
     into the genome of Nicotiana tabacum. DNA 5:473-482.
3.   Czernilofsky, A.P., R. Hain, L. Herrera-Estrella, H. Lörz, E. Goy-
     vaerts, B. Baker, and J. Schell (1986) Fate of selectable marker DNA
     integrated into the genome of Nicotiana tabacum. DNA 5:101-113.

4. Fedoroff, N. (1983) Controlling elements in maize. In Mobile Genetic Elements, J.A. Shapiro, ed. Academic Press, Inc., New York, pp. 1-63.

5. Fedoroff, N., S. Wessler, and M. Shure (1983) Isolation of the transposable controlling elements Ac and Ds. Cell 35:235-242.

6. Hain, R., P. Stabel, A.P. Czernilofsky, H.-H. Steinbiss, L. Herrera-Estrella, and J. Schell (1985) Uptake, integration, expression and genetic transmission of a selectable chimeric gene by plant protoplasts. Mol. Gen. Genet. 199:161-168.

7. Hein, T., T. Prezewozny, and O. Schieder (1983) Culture and selection of somatic hybrids using an auxotrophic cell line. Theor. Appl. Genet. 64:119-125.

8. Krens, F.H., L. Molendijk, G.J. Wullems, and R.A. Schilperoort (1982) In vitro transformation of plant protoplasts with Ti-plasmid DNA. Nature 296:72-74.

9. Leaver, C.J., P.G. Isaac, J. Bailey-Serres, I.D. Small, D.K. Hanson, and T.D. Fox (1985) Recombination events associated with the cytochrome c oxidase subunit I gene in fertile and cytoplasmic male sterile maize and sorghum. In Achievements and Perspectives in Mitochondrial Biogenesis, Vol. 11, E. Quagliarello, E.C. Slater, F. Palmieri, C. Saccone, and A.M. Kroon, eds. Elsevier Science Publishers, New York, pp. 111-122.

10. Lindsten, K., J. Vacke, and B. Gerhardson (1970) A preliminary report on three cereal virus diseases new to Sweden spread by Macrosteles and Psammotetix leafhoppers. Stat. Växtskysdanstr. Medd. 14:285-297.

11. Nagy, F., G. Lázár, L. Menczel, and P. Maliga (1983) A heteroplasmic state induced by protoplast fusion is a necessary condition for detecting rearrangements in Nicotiana mitochondrial DNA. Theor. Appl. Genet. 66:203-207.

12. Palmer, J.D., and C.R. Shields (1984) Tripartite structure of the Brassica campestries mitochondrial genome. Nature 307:437-440.

13. Paszkowski, J., R.D. Shillito, M. Saul, V. Mandak, T. Hohn, B. Hohn, and I. Potrykus (1984) Direct gene transfer to plants. EMBO J. 3:2717-2722.

14. Vacke, J. (1972) Host plants range and symptoms of Wheat Dwarf Virus. In Vedecké Práce (Výzkumných Ústavu Rostlinné Výroby, V. Praze-Ruzyni, Vol. 17, CAZ-Ustav vedeckotechnickych Informaci, pp. 151-161.

15. Wirtz, U., J. Schell, and A.P. Czernilofsky (1986) Recombination of selectable marker DNA in Nicotiana tabacum. DNA (submitted for publication).

16. Zambryski, P., L. Herrera-Estrella, M. De Block, M. Van Montagu, and J. Schell (1984) The use of the Ti-plasmid of A. tumefaciens to study the transfer and expression of foreign DNA in plant cells: New vectors and methods. In Genetic Engineering: Principles and Methods, Vol. 6, J.K. Setlow and A. Hollaender, eds. Plenum Press, New York, pp. 253-278.

GENETIC TOOLS FOR THE ANALYSIS OF GENE EXPRESSION IN PLANTS

Csaba Koncz,[1,2] Norbert Martini,[1]
Zsuzsanna Koncz-Kalman,[1] Olle Olsson,[1]
Andrea Radermacher,[1] Aladar Szalay,[3]
and Jeff Schell[1]

[1]Max-Planck-Institut für Züchtungsforschung
D-5000 Köln 30, Federal Republic of Germany

[2]Institute of Genetics
Biological Research Center
Hungarian Academy of Sciences
H 6701 Szeged, Hungary

[3]Boyce Thompson Institute of Plant Research
Cornell University
Ithaca, New York 14853

INTRODUCTION

The analysis of gene expression in plants is often based on correlations between data obtained by a variety of means: biochemical, physiological, and molecular genetic studies on the one hand, and classical genetic tools on the other hand. Among the techniques applied to the study of plant genes are screening of various genomic and complementary DNA (cDNA) libraries by synthetic oligonucleotides, gene- or organ-specific cDNAs, or antibody probes, in vitro translation of hybrid-released mRNAs, two-dimensional protein gel electrophoresis, immunoblotting, and transcript mapping (7,10). However, for an in depth understanding of how certain genes are regulated, alternative approaches are needed.

The method of transposon gene tagging provides a straightforward approach to molecular studies (27). Nevertheless, for the vast majority of isolated genes the usual method for studying gene regulation has been the identification of cis-regulatory sequences involved in the modulation of transcription of genes introduced in transgenic (host or nonhost) plants. To achieve this, chimeric genes containing an appropriate reporter gene, the expression of which is regulated by sequences under study, have to be reintroduced into plant cells. Two general transformation methods are currently used for this purpose.

197

For transient gene expression assays, the methods mainly used have been direct DNA transformation and electroporation (11,29). When organ-specific gene expression has to be studied, however, the Agrobacterium-mediated gene transfer system has been found to be the method of choice (9,28). Since the DNA transfer from agrobacteria to plant cells occurs in a regulated fashion, this system allows the use of techniques of bacterial genetics for the analysis of gene expression in plants. In this chapter we intend to explore some of these possibilities.

NEW DEVELOPMENTS IN AGROBACTERIUM-PLANT GENE TRANSFER SYSTEMS

Agrobacterium Ti plasmids represent a naturally evolved plant gene transfer system. A defined segment of such plasmids, called transfer DNA (T-DNA), which is bordered by 25-bp repeated sequences, is transferred from agrobacteria to the plant cell genome as a result of an interaction between these organisms (36). Bacterial genes, induced by specific metabolites of plant cell wall biosynthesis, are located in the virulence (Vir) region of Ti plasmids and govern this T-DNA transfer process (32). The products of some of these Vir genes (e.g., VirD) specifically recognize the 25-bp T-DNA border repeats, independently of whether these border sequences are linked or unlinked to the Vir loci. As a result of this specific interaction, a T-DNA intermediate is formed which is transferred to plant cells and integrated in their nuclear DNA by an as yet unknown mechanism (31).

Agrobacterium Ti plasmids were adapted for gene transfer purposes. Some of the more recent Ti plasmid-derived plant vector systems, referred to as binary systems, have two elements: a T-DNA-deficient helper Ti plasmid, providing virulence functions, and a broad host range vector, carrying cloning sites and marker genes for identification of transformed plant cells. The position of the T-DNA segment in these vectors is determined by the location and polarity of the 25-bp repeated sequences (1,5,19,20,33).

We developed such a binary vector system having a number of novel features: the different elements involved in plant gene transfer vectors, such as plant selectable or screenable marker genes flanked by 25-bp T-DNA border repeats, cloning sites, appropriate bacterial markers, and broad host range plasmid replication and mobilization functions, were all united in a single, small plant vector cassette (Fig. 1). The basic element of this cassette is a conditional mini-RK2 replicon which is maintained and mobilized by trans-acting functions derived from plasmid RK2. The trans-acting functions were introduced into both Escherichia coli and Agrobacterium hosts. This vector cassette can be inserted easily in various plasmids, in transposons, and in phage derivatives, which all thereby acquire plant gene vector functions. Genetic elements introduced between the 25-bp repeats of the cassette become part of the T-DNA unit, while others inserted outside of this segment provide other relevant functions (e.g., as carrier replicons).

Such combinations allow for the easy construction of plant gene vectors with different properties. The genes to be analyzed in plants are first introduced in the appropriate vectors, which can subsequently be mobilized from E. coli to various Agrobacterium hosts that provide RK2 helper functions for vector maintenance. A further practical advantage provided by this system is that the vectors can also be mobilized back from Agrobacterium to E. coli, due to the presence of RK2 plasmid mobilization functions in Agrobacterium hosts. This facilitates the analysis of

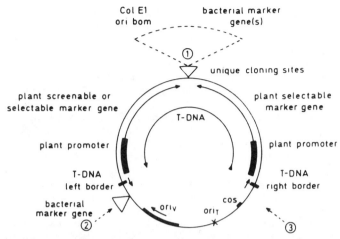

Fig. 1.   Schematic design of plant vector cassettes. Position of the T-DNA unit, polarity of T-DNA border sequences, and direction of replication initiated at RK2 $\underline{ori}_V$ sequences are labeled by arrows inside the circle. Arrows 1, 2, and 3 show unique restriction endonuclease cleavage sites which can be used to introduce new elements into the cassettes. Notation "cos" designates the assembly recognition sequence for bacteriophage λ; ori_T is required for conjugative transfer of the plasmid under control of RK2.

the structural integrity of recombinant vectors prior to plant transformation. The detailed use of this system was recently described (20).

PLASMID VECTORS

     A series of plasmid vectors was constructed by combining various pBR322 derivatives with a plant vector cassette containing a chimeric neomycin phosphotransferase (NPTII) gene as a selectable marker. These vectors were functionally characterized by transformation of Nicotiana tabacum, N. plumbaginifolia, Medicago varia, and Arabidopsis thaliana plants. The majority of transformed plants, obtained using different vectors and selected on kanamycin-containing media after protoplast co-cultivation and tissue infection experiments, were shown to carry only single T-DNA insertions. In plants containing multiple insertions the different T-DNA segments were not found to be in a tandem array. No alteration of the internal structure of the T-DNAs was detected in the transformed plants, indicating that the T-DNA units of the vectors were transferred and integrated without rearrangements.

     To illustrate the application of these vectors, the expression of two T-DNA-derived genes, the nopaline synthetase (NOS) gene and gene 5, was compared in transgenic plants. The analysis of gene 5 expression was of interest because the function of this T_L-DNA-encoded gene of pTiAch5 is not yet known. This gene is thought to be expressed at a low level because its transcript is barely detectable in tumors (37). The promoter of both genes was fused to an enzymatic promoter probe and vectors harboring fusions with both promoters were constructed. The promoter probe genes were similar in size and coupled to identical 3' polyadenylation sequences. The analysis of a large number of transformants showed that the amount of steady-state transcripts derived from the nopaline synthetase promoter is only twice as much as that for the promoter of gene 5. This observation indicated that the low steady-state level of gene 5 transcript in octopine crown gall tumors is not due to weak promoter activity. In nopaline crown gall tumors, it was previously shown that the level of gene 5 transcript is similar to that of the nopaline synthetase gene (37). In view of the fact that the overall homology between the DNA sequences of gene 5 in octopine and nopaline T-DNA regions is very high in the coding regions as well as in the 5' upstream regions, but breaks down 42 bp before the first polyadenylation site, it is conceivable that the 3' end of gene 5 may influence the steady-state level of its transcript in octopine-type tumors. Transcript analysis and comparison of the expression of marker enzymes indicated that the promoter of gene 5 is active in a tissue-specific fashion, while the nopaline synthetase promoter is constitutive and active in all tissues.

The gene 5 promoter is callus/stem-specific. The expression of gene 5 promoter fusions is barely detectable in fully developed leaves; however, it can be fully restored by treating leaf tissue with high auxin/low cytokinin hormone combinations. Conversely, a high cytokinin/low auxin treatment diminishes the gene 5 promoter activity in callus and stem tissues. This observation encouraged a more detailed analysis of the gene 5 promoter and provided a documented instance in which the expression of a gene derived from a prokaryotic host (Agrobacterium Ti plasmid) apparently was influenced by plant growth factors.

TRANSPOSON Tn5-DERIVED GENE TRANSFER AND PROMOTER PROBE VECTORS

Transposon Tn5 is a powerful tool for bacterial genetics. It is efficiently used for generating promoter and gene fusions as well as for mapping and cloning of gene mutations (3,4,6,24). In order to develop a similar technique for plant gene analysis, modified Tn5 transposons were constructed. A plant vector cassette was inserted in Tn5 in a position that does not affect its transposition properties to create Tn5-PV. Tn5-PV shares the properties of both Tn5 and plant gene vectors. It carries the replication and conjugational transfer origin sequences of plasmid RK2 linked to plant selectable and screenable marker genes (NOS promoter-NPTII, octopine synthetase) and to the 25-bp border repeats of Ti plasmid T-DNA. Tn5-PV was inserted into the chromosome of E. coli. Random Tn5-PV insertions were isolated easily in plasmids transformed into such a transposon donor E. coli strain by using "gene dosage" selection on neomycin gradient plates (30). After mapping, plasmids carrying Tn5-PV inserts were mobilized from E. coli to Agrobacterium with the help of plant vector cassette functions. Due to the orientation of the T-DNA 25-bp repeats toward the ends (IS50L and IS50R) of Tn5-PV, insertion of Tn5-PV in a plasmid resulted in a plant vector construction which transferred the target plasmid in its entirety to plant cells. As a consequence, any DNA sequence cloned in any E. coli plasmid vector can be randomly mutagenized in E. coli by Tn5-PV insertion, and the mutagenized DNA segments can be transferred to plant cells for functional analysis after mobilization to Agrobacterium. Coding regions in a large, cloned DNA sequence can be mapped by the analysis of resulting transcripts in transformed plants. Simultaneously, genes not affected by transposon insertions can be identified and their level of expression can be compared to that of co-transferred chimeric plant marker genes carried by Tn5-PV. The general scheme of Tn5-PV mutagenesis is outlined in Fig. 2.

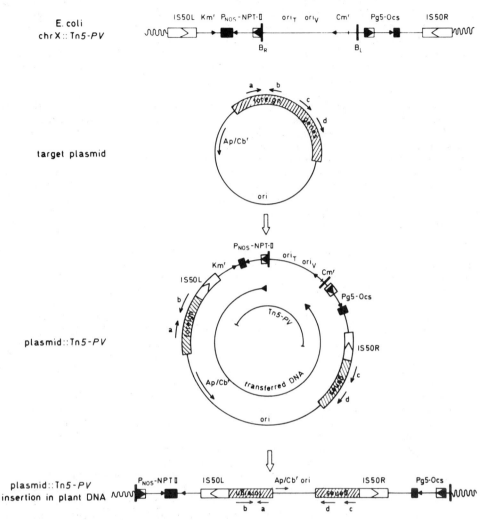

Fig. 2.   General scheme of Tn5-PV-mediated mutagenesis and gene transfer.
The Tn5-PV insertions are isolated in a target plasmid by using
an E. coli donor strain (chrX::Tn5-PV).   A structure similar to
Agrobacterium binary plant vectors is formed by Tn5-PV insertion.
The target plasmid linked to Tn5-PV is transferred into the plant
cell and integrated into the nuclear genome.   Notations a, b, c,
and d designate putative coding sequences in a foreign DNA cloned
in the target plasmid.   Inversion of the a, b, c, and d sequences
occurs during the integration of plasmid::Tn5-PV derivatives into
plant DNA. Km^r, Cm^r: bacterial kanamycin and chloramphenicol
resistance genes; ori_V, ori_T: replication and transfer origin
sequences of plasmid RK2; B_R, B_L: right and left border sequences of Ti plasmid T-DNAs; P_{NOS}-NPTII: chimeric neomycin
phosphotransferase gene transcribed by the promoter of the nopaline synthetase gene; Ocs: octopine synthetase gene; Pg5:   the
promoter of T_L-DNA-encoded gene 5.

To demonstrate the applicability of this approach, a known DNA segment, i.e., the T-DNA of pTiC58 carried by the plasmid pGV354, was subjected to mutational analysis by Tn5-PV. The function and structure of tumor-
inducing T-DNA genes located on pGV354 were analyzed in detail previously
(18,37). It was demonstrated with the help of this model system that
Tn5-PV can both mutagenize and elicit Agrobacterium-mediated transfer of
the mutagenized T-DNA segment to different plants. When the structure of
pGV354::Tn5-PV derivatives, as present in E. coli, was compared to the
structure of the transferred DNA in transformed plant cells, the data fit
the model for the mechanism of transfer and integration as depicted in
Fig. 2. No rearrangements of pGV354::Tn5-PV sequences occurred during
transfer from E. coli to the plant nucleus via Agrobacterium. There also
was a strict correlation between the precise site of Tn5-PV insertions in
pGV354, the absence or presence of T-DNA-encoded transcripts, and the expected organogenic properties of the transformed plant tissues. These results, described in detail elsewhere (21), demonstrated that Tn5-PV can
provide a direct and simple method for the transfer and the transcriptional
and functional analysis of large, cloned DNA segments in plants.

In bacteria, Tn5 derivatives have been successfully used to identify
and characterize promoter and protein export signal sequences (3,24). To
follow this analogy, Tn5-related plant vectors were constructed for isolation of transcriptional or translational fusions in plant genes. The left
IS50 sequence of Tn5 was shortened to retain only the 35-bp sequence necessary for transposition. This sequence was fused to a eukaryotic promoter
probe gene, such as the NPTII gene supplemented with a 3' polyadenylation
signal. Finally, a plant vector cassette, containing 25-bp T-DNA repeats,
conditional plasmid replication and mobilization functions, and a bacterial
Km^r gene from Tn903, was placed in the central position of this modified
Tn5. In certain derivatives the plant vector cassette also carries a dominant plant selectable marker gene (e.g., a hygromycin phosphotransferase
chimeric gene driven by the NOS promoter). The scheme of the mutagenesis
and gene transfer for these Tn5 derivatives is identical to that shown for
Tn5-PV. Insertion of such a promoter probe transposon (e.g., Tn5-PR2) in a
plant DNA sequence cloned in a plasmid can result in the formation of transcriptional or translational plant gene-reporter gene fusions. These
fusions will confer a dominant antibiotic resistance phenotype to plants
and can be either directly selected after the transfer of plasmids with
promoter probe Tn5 inserts to plant cells via Agrobacterium, or can be
screened in different organs of the transformed and regenerated transgenic
plants by enzymatic assay.

Plant gene fusions identified by the simple tool of transposon mutagenesis can be readily isolated from the mutagenized plasmids and further
characterized. This method can help the analysis of the expression of
known genes and should also facilitate the isolation of new plant promoters
active in a tissue-specific fashion.

VECTORS FOR THE USE OF T-DNA INSERTS AS GENE TAGS

Agrobacterium-mediated gene transfer results in a T-DNA insertion in
the plant nuclear genome. The T-DNA can therefore be considered as a
mutator element which can cause insertional inactivation of plant genes.
The integration of the T-DNA appears to be random with regard to the chromosomal location of T-DNA insertions. Whether or not the integration of
the T-DNA has a defined sequence specificity is not yet known. Assuming

that T-DNA integration is not specific for particular sequences, it can be used in plants to isolate in situ gene fusions. A number of vectors were therefore constructed in which the coding sequence of a selectable marker gene lacking transcription initiation sequences was fused to the 25-bp border sequence of the T-DNAs. The integration of these T-DNAs in transcribed plant chromosomal loci can be readily identified because the neomycin (NPTII) or the hygromycin B phosphotransferase (HPT) genes will give a dominant antibiotic resistance phenotype to plant cells carrying an insertionally activated selectable marker gene.

Two sets of vectors with NPTII marker genes were constructed (Fig. 3). In type I vectors the initiation codon of the NPTII coding sequence was retained, while in type II vectors it was removed. In type II vectors the NPTII sequence was fused in all three reading frames to the 25-bp border sequence (26). These constructions were also provided with a constitutively expressed hygromycin selectable marker gene. This allows the selection for transformed plants by hygromycin resistance. These plants can subsequently be screened for the organ- or tissue-specific expression of the NPTII marker gene. In order to facilitate the rescue by cloning of independent T-DNA insertions, the vectors also carry a plasmid replicon and a bacterial marker gene in their T-DNA segment.

The T-DNA insertions flanked by the mutated plant gene sequences can readily be reisolated in E. coli by digestion, religation, and transformation of plant DNAs from different transformed plants (20,22). By genetic crosses it is possible to ascertain that a given mutant phenotype is linked to the locus carrying the T-DNA insert.

Transformed diploid plants will be hemizygotic for the mutations caused by the T-DNA insertions. Therefore, insertions in diploids can only be correlated with mutant phenotypes in homozygote progeny of the transformed plants. Alternatively, haploid plants can be used for easier detection of mutations.

In order to show the applicability of the T-DNA-mediated gene tagging approach, gene fusions were isolated in allotetraploid N. tabacum (SR1) and

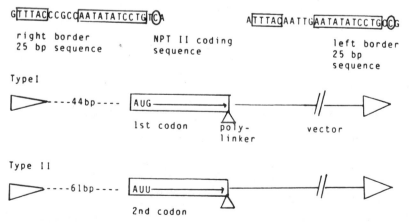

Fig. 3.   Schematic representation of type I and type II vectors used for T-DNA-mediated gene tagging.

haploid N. plumbaginifolia plants by using either protoplast co-cultivation (25) or leaf-disc infection (17) methods followed by a complex screening scheme. In experiments involving direct selection for kanamycin-resistant transformed plant cells, the frequency of transformation was 5% to 10% of that obtained with control vectors carrying NPTII genes transcriptionally driven by known promoters (P_{NOS}, $T_R Pl'$). This frequency varied according to the hormone combination and the level of kanamycin concentrations used in the different transformation experiments. When the transformed plants were first selected on hygromycin and then screened for the expression of the promoter probe marker gene, NPTII activity was detected in one-third of all transformed and hygromycin-resistant calli.

In tobacco, culture media will determine whether transformed cells will grow as calli or regenerate shoots and roots (18,34). Accordingly, certain gene fusions, e.g., those expressed only in leaves or only in roots, will not be selected in callus cultures. Therefore, appropriate hormonal conditions should be used to isolate gene fusions expressed in a tissue-specific fashion. In haploid N. plumbaginifolia, any insertion resulting in an auxotrophic mutation may cause lethality. Therefore culture media should also be supplemented with amino acids, vitamins, etc. Figure 4 shows the tissue specificity of some gene fusions isolated with type I vectors in N. tabacum SR1 plants by selecting for callus formation in the presence of kanamycin. Calli containing gene fusions and expressing the NPTII enzyme were regenerated to plants in the absence of selection. These plants were recurrently tested in the presence of kanamycin. The tissue specificity of the NPTII gene fusions was easily detected because the plants showed a rapid death and degeneration of tissues in which the NPTII selectable marker was not expressed (e.g., plants with stem-specific fusions lost their leaves; the leaves of plants containing root/stem-specific NPTII fusions were bleached, etc.). In haploid N. plumbagini-folia, where the appearance of a mutant phenotype should be apparent imme-diately after transformation, calli and transformed plants carrying 800 independent gene fusions were screened for possible deficiencies in amino acid metabolism, photosynthesis, differentiation, and morphological traits. No auxotrophic mutants turned up in these screens, but lines altered in leaf and flower morphology and several albinos were obtained. Their char-acterization will be described elsewhere (C. Koncz et al., ms. in prep.).

In seed germination assays, the isolated gene fusions showed dominant Mendelian, single- and, in a few cases, double-factor inheritance of the NPTII marker. This test is reliable only for gene fusions expressed in seedlings. Additional tests and hybridization data indicated that in some plants showing single-factor inheritance of the NPTII marker, additional silent copies of vector T-DNAs were nevertheless present.

In transformants obtained by type II vectors (Fig. 3), allowing forma-tion of translational gene fusions only, NPTII fusion proteins of different sizes were indeed detected, while most transformants selected by type I vectors, providing both transcriptional and translational fusions, synthe-sized normal-size NPTII enzyme proteins. This observation was not expect-ed, since the statistical probability for the integration of the vector T-DNA into coding sequences should be higher than that for the integration of the T-DNA in transcriptional leader sequences.

Many other intriguing questions remain to be answered, such as: (a) can one select for insertions in introns?, (b) is the high frequency appearance of transformants carrying putative gene fusions due to the

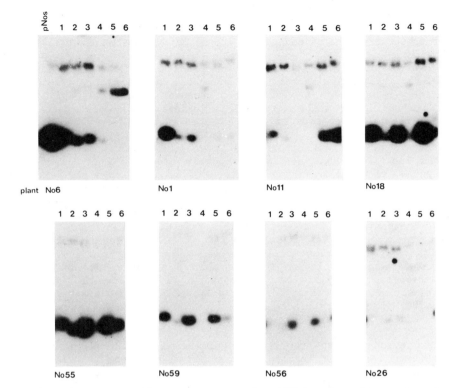

Fig. 4. Tissue-specific expression of a NPTII selectable marker in Nicotiana tabacum plants transformed by type I NPTII promoter probe
vectors. NPTII activities in callus (lane 1), upper stem and
leaf primordia (lane 2), upper stem (lane 3), leaves (2nd and
3rd) (lane 4), lower stem (lane 5), and root (lane 6). The
sample was taken out of 600 independent lines carrying transcriptional and translational NPTII fusions. The NPTII assay is stan-
dardized for equal amount of protein in the extracts. pNO, control extract from callus tissue containing a chimeric pNOS-NPTII
gene.

preferential integration of the vector T-DNA in transcriptionally active
sequences which are moderately repeated?, and (c) does the selection for
higher levels of antibiotic resistance select for the specific amplification of promoter probe sequences? All these questions should be answered
by further molecular studies of reisolated gene fusions.

EXPRESSION VECTORS AND ALTERNATIVE REPORTER PROTEINS

The DNA sequences coding for reporter proteins have been used for the
construction of plant chimeric genes. Previous work has demonstrated that
a number of bacterial enzymes can be expressed and used as selectable and
screenable markers in transgenic plants, e.g., neomycin phosphotransferase
(NPTII) (15,16), chloramphenicol acetyl transferase (CAT) (16), β-galactosidase (14), and hygromycin phosphotransferase (33). All of these enzymes

require relatively complex assay procedures. The results of CAT or β-galactosidase assays are not easily quantified, due to nonspecific reactions or to the presence of endogenous enzyme activities in plant cells.

To overcome these limitations we chose and tested the light-emitting bacterial luciferase as a marker for plant cell transformation. The bacterial luciferase enzyme is a heterodimer, composed of two polypeptide subunits, Luxα and Luxβ, which catalyze the oxidation of long chain fatty aldehydes (12). The reaction requires reduced flavin mononucleotide (FMN) and molecular oxygen and results in the emission of blue-green light, easily measurable by a scintillation counter or luminometer (13). Genes involved in the bioluminescence have recently been isolated from Vibrio harveyi and V. fischeri in E. coli. The luxA and luxB genes are part of a single transcriptional unit in V. harveyi and encode the α and β subunits of luciferase (2,8). Escherichia coli cultures expressing luxA and luxB genes are bioluminescent when an aldehyde substrate (e.g., n-decanal) is supplied, indicating that viable cells can take up the substrate aldehydes (2). In order to obtain expression and to permit correct translation of luxA and luxB genes in plant cells, the genes were separated and possible extra translational initiation codons, located in their 5' untranslated leader sequences, were removed. The constructed luxA and luxB "translational-transcriptional" cassettes were inserted in a plant expression vector, pPCV701, and thereby placed under the transcriptional control of the T_R-DNA 1' and 2' promoters (35), as shown in Fig. 5.

After introduction of the resulting plasmid, pPCV701luxA&B, into tobacco and carrot cells by Agrobacterium-mediated or direct DNA transformation, it was possible to demonstrate the expression of luciferase genes by measuring bioluminescence and showing the presence of the α and β luciferase subunits by immunoblotting in the transformed cells. Both luxA and luxB genes were expressed simultaneously and to similar levels in transformed protoplasts, calli, and organs of regenerated plants. Due to the great sensitivity of the luciferase assay, the chimeric luxA&B genes could be used to demonstrate DNA uptake and gene expression in carrot protoplasts as early as 8 hr after electroporation.

In view of the fact that specific luciferase activity can easily and quantitatively be detected in plant cell extracts, this enzyme appears to be suited as a convenient reporter to monitor the transcriptional regulation of chimeric genes and the transcriptional activity of promoter 5' upstream sequences in transgenic plants as well as in transient gene expression assays. All bacterial enzymes shown to be expressed in plants thus far were of a single subunit type. The heterodimeric V. harveyi luciferase also provided a suitable system to test for the assembly of a complex bacterial enzyme in plant cells, thus opening the way for expression of a multicomponent, heterologous enzyme system in higher plants (23).

CONCLUSION

We have described examples for the application of techniques of bacterial genetics in plant gene analysis. In view of the largely methodological character of this chapter, we do not think that a sophisticated conclusion is required. Instead, we would like to encourage further development in the use of these and similar approaches. They allow plant molecular geneticists to work with the simple tools which have been used with such striking success in the analysis of gene regulation in bacteria and yeasts.

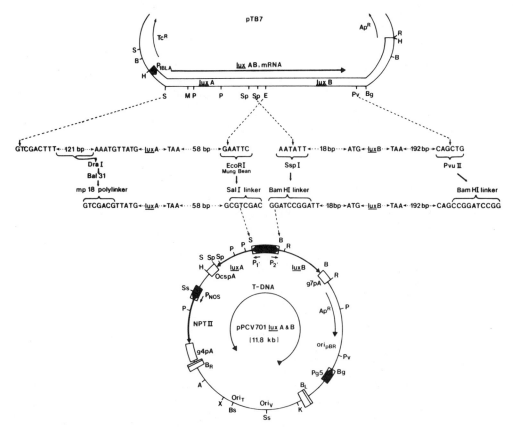

Fig. 5.   Construction and cloning of <u>Vibrio</u> <u>harveyi</u> luciferase <u>luxA</u> and <u>luxB</u> gene cassettes in the plant expression vector pPCV701. $P1_{BLA}$: P1 promoter of β-lactamase gene used for expression of luxA&B transcriptional unit in <u>E. coli</u> plasmid pTB7 (2); P1' and P2': promoters of T_R-DNA-encoded genes 1' and 2'; Pg5 and P_{NOS}: promoters of gene 5 and nopaline synthetase genes; g4pA, OcspA, g7pA: polyadenylation sequences derived from T_L-DNA-encoded gene 4, the octopine synthetase gene, and gene 7; ori_{pBR}: replication origin of pBR322.   A, ApaI; B, BamHI; Bg, BglII; Bs, BstEII; H, HindIII; K, KpnI; M, MaeI; P, PstI; Pv, PvuII; R, EcoRI; S, SalI; X, XhoI; Ss, SstII; Sp, SspI.

REFERENCES

1. An, G., B.D. Watson, S. Stachel, M.P. Gordon, and E.W. Nester (1985) New cloning vehicles for transformation of higher plants. <u>EMBO J.</u> 4:277-284.

2. Baldwin, T.O., T. Berends, T.A. Bunch, T.F. Holzman, S.K. Rausch, L. Shamansky, M.L. Treat, and M.M. Ziegler (1984) Cloning of the luciferase structural genes from <u>Vibrio</u> <u>harveyi</u> and expression of bioluminescence in <u>Escherichia</u> <u>coli</u>. <u>Biochemistry</u> 23:3663-3667.

3. Bellofatto, V., L. Shapiro, and D.A. Hodgson (1984) Generation of a Tn<u>5</u> promoter probe and its use in the study of <u>Caulobacter</u> <u>crescentus</u>. <u>Proc. Natl. Acad. Sci., USA</u> 81:1035-1039.

4. Berg, D.E., and C.H. Berg (1983) The procaryotic transposable element Tn5. Bio/Technology 1:417-435.
5. Bevan, M. (1984) Binary Agrobacterium vectors for plant transformation. Nucl. Acids Res. 12:8711-8721.
6. De Bruijn, F.J., and J.R. Lupski (1984) The use of transposon Tn5 mutagenesis in the rapid generation of correlated physical and genetical maps of DNA segments cloned into multicopy plasmids--Review. Gene 27:131-149.
7. Dodds, J.H., ed. (1985) Plant Genetic Engineering, Cambridge University Press, Cambridge, England.
8. Engebrecht, J., K. Nealson, and M. Silverman (1983) Bacterial bioluminescence: Isolation and genetic analysis of functions from Vibrio fischeri. Cell 32:773-781.
9. Fluhr, R., C. Kuhlemeyer, F. Nagy, and N.H. Chua (1985) Organ specific and light induced expression of plant genes. Science 232:1106-1112.
10. Freeling, M., ed. (1985) Plant Genetics (UCLA Symposia on Molecular and Cellular Biology, New Series Vol. 35), Alan R. Liss, Inc., New York.
11. Fromm, M., L.P. Taylor, and V. Walbot (1985) Expression of genes transferred into monocot and dicot plant cells by electroporation. Proc. Natl. Acad. Sci., USA 82:5824-5828.
12. Hastings, J.W., and K.H. Nealson (1977) Bacterial bioluminescence. Ann. Rev. Microbiol. 51:549-595.
13. Hastings, J.W., T.O. Baldwin, and M.Z. Nicoli (1978) Bacterial luciferase: Assay, purification and properties. In Bioluminescence and Chemiluminescence (Methods in Enzymology, Vol. LVII), M.A. DeLuca, ed. Academic Press, Inc., New York, pp. 135-152.
14. Helmer, G., M. Casabadan, M. Bevan, L. Kayes, and M.-D. Chilton (1984) A new chimeric gene as a marker for plant transformation: The expression of Escherichia coli β-galactosidase in sunflower and tobacco cells. Bio/Technology 1:520-527.
15. Herrera-Estrella, L., A. Depicker, M. Van Montagu, and J. Schell (1983) Expression of chimeric genes transferred into plant cells using a Ti-plasmid derived vector. Nature 303:209-213.
16. Herrera-Estrella, L., M. De Block, E. Messens, J.P. Hernalsteens, M. Van Montagu, and J. Schell (1983) Chimeric genes as dominant selectable markers in plant cells. EMBO J. 2:987-995.
17. Horsch, R.B., J.E. Fry, N.L. Hoffman, D. Eichholz, S.G. Rogers, and R.T. Fraley (1985) A simple and general method for transferring genes into plants. Science 227:1229-1231.
18. Joos, H., D. Inze, A. Caplan, M. Sormann, M. Van Montagu, and J. Schell (1983) Genetic analysis of T-DNA transcripts in nopaline crown galls. Cell 32:1057-1067.
19. Klee, H.J., M.F. Yanofsky, and E.W. Nester (1985) Vectors for transformation of higher plants. Bio/Technology 3:637-642.
20. Koncz, C., and J. Schell (1986) The promoter of T_L-DNA gene 5 controls the tissue-specific expression of chimaeric genes carried by a novel type of Agrobacterium vector. Mol. Gen. Genet. 204:383-396.
21. Koncz, C., Zs. Koncz-Kalman, and J. Schell (1986) Transposon Tn5 mediated gene transfer into plants. Mol. Gen. Genet. (in press).
22. Koncz, C., F. Kreuzaler, Zs. Kalman, and J. Schell (1984) A simple method to transfer, integrate, and study expression of foreign genes, such as chicken ovalbumin and α-actin in plant tumors. EMBO J. 3: 1597-1603.
23. Koncz, C., O. Olsson, W.H.R. Langridge, J. Schell, and A. Szalay (1986) Expression and functional assembly of bacterial luciferase in plants. Proc. Natl. Acad. Sci., USA (in press).

24. Manoil, C., and J. Beckwith (1985) Tn phoA: A transposon probe for protein export signals. Proc. Natl. Acad. Sci., USA 82:8129-8133.
25. Marton, L., G.J. Wullems, L. Molendijk, and R.A. Schilperoort (1982) In vitro transformation of cultured cells from Nicotiana tabacum by Agrobacterium tumefaciens. Nature 277:129-131.
26. Reiss, B., R. Sprengel, and H. Schaller (1984) Protein fusions with the kanamycin resistance gene from transposon Tn5. EMBO J. 3:3317-3322.
27. Saedler, H., U. Bonas, A. Gierl, B.J. Harrison, R.B. Klösgen, E. Krebbers, P. Nevers, P.A. Peterson, Zs. Schwarz-Sommer, H. Sommer, K. Upadhyaya, and U. Wienand (1984) Transposable elements in Antirrhinum majus and Zea mays. Cold Spring Harbor Symp. Quant. Biol. 49:355-361.
28. Schell, J., H. Kaulen, F. Kreuzaler, P. Eckes, S. Rosahl, L. Willmitzer, A. Spena, B. Baker, L. Herrera-Estrella, and N. Fedoroff (1985) Transfer and regulation of expression of chimeric genes in plants. Cold Spring Harbor Symp. Quant. Biol. 50:421-431.
29. Shillito, R.D., M.W. Saul, J. Paszkowski, M. Müller, and I. Potrykus (1985) High efficiency direct gene transfer to plants. Bio/Technology 3:1099-1103.
30. Simon, R. (1984) High frequency mobilization of Gram-negative bacterial replicons by the in vitro constructed Tn5-Mob transposon. Mol. Gen. Genet. 196:413-420.
31. Stachel, S.E., B. Timmerman, and P. Zambryski (1986) Generation of single stranded T-DNA molecules during the initial stages of T-DNA transfer of A. tumefaciens to plant cells. Nature 322:706-716.
32. Stachel, S.E., E. Messens, M. Van Montagu, and P. Zambryski (1985) Identification of signal molecules produced by wounded plant cells that activate T-DNA transfer in Agrobacterium tumefaciens. Nature 318:624-630.
33. Van den Elzen, P.J.M., K.Y. Lee, J. Townsend, and J.R. Bedbrook (1985) Simple binary vectors for DNA transfer to plant cells. Plant Mol. Biol. 5:149-154.
34. Vasil, I.K., ed. (1984) Cell Culture and Somatic Cell Genetics of Plants, Vol. 1, Academic Press, Inc., New York.
35. Velten, J., and J. Schell (1985) Selection-expression plasmid vectors for use in plants. Nucl. Acids Res. 13:6981-6998.
36. Wang, K., L. Herrera-Estrella, M. Van Montagu, and P. Zambryski (1984) Right 25 bp terminus sequence of the nopaline T-DNA is essential for and determines direction of DNA transfer from Agrobacterium to the plant genome. Cell 38:455-462.
37. Willmitzer, L., P. Dhaese, P. Schreier, W. Schmalenbach, M. Van Montagu, and J. Schell (1983) Size, location and polarity of T-DNA encoded transcripts in nopaline crown gall tumors: Common transcripts in octopine and nopaline tumors. Cell 32:1045-1056.

ROSTER OF SCIENTIFIC ORGANIZING COMMITTEE,
CHAIRMEN, SPEAKERS, AND PARTICIPANTS

Aapoca, Alpo, Calgene, Inc., Davis, CA 95616
Ahlquist, Paul G., University of Wisconsin, Madison, WI 53706
Alexander, Danny, Los Altos Hills, CA 94022
Alpert, Kevin B., University of California, Davis, CA 95616
Altenbach, Susan B., ARCO Plant Research Institute, Dublin, CA 94568
Anderson, Lars, U.S. Department of Agriculture, Agricultural Research
   Service, Davis, CA 95616
Anderson, Olin D., U.S. Department of Agriculture, Agricultural Research
   Service, Albany, CA 94710
Archer, Kathleen, Cornell University, Ithaca, NY 14853
Aromand, Navid, University of California, Davis, CA 95616
Arulsekar, S., University of California, Davis, CA 95616
Axtell, John D., Purdue University, West Lafayette, IN 47907

Baergen, Kathleen, University of California, Davis, CA 95616
Ballo, Barbara, ARCO Plant Cell Research Institute, Dublin, CA 94568
Baran, George J., Minnetonka, MN 55343
Barash, Isaac, Tel-Aviv University, Tel-Aviv, Israel
Baribault, Tom, Cleveland Heights, OH 44121
Barsky-Shoaf, Debonny, University of California, Davis, CA 95616
Barton, Carolyn, San Carlos, CA 94070
Baszczynski, Chris L., Allelix, Inc., Mississauga, Ontario, Canada L4V 1P1
Beachy, Roger N., Washington University, St. Louis, MO 63130
Bedbrook, John, Advanced Genetic Sciences, Inc., Oakland, CA 94608
Belanger, Faith C., University of Illinois, Urbana, IL 61801
Belzice, Francois, University of California, Davis, CA 95616
Ben-hayyim, Gozal, ARCO Plant Cell Research Institute, Dublin, CA 94568
Bennett, Alan B., University of California, Davis, CA 95616
Bernardin, John E., U.S. Department of Agriculture, Agricultural Research
   Service, Albany, CA 94710
Bertoni, Gregory, Corvallis, OR 97330
Black, Diane, University of California, La Jolla, CA 92093
Black, Favreau M., Advanced Genetic Sciences, Inc., Oakland, CA 94608
Blechl, Ann E., U.S. Department of Agriculture, Agricultural Research
   Service, Albany, CA 94710
Bloksberg, Leonard N., University of California, Davis, CA 95616
Bogorad, Lawrence, Harvard University, Cambridge, MA 02138
Bohnert, Hans J., University of Arizona, Tucson, AZ 85721
Bond-Nutter, Diane, Advanced Genetic Sciences, Inc., Oakland, CA 94608
Boulay, Michel Paul, University of California, Davis, CA 95616
Boyd, Richard A., Santa Monica, CA 90404
Braam, Janct, Palo Alto, CA 94301-1416
Breidenbach, R.W., University of California, Davis, CA 95616

Briggs, Steve, Johnston, IA 50131
Brink, Don, Cleveland, OH 44128
Brown, Chuck, Prosser, WA 99350
Bruening, George, University of California, Davis, CA 95616
Burgess, Diane, Advanced Genetic Sciences, Inc., Oakland, CA 94608

Campbell, Donald E., U.S. Department of Agriculture, Agricultural Research
  Service, Albany, CA 94710
Cannon, Catherine, San Jose, CA 95112
Carlson, Don M., University of California, Davis, CA 95616
Carnes, Michael G., Creve Coeur, MO 63141
Chang, Caren, Pasadena, CA 91125
Chay, Catherine, University of California, Davis, CA 95616
Chetelat, Roger, University of California, Davis, CA 95616
Choe, Hyung Tae, University of California, Davis, CA 95616
Clouse, Steven D., The Salk Institute, San Diego, CA 92138
Clutter, Mary E., National Science Foundation, Washington, D.C. 20550
Cohen, Daniel B., University of California, Davis, CA 95616
Colby, Sheila, University of California, Davis, CA 95616
Colwell, Gregg, Corvallis, OR 97330
Comai, Luca, Calgene, Inc., Davis, CA 95616
Corbin, David R., The Salk Institute, San Diego, CA 92138
Cornish, Edwina, University of Melbourne, Victoria, Australia
Cramer, Carole L., The Salk Institute, San Diego, CA 92138
Crawford, Nigel, Stanford University Medical Center, Stanford, CA 94305
Crosby, William L., Saskatoon, Saskatchewan, Canada S7N 0W9
Cross, John W., Hayward, CA 94545
Crossman, Curt C., Woodland, CA 95695
Crossway, Anne, Calgene, Inc., Davis, CA 95616
Crouch, Martha L., Indiana University, Bloomington, IN 47405
Czarnecka, Eva, University of Florida, Gainesville, FL 32611
Czernilofsky, Armin Peter, Max-Planck-Institut für Zuchtungsforschung,
  Köln, D-5000 Federal Republic of Germany

Damon, Susan, University of California, Davis, CA 95616
Dandekar, Abhaya M., University of California, Davis, CA 95616
Daubert, Steve, University of California, Davis, CA 95616
Dean, Caroline, Advanced Genetic Sciences, Inc., Oakland, CA 94608
Dean, Victoria, Advanced Genetic Sciences, Inc., Oakland, CA 94608
Deaton, Randy, Monsanto Company, Chesterfield, MO 63198
De Francesco, Laura, University of California, Los Angeles, CA 90024
Del Campillo, Elena, University of California, Berkeley, CA 94720
Delauney, Ashton J., McGill University, Montréal, Quebec, Canada H3A 1B1
Della Penna, Dean, University of California, Davis, CA 95616
Della-Cioppa, Monsanto Company, Chesterfield, MO 63198
Dellaporta, Stephen L., Yale University, New Haven, CT 06510
Demmin, Scott, Riverside, CA 92507
De Souza, Edna Riemke, University of California, Davis, CA 95616
De Verna, Joseph W., University of California, Davis, CA 95616
De Wet, Jeffrey R., Stanford University, Stanford, CA 94305
Dietrich, Bob, University of California, Davis, CA 95616
Dietrich, Margaret, University of Missouri, Columbia, MO 65211
Dietz, Antje, Stanford University, Stanford, CA 94305
Dooner, Hugo, Advanced Genetic Sciences, Inc., Oakland, CA 94608
Duncan, Roger, University of California, Davis, CA 95616
Durzan, Don J., University of California, Davis, CA 95616
Dvorak, Jan, University of California, Davis, CA 95616

Ecker, Joseph R., Stanford University, Stanford, CA 94305
Edwards, Carla, Palo Alto, CA 94301
El-Sheikh, Adel, Fullerton, CA 92633
English, James, Advanced Genetic Sciences, Inc., Oakland, CA 94608
Epp, Melvin D., ARCO Plant Research Institute, Dublin, CA 94568
Esen, Asim, Virginia Polytechnic Institute, Blacksburg, VA 24061
Estilai, Ali, University of California, Riverside, CA 92521
Etzler, Marilynn, University of California, Davis, CA 95616
Evans, Paula, U.S. Department of Agriculture, Agricultural Research
   Service, Albany, CA 94710

Falkenberg, Rick, Merced, CA 95344-0168
Feldmann, Kenneth A., Zoecon Corporation, Palo Alto, CA 94304
Fenoll, Carmen, University of California, La Jolla, CA 92093
Ferl, Robert, University of Florida, Gainesville, FL 32611
Fillatti, JoAnne J., Calgene, Inc., Davis, CA 95616
Firoozabady, Ebrahim, Agrigenetics Advanced Science Company, Madison, WI
   53716
Fischer, Robert, University of California, Berkeley, CA 94720
Fitzmaurice, Leona Claire, SIBIA, Inc., La Jolla, CA 92037
Flashman, Stuart, Richmond, CA 94804
Fornari, Chester S., U.S. Department of Agriculture, Agricultural Research
   Service, Albany, CA 94710
Fox, Cheryl, Northrup King Company, Stanton, MN 55057
Foxe, Michael J., University College, Dublin, Ireland
Fraley, Robert T., Monsanto Company, Chesterfield, MO 63198
Francis, David M., University of California, Davis, CA 95616
Frankel, Rafael, The Volcani Center, Bet Dagan, Israel
Freedman, Rover P., Diatech, Ltd., London, England
Freeling, Michael, University of California, Berkeley, CA 94720
Frehner, Marco, University of California, Davis, CA 95616
Frome, Matther J., Los Angeles, CA 90025
Fujii, Dwight S., University of California, Davis, CA 95616
Fujikura, Yuzo, ARCO Plant Research Center, Dublin, CA 94568
Furter, Rolf M., University of Washington, Seattle, WA 98195
Fuson, Gayle, University of California, Davis, CA 95616

Gaffney, Thomas, University of California, Davis, CA 95616
Gamborg, Oluf L., Colorado State University, Fort Collins, CO 80523
Gaynor, John J., South Plainfield, NJ 07080
Gee, Doreen, University of California, Davis, CA 95616
Gilchrist, David G., University of California, Davis, CA 95616
Glascock, Christopher, University of California, Davis, CA 95616
Glassman, Kimberly F., Molecular Genetics, Inc., Minnetonka, MN 55343
Golman, Ron, Alamo, CA 94507
Gomez-Lim, Miguel A., University of California, Los Angeles, CA 90024
Gonzales, Robert A., Ardmore, OK 73402
Goodman, Robert M., Calgene, Inc., Davis, CA 95616
Goodrich, Marta, University of California, Davis, CA 95616
Graham, Madge Yang, Ohio State University, Columbus, OH 43210
Graham, Terry, Ohio State University, Columbus, OH 43210
Grayburn, W. Scott, University of Washington, Seattle, WA 98195
Greene, Frank C., U.S. Department of Agriculture, Agricultural Research
   Service, Albany, CA 94710
Greenlee, Judith K., Stanford University, Stanford, CA 94305
Gregory, Boni, University of California, Davis, CA 95616
Grill, Laurence K., Zoecon Corporation, Palo Alto, CA 94304

Gruissem, Wilhelm, University of California, Berkeley, CA 94720
Guilfoyle, Tom J., University of Missouri, Columbia, MO 65211
Gupta, Pramod Kumar, University of California, Davis, CA 95616
Gutierrez, Marco V., University of California, Davis, CA 95616

Hadley, Ray G., Plant Genetics, Inc., Davis, CA 95616
Hall, Benjamin D., University of Washington, Seattle, WA 98195
Hanson, Maureen, Cornell University, Ithaca, NY 14853
Harada, John J., University of California, Davis, CA 95616
Harber, James J., Arcata, CA 95521
Hari, V., Bloomfield Hills, MI 48013
Harpster, Mark, Advanced Genetic Sciences, Inc., Oakland, CA 94608
Harriman, Bob, Lafayette, IN 47904
Heath-Pagliuso, Sharon, University of California, Davis, CA 95616
Heffner, Landon, Camino, CA 95709
Heller, Renu A., Stanford, CA 94305
Hess, Charles E., University of California, Davis, CA 95616
Hess, Dan F., Zoecon Corporation, Palo Alto, CA 94304-0859
Heupel, Rick C., U.S. Department of Agriculture, Agricultural Research
  Service, Albany, CA 94710
Holwerda, Barry C., University of Saskatchewan, Saskatoon, Saskatchewan,
  Canada
Houck, Catherine, Calgene, Inc., Davis, CA 95616
Hudspeth, Richard, Pasadena, CA 91105
Huffaker, R.C., University of California, Davis, CA 95616
Hulbert, Scot, University of California, Davis, CA 95616
Hunter, Alan, University College, Dublin, Ireland

Ishii, Chizu, Stanford University, Stanford, CA 94305-2493

Jacobs, Joseph, University of California, Davis, CA 95616
Jelaska, Sibila, Zagreb, Yugoslavia
Jensen, Jens Stougaard, University of Aarhus, Aarhus, Denmark
Jofuku, Diane, University of California, Los Angeles, CA 90024
John, Maliyakal E., Agracetus, Middleton, WI 53562
Johnson, Duane C., Colorado State University, Fort Collins, CO 80523
Johnson, Sheila M., University of California, Davis, CA 95616
Jones, Jonathan, Advanced Genetic Sciences, Inc., Oakland, CA 94608
Jorgensen, Rich, Advanced Genetic Sciences, Inc., Oakland, CA 94608
Judelson, Howard S., University of California, Davis, CA 95616

Kado, Clarence, University of California, Davis, CA 95616
Kahler, Alex L., Slater, IA 50244
Kahn, I.A., Riverside, CA 92507
Kamaruzaman, Bin Mohammad, Virginia Polytechnic Institute, Blacksburg, VA
  24061
Kasarda, Donald D., U.S. Department of Agriculture, Agricultural Research
  Service, Albany, CA 94710
Katayama, Carol, Advanced Genetic Sciences, Inc., Oakland, CA 94608
Keathley, Daniel, Michigan State University, East Lansing, MI 48824
Keith, Brian, Rockefeller University, New York, NY 10021
Kelly, Jeffrey, University of California, Davis, CA 95616
Kerk, Nancy, Yale University, New Haven, CT 06511
Key, Joe L., University of Georgia, Athens, GA 30602
Khush, Ranjiu, University of California, Davis, CA 95616
Kidd, George, Milwaukee, WI 53211
Kim, Leo, Modesta, CA 95352

Kleinhofs, Andris, Washington State University, Pullman, WA   99163
Koncz, Csaba, Max-Planck-Institut für Zuchtungsforschung, Köln, D-5000
   Federal Republic of Germany
Korhonen-Lehto, Kirsi Marpit, Riverside, CA   92507
Kosuge, Tsune, University of California, Davis, CA   95616
Kramer, Vance, CIBA-GEIGY, Research Triangle Park, NC   27709

Labovitz, Jeffrey, Hayward, CA   94545
Ladyman, Juanita A.R., Modesta, CA   95350
Lagarias, J. Clark, University of California, Davis, CA   95616
Lagrimini, Mark, CIBA-GEIGY, Research Triangle Park, NC   27709
Lamb, Christopher J., The Salk Institute, San Diego, CA   92138
Landry, Benoit S., University of California, Davis, CA   95616
Lapushner, Dvora, The Volcani Center, Bet Dagan, Israel
Larkins, Brian, Purdue University, West Lafayette, IN   47907
Lassmer, Michael, University of California, Davis, CA   95616
Lawrence, Robert H., White Plains, NY   10625
Lee, Gregory J., University of California, Davis, CA   95616
Lee, Kathy, Advanced Genetic Sciences, Inc., Oakland, CA   94608
Leong, Merlin, University of Victoria, Victoria, British Columbia, Canada
   V8W 2Y2
Levings, Charles S., North Carolina State University, Raleigh, NC
   27695-7614
Lifschytz, Eliezer, Israel Institute of Technology, Haifa, Israel
Lillis, Marcella, Princeton, NJ   08540
Lin, Jhy-Jhu, Cornell University, Ithaca, NY   14853
Lindhout, Pim, Wageningen, The Netherlands
Lindsey, Hilde, San Francisco, CA   94116
Litts, Jim, Oregon State University, Corvallis, OR   97331
Loh, Willie, Cinnaminson, NJ   08077
Lois, Augusto F., Los Angeles, CA   90066
Low, Ann L., Denver, CO   80220
Luh, Bor S., University of California, Davis, CA   95616

Malik, Vedpal Singh, New York, NY   10021
Mangano, Mary Lou, Pfizer, Inc., Groton, CT   06340
Marrero-Dominguez, Antonio, University of California, Davis, CA   95616
Martensen, Ann, University of California, Davis, CA   95616
Martin, George C., University of California, Davis, CA   95616
Martin, Lori, University of California, Davis, CA   95616
Mascia, Peter N., Monsanto Zoo, Chesterfield, MO   63198
Mathews, M.A., University of California, Davis, CA   95616
Mau, Christopher, University of California, Los Angeles, CA   90024
Maxwell, Carl A., University of California, Davis, CA   95616
Mazelis, Mendel, University of California, Davis, CA   95616
McClure, Bruce, University of Missouri, Columbia, MO   65211
McCue, Kent, University of California, Davis, CA   95616
McDermott, Joseph, University of California, Davis, CA   95616
McDonald, Bruce A., University of California, Davis, CA   95616
McGrath, J. Mitchell, University of California, Davis, CA   95616
Mejia, Patricia Leon, Stanford University, Stanford, CA   94305
Menon, A. Satish, Harvard Medical School, Boston, MA   02115
Meredith, Carole, University of California, Davis, CA   95616
Merlo, Don, Agrigenetics Advanced Science Company, Madison, WI   53716
Mestel, Rosie, University of California, Davis, CA   95616
Metzler, Mary, New Haven, CT   06511
Michalska, Anna, Stacia Hodowli Roslin, Warsaw, Poland

Michelmore, Richard, University of California, Davis, CA 95616
Momma, Takayuki, Max-Planck-Institut für Zuchtungsforschung, Köln, D-5000
    Federal Republic of Germany
Moran, Marilyn, Unilever Research Colworth House, Bedford, England MK441LQ
Mossie, Kevin, Pasadena, CA 91125
Moussatos, Liana, University of California, Davis, CA 95616
Mundy, John W., New York, NY 10027

Naito, Satoshi, Washington University, St. Louis, MO 63130
Napoli, Carolyn, University of California, Berkeley, CA 94720
Narayanan, K.R., Homestead, FL 33031
Nasrallah, June, Cornell University, Ithaca, NY 14853
Neale, David B., University of California, Davis, CA 95616
Nevine, Donald J., University of California, Davis, CA 95616
Nguyen, Truyen, McGill University, Montréal, Quebec, Canada H3A 1B1
Nivison, Helen T., Cornell University, Ithaca, NY 14853
Nolan, Randall C., Washington University, St. Louis, MO 63130
Nonaka, Mas, Moraga, CA 94556
Nutter, Robert C., Richmond, CA 94804

Oard, James, University of California, Davis, CA 95616
Oard, Margi, University of California, Davis, CA 95616
Okamuro, Jack K., University of California, Los Angeles, CA 90024
Olson, Pam, Richmond, CA 94804
Omeilan, Joe, University of California, Davis, CA 95616
O'Neill, Sharman D., University of California, Davis, CA 95616
Osteryoung, Katherine, University of California, Davis, CA 95616
Ott, Russ, University of California, Davis, CA 95616

Padgette, Stephen R., Monsanto Company, Chesterfield, MO 63198
Palmen, Peter E., San Francisco, CA 94108
Palys, Joe, University of California, Davis, CA 95616
Parrish, Fred, New Orleans, LA 70124
Patena, Lilian F., University of California, Davis, CA 95616
Pellow, John W., Pasadena, CA 91105
Peterman, T. Kaye, Massachusetts General Hospital, Boston, MA 02139
Peters, Ingrid, University of California, Davis, CA 95616
Peterson, Thomas Michael, University of California, Davis, CA 95616
Phillips, D.A., University of California, Davis, CA 95616
Pierce, Dorothy A., Richmond, CA 94804
Pillay, Datta T.N., Windsor, Ontario, Canada N9B 3P4
Pinson, Shannon, University of California, Davis, CA 95616
Pokalsky, Ann, Calgene, Inc., Davis, CA 95616
Ponz, Fernando, University of California, Davis, CA 95616
Poutre, Candace G., ARCO Plant Research Institute, Dublin, CA 94568
Preiss, Jack, Michigan State University, East Lansing, MI 48824
Punja, Zamir K., University of California, Davis, CA 95616

Quail, Peter H., University of Wisconsin, Madison, WI 53706
Qualset, Calvin O., University of California, Davis, CA 95616
Quatrano, Ralph, DuPont Experimental Station, Wilmington, DE 19898
Quayle, Tom, University of California, Davis, CA 95616

Rabson, Robert, U.S. Department of Energy, Washington, D.C. 20545
Ralston, Edward, Advanced Genetic Sciences, Inc., Oakland, CA 94608
Ramage, Robert T., University of Arizona, Tucson, AZ 85721

Ramagopal, S., U.S. Department of Agriculture, Agricultural Research
Service, Aiea, HI 96701
Rawal, Kanti M., San Leandro, CA 94577
Reed, Kathryn M., Des Moines, IA 50322
Reilly, Ann, Watsonville, CA 95076
Riggs, Lawrence A., Berkeley, CA 94709
Rivka, Barg, The Volcani Center, Bet Dagan, Israel
Roberto, Frank, University of California, Davis, CA 95616
Robinson, Nina L., University of California, Davis, CA 95616
Rocha-Sosa, Mario, Max-Planck-Institut für Zuchtungsforschung, Köln, D-5000
Federal Republic of Germany
Rodriquez, Raymond L., University of California, Davis, CA 95616
Rutger, J. Neil, U.S. Department of Agriculture, Agricultural Research
Service, Davis, CA 95616
Ryan, Clarence A., Washington State University, Pullman, WA 99164-6340
Ryan, Frederick J., University of California, Davis, CA 95616

Saghai, M.A., University of California, Davis, CA 95616
Salts, Yehiam, The Volcani Center, Bet Dagan, Israel
Sandler, Steven J., Advanced Genetic Sciences, Inc., Oakland, CA 94608
Sandmeier, Ruedi, Northrup King Research, Stanton, MN 55057
Sanger, Margaret, University of California, Davis, CA 95616
Scalry, Alader A., Cornell University, Ithaca, NY 14853
Scarafia, Lilana, CIBA-GEIGY, Research Triangle Park, NC 27708
Schachman, Howard K., University of California, Berkeley, CA 94720
Schettini, Terry M., University of California, Davis, CA 95616
Schneider, Michel, University of California, La Jolla, CA 92093
Shaw, D.S., University of California, Davis, CA 95616
Shaw, Joe, University of California, Davis, CA 95616
Sheikholeslam, Shahla, Zoecon Corporation, Palo Alto, CA 94304
Shields, Clark, University of California, Davis, CA 95616
Shillito, R.D., CIBA-GEIGY, Research Triangle Park, NC 27709
Shotwell, Mark, Purdue University, West Lafayette, IN 47907
Silva, Oswaldo Da Costa E., University of California, Davis, CA 95616
Silvas, Javier S., Sinaloa, Mexico
Silverstone, Sara, University of California, Davis, CA 95616
Simon, Rudiger, Köln, Federal Republic of Germany
Siu, Naomi, Watsonville, CA 95077
Smith, Alan G., Monsanto Company, Chesterfield, MO 63198
Smith, Jane A., University of California, Berkeley, CA 94720
Smith, Michael, University of British Columbia, Vancouver, British
Columbia, Canada V6R 4K3
Smith, Wendy Ann, Princeton, NJ 08540
Somerville, C.R., Michigan State University, East Lansing, MI 48824
Spielmann, Albert, ARCO Plant Research Institute, Dublin, CA 94568
Spoirs, Jim, CSIRO, North Ryde, NSW, Australia
Stamp, James A., University of California, Davis, CA 95616
Stayton, Mark, Advanced Genetic Sciences, Inc., Oakland, CA 94608
Stermer, Bruce A., University of California, Davis, CA 95616
Stiekema, W.J., Research Institute ITAL, Wageningen, The Netherlands
Stockinger, Eric J., Riverside, CA 92507
Strick, Christine, Cornell University, Ithaca, NY 14853
Stuart, David, Plant Genetics, Inc., Davis, CA 95616
Sun, Samuel S.M., ARCO Plant Research Institute, Dublin, CA 94568
Suslow, Trevor V., Advanced Genetic Sciences, Inc., Oakland, CA 94608

Taha, Fayza A., Cairo University, Giza, Egypt
Tamaki, Stanley, University of California, Riverside, CA 92521
Tanksley, Steven D., Cornell University, Ithaca, NY 14853
Taylor, Allan, Montana State University, Bozeman, MT 59717
Taylor, Loverine P., Stanford, CA 94305
Temple, Steve, University of California, Davis, CA 95616
Tilton, Varien, San Leandro, CA 94577
Timothy, David H., North Carolina State University, Raleigh, NC 27695-7620
Tobin, Elaine M., University of California, Los Angeles, CA 90024
Tolin, Sue A., Virginia Polytechnic Institute, Blacksburg, VA 24061
Tsay, Shang-shang, Irvine, CA 92715
Tucker, Mark L., University of California, Berkeley, CA 94720

Valentine, Raymond C., University of California, Davis, CA 95616
Varner, Joseph E., Washington University, St. Louis, MO 63130
Verma, Desh Pal S., McGill University, Montréal, Quebec, Canada H3A 1B1
Vinizky, Itamar, University of California, Davis, CA 95616
Vu, Thanh, Fremont, CA 94536

Walbot, Virginia, Stanford University, Stanford, CA 94305
Waldron, Clegg, Lilly Corporate Center, Indianapolis, IN 46285
Walker, Andrew, University of California, Davis, CA 95616
Wallner, Stephen J., Colorado State University, Fort Collins, CO 80523
Walter, Michael H., The Salk Institute, San Diego, CA 92138-9216
Ward, Michael R., University of California, Davis, CA 95616
Warner, Robert L., Washington State University, Pullman, WA 99164-6420
Watanabe, Nancy M., University of California, Davis, CA 95616
Weck, Edward, Richmond, CA 94804
Weeks, Donald, Zoecon Corporation, Palo Alto, CA 94304
West, Joanne A., Zoecon Corporation, Palo Alto, CA 94304
Whalen, Maureen, University of California, Berkeley, CA 94720
Whitaker, John R., University of California, Davis, CA 95616
Wiebe, Wayne, Woodland, CA 95695
Wilson, Claire M., Council for Research Planning in Biological Sciences,
    Washington, D.C. 20036-2077
Wilson, Kate, Massachusetts General Hospital, Boston, MA 02114
Wilson, Sandy, University of California, Davis, CA 95616
Wing, Rod A., University of California, Davis, CA 95616
Wu, Bor-wen, Irvine, CA 92715
Wu, Fang-sheng, Zoecon Corporation, Palo Alto, CA 94304

Yamada, Tetsuji, University of California, Davis, CA 95616
Yan-yu, Dong, University of California, Davis, CA 95616
Yip, Ryan, U.S. Department of Agriculture, Agricultural Research Service,
    Albany, CA 94710
Yoder, John I., University of California, Davis, CA 95616
Yost, Susan Connolly, Des Moines, IA 50322

Zabel, Pim, Wageningen, The Netherlands
Zahnley, James C., U.S. Department of Agriculture, Agricultural Research
    Service, Albany, CA 94710
Zarowitz, Mike, San Carlos, CA 94070
Zelcer, Aaron, Bet Dagan, Israel
Zemetra, Robert, University of Idaho, Moscow, ID 83843

INDEX

219